Canon

THE ULTIMATE WORLD CUP FACT AND QUIZ BOOK

Canon

THE ULTIMATE WORLD CUP FACT AND QUIZ BOOK

Frank Nicklin

Cartoons by

Peter Coupe

STOPWATCH

Published by Stopwatch Publishing Limited
443 Oxford St
London W1R 1DA

For Bookmart Limited
Desford Road
Enderby
Leicester LE9 5AD

This edition published 1998

ISBN 1 - 900032 - 72 - 4

Printed in Finland

FOREWORD

Canon is delighted to have been associated with World Cup football since 1978 when we first became a sponsor at the finals in Argentina. Nearer to home, we were the first ever sponsor of the English Football League in the early 1980s, and have more recently been an associate sponsor of Team England.

Our sponsorship of this World Cup Fact and Quiz Book is therefore very appropriate in the year that marks the twentieth anniversary of our involvement with the competition. The range and diversity of the questions should tax even the most dedicated followers of the game, and I hope the sheer volume of quizzes and facts will provide many hours of enjoyment.

Martin Laws
Managing Director
Canon (UK) Ltd

CONTENTS

World Cup Quiz Book

QUIZ CONTENTS

True or False?

Quiz 1

True or False?

1. **The first World Cup took place in Uruguay in 1930.**
2. Uruguay were the first country to win the World Cup.
3. **Edson Arantes do Nascimento played for Argentina in four World Cup tournaments.**
4. Edson Arantes do Nascimento was better known as Zico.
5. **England beat Portugal in the 1966 World Cup Final.**
6. Eusebio of Portugal was the top scorer in the 1966 World Cup tournament in England.
7. **A dog called Biggles found the stolen World Cup trophy in a London garden.**
8. The fastest goal to be scored in a finals series was Bryan Robson's in Spain in 1982.
9. **Bryan Robson was captain of England in the 1982 series.**
10. Ray Wilkins was sent off in a World Cup match.
11. **Diego Maradona scored three goals against England in 1986.**
12. Maradona claimed it was 'the hand of God' that helped him to score the first goal.
13. **Wales have never played in a World Cup finals series.**
14. Brazil beat West Germany in the Final of 1970.
15. **Gerd Muller scored two hat-tricks for West Germany in the 1970 World Cup finals.**

ANSWERS: 1.True 2.True **3.False - he played for Brazil.** 4.False - he was Pele **5.False - they beat West Germany** 6.True - he scored nine **7.False - it was Pickles** 8.True - in 27 seconds **9.False - it was Mick Mills of Ipswich** 10.True - against Morocco in 1986 **11.False - he scored two** 12.True **13.False - they played once in 1958** 14.False - they beat Italy **15.True**

Quiz 2

True or False?

1. **Argentina won their second World Cup Final in eight years in 1986.**
2. Argentina played in three World Cup Finals in four consecutive series.
3. **Geoff Hurst scored a hat-trick for England in the 1966 Final.**
4. England's other goal in the 1966 Final was scored by Alan Ball.
5. **Alf Ramsey was knighted before the 1966 Final.**
6. Martin Peters played county cricket once for Essex.
7. **The highest score in a World Cup qualifying round match was 17-0 by Iran against The Maldives in 1997.**
8. The previous highest was 13-0 by New Zealand against Fiji in 1981.
9. **The World Cup trophy won outright by Brazil was named after a Frenchman.**
10. His name was Jules Verne.
11. **The first European country to stage the World Cup finals was France in 1934.**
12. The second European country to stage the finals was France in 1938.
13. **Italy won the 1934 World Cup Final.**
14. France won the 1938 World Cup Final.
15. **Just Fontaine scored 13 goals for France in the 1958 finals in Sweden.**

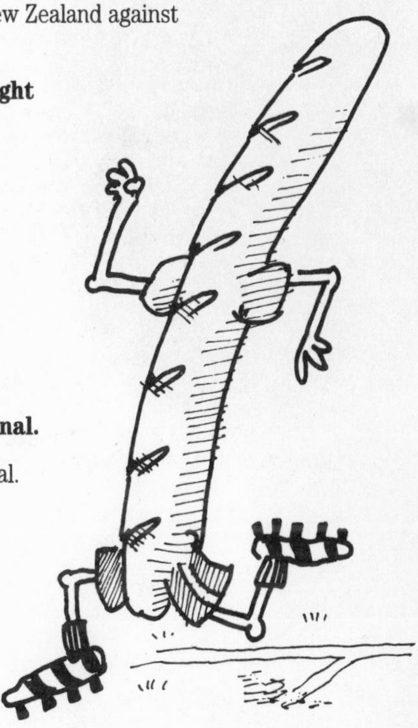

ANSWERS: 1.True 2.True - 1978-86-90 **3.True** 4.False - it was Martin Peters **5.False** 6.False - it was Geoff Hurst **7.True** 8.True **9.True** 10.False - it was Jules Rimet **11.False - it was Italy** 12.True **13.True** 14.False - Italy again **15.True**

Quiz 3

True or False?

1. **Bobby Moore was presented with the World Cup in 1966 by the Prime Minister.**
2. West Germany beat Brazil in the 1974 World Cup Final.
3. **The 1974 World Cup Final was in Munich.**
4. Gerd Muller was West Germany's captain in the 1974 Final.
5. **Uruguay were the first World Cup holders not to defend it.**
6. The 1970 World Cup Final referee was an Englishman.
7. **The 1974 Final was refereed by a Welshman.**
8. Uwe Seeler was West Germany's captain in the 1966 World Cup Final at Wembley.
9. **Two penalties were awarded to West Germany in the 1974 Final against Holland.**
10. Gerd Muller converted a penalty for West Germany in the 1974 Final.
11. **England reached the quarter-final stage of the 1974 finals.**
12. England reached the quarter-final stage of the 1978 finals.
13. **Twenty-six more goals were scored in the 1994 USA finals than in the 1990 Italy finals.**
14. Paul McGrath captained the Republic of Ireland team in the United States in 1994.
15. **England won only one match in the 1994 tournament in USA.**

ANSWERS: 1.False - the Queen presented it 2.False - they beat Holland **3.True** 4.False - it was Franz Beckenbauer **5.True** 6.False - it was an East German **7.False - it was Jack Taylor of England** 8.True **9.False - each side had one** 10.False - it was Paul Breitner **11.False - they failed to qualify** 12.False again - same reason! **13.True** 14.False - it was Andy Townsend **15.False - they failed to qualify**

Quiz 4

True or False?

1. **Fifteen European countries qualified for the 1998 finals in France.**
2. Fifteen countries from the whole world competed in the 1938 finals in France.
3. **Scotland qualified for the finals for the fifth consecutive time in 1990.**
4. Scotland beat Brazil in their group match in 1990.
5. **Italy beat Brazil 2-0 in the match to decide third place in 1978.**
6. Poland beat Brazil 1-0 in the third-place match in 1974.
7. **England's first-ever World Cup action was a qualifying match against Northern Ireland in November 1949 in Manchester.**
8. The first-ever match was against Wales at Wembley and England won 4-1.
9. **Jackie Milburn scored three in England's World Cup qualifying game against Wales in 1949.**
10. Jackie Milburn scored four in their 1949 qualifying match against Northern Ireland.
11. **England played three matches in their first World Cup finals in Brazil in 1950.**
12. They were captained in all their games by Billy Wright of Wolves.
13. **England lost two of their games in the 1950 finals to USA and Spain, both by the only goal.**
14. England's wingers in the match with Spain in 1950 were Stanley Matthews and Tom Finney.
15. **Scotland's first-ever World Cup qualifier was against Northern Ireland in Belfast in 1949, the Scots winning 8-2.**

ANSWERS: 1.True 2.True **3.True** 4.False - Brazil won 1-0 **5.False - Brazil won 2-1** 6.True **7.False - it was the second** 8.False - it was at Cardiff **9.True** 10.False - it was Jack Rowley of Manchester United **11.True** 12.True **13.True** 14.True **15.True**

Quiz 5

True or False?

1. **Cameroon are known as the Lions of Africa.**
2. Their ageing star player Roger Milla changed his name from Miller.
3. **Cameroon first qualified for the World Cup finals in 1986.**
4. They were never beaten in their first appearance in the finals.
5. **They won more matches than they drew in the 1982 finals.**
6. Argentina were the first country to have a player sent off in a World Cup Final.
7. **They had two men sent off in the same Final.**
8. The 2002 World Cup finals will have joint hosts, Japan and North Korea.
9. **Nigeria first appeared in the finals stage in 1994.**
10. Mexico were banned from the World Cup in 1986 because of irregularities in an international youth tournament.
11. **The finals of the 14th World Cup in Italy in 1990 featured four penalty shoot-outs.**
12. Argentina were involved in two penalty shoot-outs in Italy in the 1990 finals.
13. **West Germany did not play in any qualifying matches for the finals in Argentina in 1978.**
14. The average match attendance for the 1966 finals in England was a World Cup record.
15. **England played all five matches at Wembley in the 1966 finals.**

ANSWERS: **1.True** 2.True **3.False - they first played in Spain 1982** 4.True **5.False - played three, drew three** 6.True **7.True - in Italy 1990** 8.False - Japan and South Korea **9.True** 10. False - it was 1990 **11.True** 12.True **13.True - they were exempt as 1974 winners** 14. False - Brazil 1950 was then the highest. **15. False - there were six involving England.**

Quiz 6

True or False?

1. **Nigeria played three matches in their first finals.**
2. They were beaten by Italy in their last match of 1994.
3. **The match between Nigeria and Italy went into extra time.**
4. Italy played seven matches in the 1994 finals in the USA.
5. **Italy played seven matches in the 1990 finals in Italy.**
6. Italy lost one of their matches in the 1994 finals on a penalty shoot-out.
7. **The result of that shoot-out was 3-2.**
8. Italy lost one of their matches in the 1990 finals on a penalty shoot-out.
9. **The result of that shoot-out was 5-4.**
10. Italy beat England 2-1 in the 1990 series.
11. **Italy played six matches in the Mexico 1970 finals.**
12. Italy had three 0-0 results in the 1970 finals.
13. **England beat Italy 1-0 at Wembley in 1977 in a World Cup qualifying tie.**
14. England lost to Italy 2-0 in a World Cup qualifier in Rome in 1976.
15. **Kevin Keegan captained England in that 1976 Rome match.**

ANSWERS: 1.False - they played four in 1994 2.True 3.True - Italy won 2-1 4.True 5.True 6.True **7.True - against Brazil in the Final** 8.True - to Argentina in the semi-finals **9.False - it was 4-3** 10.True **11.True** 12.False - it was two, against Uruguay and Israel **13.False - England won 2-0** 14.True **15.True**

Quiz 7

True or False?

1. **Kevin Keegan captained England in the 1977 qualifying match with Italy at Wembley.**
2. Kevin Keegan scored a goal in that match.
3. **Michel Platini is president of the Organising Committee for the 1998 World Cup.**
4. Platini was a captain and also a coach of France in World Cup tournaments including qualifiers).
5. **Romania beat Sweden 5-4 in a penalty shoot-out in a quarter-final match in 1994.**
6. Romania have qualified seven times for the finals stage.
7. **Scotland have qualified seven times for the finals stage.**
8. Holland have qualified eight times for the finals stage.
9. **Iran have never qualified for the finals stage.**
10. Iraq have never qualified for the finals stage.
11. **Scotland have never progressed beyond the first round.**
12. Germany/West Germany have missed the finals only once.
13. **England have qualified for the finals stage ten times.**
14. England have never met South Africa in the World Cup.
15. **England have beaten Iran once in the World Cup.**

ANSWERS: 1.False - it was Emlyn Hughes 2.True **3.True** 4.True **5.False - Sweden won 5-4** 6.True **7.False - it's eight** 8.False - it's seven! **9.False - did it in 1978 & 1998** 10.False - they were there in 1986 **11.True** 12.False - twice **13.True** 14.True **15.False - they have never met**

Quiz 8

True or False?

1. **The first goal in England's qualifying matches for the 1998 finals was scored by Paul Gascoigne.**
2. Nick Barmby played in only one of England's eight qualifying matches for the 1998 series.
3. **Scotland's first qualifying match for 1998 ended 0-0.**
4. Their opponents in this match were Belarus.
5. **Scotland beat Latvia 2-1 in their second qualifier for 1998.**
6. Craig Brown was appointed as manager of Scotland in 1993.
7. **Kevin Gallacher scored six goals in Scotland's ten qualifying matches for 1998.**
8. Gary McAllister captained Scotland in all their ten qualifying matches for 1998.
9. **Alan Shearer was England's leading scorer in the 1998 qualifiers.**
10. Shearer scored four goals in the 1998 qualifying games.
11. **Paul Gascoigne scored three times in the 1998 qualifiers.**
12. Ian Wright scored three in the 1998 qualifiers.
13. **David Seaman missed only one of England's eight qualifying games for 1998.**
14. David Beckham also missed only one of those eight matches.
15. **Geoff Hurst played three times in England's six matches in the 1966 finals.**

ANSWERS: 1.False - was Nick Barmby 2.True **3.True** 4.False - Austria **5.False - won 2-0**
6.True **7.True** 8.False - he missed one **9.True** 10.False - it was five **11.False - it was two**
12.False - it was two **13.True** 14.False - he played in all eight **15.True**

Quiz 9

True or False?

1. **Walter Winterbottom was England's team manager in Chile for the seventh World Cup finals in 1962.**
2. Alf Ramsey played for England in all three of their matches in the Brazil finals of 1950.
3. **Nat Lofthouse scored three goals for England in two matches in the 1954 finals.**
4. England drew 4-4 with Belgium after extra time in the 1954 finals.
5. **Hungary beat El Salvador 10-0 in the 1982 finals in Spain.**
6. In six World Cup finals matches, El Salvador have won only once.
7. **Jack Charlton's Republic of Ireland team played five finals matches in Italy in 1990 and lost only one.**
8. The result of their match with Egypt in 1990 was 0-0.
9. **The Irish drew 1-1 with Holland in the 1990 finals.**
10. Niall Quinn scored for the Republic in that match.
11. **Ronald Koeman scored with a penalty for Holland in that match.**
12. Ruud Gullit scored from a penalty against West Germany in the second round in 1990.
13. **West Germany won that match 2-1.**
14. Jurgen Klinsmann scored six goals for Germany in America in the 1994 finals.
15. **Germany lost to Bulgaria in the 1994 quarter-finals.**

ANSWERS: 1.True 2.True **3.True** 4.True **5.False - El Salvador made it 10-1** 6.False - never won **7.True** 8.True **9.True** 10.True **11.False - Ruud Gullit scored** 12.False - Koeman scored **13.True** 14.False - only five **15.True**

Quiz 10

True or False?

1. **Algeria first played in the World Cup finals in 1978 in Argentina.**
2. Algeria have reached the finals stage three times.
3. **Uruguay were losing 2-1 at half-time but went on to win 4-2 against Argentina in the first Final of 1930 in Montevideo.**
4. Argentina had beaten the USA 6-1 in the semi-finals of 1930.
5. **France were beaten 1-0 by Argentina and Chile in the 1930 finals.**
6. Luxembourg have played only once in the World Cup finals stage.
7. **England once beat Luxembourg 9-0 in a qualifying round match.**
8. England played them 22 years later at Wembley in a European Championship qualifying match and again beat them 9-0.
9. **In the 1960 match against Luxembourg, Bobby Charlton and Jimmy Greaves each scored hat-tricks.**

10. England's captain that day was Jimmy Armfield.
11. **Norway played only one match in the 1938 finals in France.**
12. Italy beat them 2-0 in that match after extra time.
13. **Norway never appeared again in the finals until USA 1994.**
14. Norway drew 0-0 with Eire in the 1994 finals.
15. **Northern Ireland have played in four World Cup final series.**

ANSWERS: 1.False - it was Spain 1982 2.False - only two 3.True 4.True 5.True 6.False - never 7.True - in 1960 8.True 9.True 10.False - it was Johnny Haynes 11.True 12.False - Italy won 2-1 13.True 14.True 15.False - only three

Quiz 11

True or False?

1. **Peter McParland scored twice for Northern Ireland against West Germany in 1958.**
2. McParland also scored twice against Argentina in 1958.
3. **McParland again! Two more against Czechoslovakia in a 1958 play-off.**
4. Peru held Italy to a 1-1 draw in 1982 when the Italians won the World Cup.
5. **Italy went on to beat Brazil 3-0 in the second round that year.**
6. Paolo Rossi scored twice for Italy in that match.
7. **Rossi scored three in that year's semi-finals against Poland.**
8. Rossi scored twice in the 1982 Final against West Germany.
9. **Rossi was top scorer in the 1982 finals in Spain with seven goals.**
10. Brazil, having won the Jules Rimet Trophy outright, supplied a replacement for the finals in West Germany in 1974.
11. **England played three matches in the 1974 finals.**
12. Bobby Moore played his final match for England against Italy in a World Cup qualifying match in 1973.
13. **Poland's World Cup goalkeeper was once described as 'a clown' by Brian Clough.**
14. The Polish goalkeeper Jan Tomaszewski saved penalties against Sweden and West Germany in the 1974 finals.
15. **Which West German forward's spot-kick did he save?**

ANSWERS: 1.True 2.False - only once **3.True** 4.True **5.False - it was 3-2** 6.False - he scored three **7.False - he scored two, Italy winning 2-0** 8.False - he scored one **9.False - he was top with six** 10.True - but the offer was rejected **11.False - they failed to qualify** 12.False - it was not a World Cup match **13.True** 14.True **15.Uli Hoeness**

Quiz 12

True or False?

1. **West Germany were unbeaten in all seven matches in the 1974 finals on home soil.**
2. West Germany lost one match on their way to the World Cup Final of 1974.
3. **West Germany conceded only four goals in the seven matches of 1974.**
4. One of those goals was scored by Australia in a first-round match.
5. **Poland's Lato was the top scorer in the 1974 finals with six goals.**
6. Gerd Muller scored twice but was on the losing side against Italy in Mexico in a 1970 semi-final.
7. **France scored six against West Germany in the Sweden 1958 finals.**
8. Just Fontaine scored three for France in that match.
9. **West Germany scored in all six of their matches in the 1958 finals.**
10. Helmut Rahn scored twice for West Germany in the 1954 World Cup Final.
11. **The other German goal in that match was scored by Schaefer.**
12. West Germany scored 25 goals in six games to win the 1954 tournament.
13. **West Germany lost 7-3 to Hungary in a group match in 1954.**
14. Australia have appeared only once in World Cup final stages.
15. **They have failed to score in the World Cup final stages, although they held Chile 0-0 in a group match.**

ANSWERS: 1.False 2.True - East Germany beat them **3.True** 4.False - Australia lost 3-0 **5.False - he scored seven** 6.True - Italy won 4-3 **7.True** 8.False - he scored four **9.True** 10.True **11.False - it was Morlock** 12.True **13.False - it was 8-3** 14.True - 1974 **15.True**

Quiz 13

True or False?

1. **Australia won a point in their only World Cup finals.**
2. Australia were eliminated in the qualifying rounds for the 1998 World Cup.
3. **They were beaten by Iran at Melbourne on a penalty shoot-out.**
4. The first goal against Australia in the 1974 finals was scored by an East German.
5. **East Germany scored two more goals in the second half.**
6. West Germany scored twice in the first half against Australia in the 1974 finals.
7. **Gerd Muller made it 3-0 in the second half.**
8. Australia were unbeaten in their 11 matches in the 1974 qualifying rounds.
9. **Australia lost twice in the 1974 qualifiers.**
10. Iran beat Australia in one of the 1974 qualifying rounds.
11. **Australia beat Iran in one of the 1974 qualifying rounds.**
12. Australia played South Korea three times in the group final in October and November 1973.
13. **Australia lost one and won two against South Korea.**
14. Belgium played in three World Cup finals series before the outbreak of the Second World War.
15. **Belgium lost all their World Cup finals matches before the War.**

ANSWERS: 1.True - draw with Chile 0-0 2.True 3.False - Iran went through on away goals 4.False - own goal by Curran 5.False - the result was 2-0 6.True 7.True 8.False 9.False 10.True - by 2-0 11.True - by 3-0 in the first leg 12.True 13.False - Australia drew two, won one 14.True 15.True

Quiz 14

True or False?

1. USA beat Belgium 3-0 in the first World Cup finals match between the two teams.

2. McGhee recorded a hat-trick for the Americans.

3. Jean Nicolas scored a hat-trick for France against Belgium in the 1938 finals in France.

4. That was Belgium's only match in the 1938 finals.

5. Belgium conceded five goals against Germany in the Italy 1934 finals.

6. That was Belgium's only match in the 1934 finals.

7. Germany's scorers in that match were Kobierski (3) and Conen (2).

8. Austria qualified for their seventh World Cup finals in winning through to France 1998.

9. Their best performance was in 1954 when they reached the quarter-finals.

10. Twelve goals were scored in their quarter-final match of 1954.

11. The result of that match was Austria 8 Switzerland 4.

12. Their first finals match in 1954 was a 1-0 defeat of Scotland.

13. Their last match in the 1954 finals was against West Germany.

14. Their last match was against Uruguay in a third-place play-off.

15. Austria were beaten 3-1 in the third-place match.

ANSWERS: 1.True 2.False - he scored two **3.False - only two** 4.True **5.True** 6.True **7.False - Conen scored three, Kobierski two** 8.True **9.False - they reached the semi-finals** 10.True **11.False - Austria won 7-5** 12.True **13.False** 14.True **15.False - Austria won 3-1**

Quiz 15

True or False?

1. **Belgium's entry to the World Cup finals of 1998 was their sixth consecutive qualification for the finals.**
2. France 1998 will be their ninth World Cup finals.
3. **Belgium's best World Cup achievement was to reach the semi-finals in 1986.**
4. They played seven matches in that tournament.
5. **Two of their matches in Mexico 1986 went to extra time.**
6. Two of their matches went to penalty shoot-outs.
7. **Belgium won a penalty shoot-out against Spain 5-4.**
8. Diego Maradona scored all three Argentina goals against Belgium in the semi-finals.
9. **Maradona scored one goal in that semi-final match.**
10. France scored four goals to take third place in 1986.
11. **England eliminated Belgium in the second round in Italy 1990.**
12. David Platt scored the only goal in extra time in that match.
13. **Saudi Arabia drew 1-1 with Belgium in the 1994 finals.**
14. The Belgians beat Morocco and Holland 1-0 in 1994 group matches.
15. **Voeller and Klinsmann (2) scored in Germany's 3-2 defeat of Belgium in 1994.**

ANSWERS: 1.False - the fifth 2.False - the tenth **3.True** 4.True **5.False - three** 6.False - one
7.True 8.False - the score was 2-0 **9.False - he scored both** 10.True - Belgium 2 France 4
11.True 12.True **13.False - Belgium lost 1-0** 14.True **15.False - Voeller (2) & Klinsmann**

Quiz 16

True or False?

1. **El Salvador conceded 22 goals in their six World Cup finals matches.**
2. Belgium have beaten them twice in the World Cup.
3. **Hungary were the kiss of death for El Salvador in a 10-1 defeat where Laszlo Kiss scored four.**
4. England beat El Salvador 4-1 in the 1970 finals in Mexico.
5. **France will host the 1998 World Cup finals on their tenth appearance.**
6. Mexico will also be making their tenth finals appearance.
7. **Spain will also be making their tenth finals appearance.**
8. Yugoslavia will also be making their tenth appearance.
9. **England will be making their eleventh World Cup finals appearance.**
10. Romania will not be making their tenth finals appearance.
11. **France appeared in all three pre-Second World War finals.**
12. They played six times in pre-War finals matches, winning three.
13. **France's first British opponents in a finals series were England in Sweden 1958.**
14. France's second British opponents in the next match in Sweden were Wales.
15. **France were beaten in the semi-finals in Sweden by Brazil, for whom Pele scored a hat-trick, with Vava and Didi also scoring. Fontaine and Piantoni scored for France, who lost 5-2. The match was on June 24, 1958 and Brazil led 2-1 at half-time.**

ANSWERS: 1.True 2.True **3.False - he scored three** 4.False - they never met **5.True** 6.False - eleventh **7.True** 8.False - ninth **9.False - tenth** 10.True - seventh **11.True** 12.False - they won two **13.False - Scotland** 14.False - Northern Ireland **15.True - every single word!**

Quiz 17

True or False?

1. **France's manager in Sweden 1958 was Paul Nicolas. He was not renowned for his singing.**
2. They won third place in those 1958 finals by beating West Germany.
3. **The result was France 6 West Germany 3.**
4. Just Fontaine's four goals for France in that match included one penalty.
5. **Raymond Kopa scored from the penalty spot in that match.**
6. France beat Argentina 2-1 in the Argentina finals of 1978.
7. **France were beaten in the quarter-finals in 1978.**
8. France were beaten by England in 1966 with goals from Roger Hunt and Bobby Charlton.
9. **France lost 3-2 to Poland in the third-place play-off match in 1982.**
10. Jean-Pierre Papin scored the only goal of the match with Canada in the 1982 finals.
11. **France have never played in a World Cup Final but have won third place three times.**
12. Germany's pre-War teams played six times in two tournaments.
13. **They drew with Switzerland and lost the replay in 1938.**
14. Unified Germany of 1994 went out after four matches in the United States.
15. **Jurgen Klinsmann scored in every match in the States.**

ANSWERS: 1.True 2.True **3.True** 4.False **5.True** 6.False - they lost 1-2 **7.False - they went out after the group games** 8.False - Hunt scored both **9.True** 10.True **11.False - twice third** 12.True **13.True** 14.False - they played five **15.False - only in the first four.**

Quiz 18 True or False?

1. Greece have appeared in two World Cup finals series.

2. Greece have never scored a goal in the World Cup finals.

3. Gabriel Batistuta scored all four goals in Argentina's defeat of Greece in 1994.

4. Bulgaria and Argentina both beat Greece 4-0.

5. Haiti have played in only one World Cup finals.

6. They failed to score in three matches in that tournament.

7. Portugal beat Haiti 7-0 in a 1974 group match.

8. Italy scored only three against Haiti - all in the second half.

9. Honduras held a British Isles country to a 1-1 draw in Spain in 1982.

10. That British team was Scotland.

11. Honduras held another European side to a 1-1 draw in 1982.

12. Honduras gave away only three goals in three World Cup matches.

13. Honduras failed to win a game in the 1990 finals in Italy.

14. Iraq played in only one World Cup finals - in Mexico in 1986.

15. Iraq failed to score in their three games in 1986.

ANSWERS: 1.False - once 2.True **3.False - he got three** 4.True **5.True** 6.False - they scored two **7.False - it was Poland** 8.True **9.True** 10.False - Northern Ireland **11.True - Spain** 12.True **13.True - they didn't qualify** 14.True **15.False - they scored once against Belgium**

Quiz 19 True or False?

1. Paraguay played in their third World Cup finals in Mexico in 1986.

2. Paraguay won three points in their three group games in Mexico in 1986.

3. Paraguay won four points in their group games in Sweden in 1958.

4. Scotland beat Paraguay 3-2 in their group match in 1958.

5. Just Fontaine scored two of the seven French goals against Paraguay in 1958.

6. Paraguay have won three of their 11 matches in the World Cup finals.

7. Paraguay have lost only four of their 11 matches in the World Cup finals.

8. Gary Lineker scored two of England's four goals against Paraguay in the 1986 World Cup finals.

9. Peter Beardsley scored for England in that match with Paraguay in Mexico in 1986.

10. Jackie Mudie, one of the Scotland scorers in 1958 against Paraguay, was a Blackburn player.

11. Poland lost their only match in their first finals appearance.

12. One Polish player scored four goals in that match.

13. A Brazilian player scored four goals in that match.

14. Brazil beat Poland 7-5 in that match.

15. They played extra time in that match.

ANSWERS: 1.False - fourth 2.False - they won four points **3.False - they won three** 4.False - Paraguay won 3-2 **5.False - he scored a hat-trick** 6.True **7.True** 8.False - England scored three **9.True** 10.False - he played for Blackpool **11.True** 12.True - it was Willimowski **13.True - Leonidas** 14.False - Brazil won 6-5 **15.True**

Quiz 20 True or False?

1. **Wetterstroem scored five goals for Sweden against Cuba in the 1938 finals.**
2. Sweden beat Cuba 8-0 in that match.
3. **This was the first of only two finals appearances by Cuba.**
4. Cuba played Romania twice in their World Cup finals games in France in 1938.
5. **Cuba scored five times against Romania in 1938.**
6. Romania scored four in their two games against Cuba in 1938.
7. **Czechoslovakia have appeared eight times in World Cup finals series.**
8. Romania lost 2-1 to the Czechs in a first-round match at the finals of 1934 in Italy.
9. **Czechoslovakia lost 3-1 to Germany in the semi-finals of 1934.**
10. The World Cup Final of 1934 stood at 0-0 after 90 minutes in Rome.
11. **Orsi and Schiavio scored to give Italy a 2-0 victory over the Czechs in extra time.**
12. The result of that match was: Italy 1 Czechoslovakia 0 after extra time.
13. **Italy won on a penalty shoot-out by 4-3 in that 1934 Final.**
14. The result of the 1934 World Cup Final after extra time was: Italy 2 Czechoslovakia 1.
15. **Puc, of course, was the Czechoslovakian scorer in the 1934 Final.**

ANSWERS: 1.False - he scored four 2.True **3.False - they appeared only once** 4.True **5.True** 6.True **7.True** 8.True **9.False - they won 3-1** 10.True **11.False** 12.False **13.False - no shoot-outs in those days** 14.True - got it! **15.Of course**

Quiz 21

True or False?

1. **Czechoslovakia met Brazil twice in the World Cup finals of 1938.**
2. Brazil won both games.
3. **Two of the Czechs' three games in 1938 went to extra time.**
4. In 1938, Czechoslovakia scored three in extra time against Holland after 90 goalless minutes.
5. **Czechoslovakia lost all three of their finals games in 1954 in Switzerland.**
6. They scored only one goal in those 1954 finals matches.
7. **The Czechs drew with West Germany 2-2 in 1958.**
8. They scored six against Argentina in their next match.
9. **Czechoslovakia have twice played in the World Cup Final.**
10. They had won four of their five matches to reach the Final in Chile in 1962.
11. **Czechoslovakia played in only four finals series after 1962.**
12. Bilek scored from the penalty spot twice for the Czechs in 1990.
13. **The Dutch East Indies played only two matches in their single World Cup finals appearance in 1938.**
14. Hungary beat them 7-0 in the 1938 finals.
15. **East Germany appeared only once in a finals stage of the World Cup.**

ANSWERS: **1.True** 2.False - one was a draw **3.True** 4.True **5.False - they played only two** 6.False - they didn't score **7.True** 8.True **9.True** 10.False - won three **11.False - only three** 12.True **13.False - they played one** 14.False - it was 6-0 **15.True**

Quiz 22

True or False?

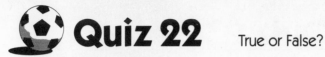

1. **East Germany played five matches in two groups in the 1974 finals in West Germany.**
2. The East played the West twice in those finals.
3. **East Germany were beaten only twice - by Brazil and Holland.**
4. East Germany drew with Argentina and Chile in 1974.
5. **Egypt have played in two World Cup finals series.**
6. Egypt were beaten by Eire and England in the same World Cup finals.
7. **Costa Rica have won more finals matches than they have lost.**
8. Costa Rica have lost more than they have won.
9. **Sweden and Scotland have both been beaten by Costa Rica in the World Cup finals.**
10. Hungary's last World Cup finals match was in Italy in 1990.
11. **Hungary's last World Cup finals match was against France in 1986.**
12. All six Soviet goals against Hungary in 1986 were scored by different players.
13. **Hungary's World Cup Final appearance in 1938 was their fifth match in the series.**
14. Szengeller was Hungary's crackshot marksman in 1938 with seven goals in three matches.
15. **Szengeller scored both goals in the Final which Italy won 4-2.**

ANSWERS: 1.False - played six 2.False - once **3.True** 4.True **5.True** 6.False - England won, Eire drew **7.False** 8.False - won two, lost two **9.True - in 1990** 10.False - they didn't qualify **11.True** 12.False - five players **13.False - their fourth** 14.True **15.False - he didn't score**

Quiz 23

True or False?

1. Hungary met Wales twice in 1958 in Sweden.

2. John Charles and Ivor Allchurch each scored in those matches.

3. Wales won one and drew one with Hungary in 1958.

4. Lajos Tichy, a goalscoring giant for Hungary, scored in all four of their finals matches in 1958.

5. Sandor Kocsis scored ten goals for Hungary in the 1954 finals.

6. Kocsis had hat-tricks in the first two games of 1954.

7. Kocsis and Puskas scored Hungary's goals in the 3-2 Final defeat by West Germany.

8. Hungary scored 27 times in the 1954 finals.

9. Tichy was on target with both goals against England in their first group match of the 1962 finals.

10. Tichy got three and Albert two in the 6-1 defeat of Bulgaria in 1962.

11. Tichy got two and Albert three in that match.

12. Nobody scored for Hungary against Argentina and Czechoslovakia in 1962.

13. Nandor Hidegkuti scored in three of Hungary's five matches in 1954.

14. Hungary won three matches in the Argentina finals of 1978.

15. Hungary scored once in each of those matches.

ANSWERS: **1.**True **2.**True **3.**True **4.**False - he got four in three matches **5.**True **6.**True **7.**False - Puskas & Czibor **8.**True **9.**False - he scored one **10.**False **11.**True **12.**True **13.**True **14.**False - lost all three **15.**True

Quiz 24

True or False?

1. **The Soviet Union played in seven World Cup finals series before trading as Russia in 1994.**
2. The Soviets first played in the finals in 1962 in Sweden.
3. **Their first World Cup finals match was against England.**
4. They drew 2-2 in that match after leading 1-0 at half-time.
5. **Derek Kevan scored from the penalty spot for England against the Soviets in 1958.**
6. Johnny Haynes captained England in that match.
7. **England's last match before the World Cup of 1958 was also against the Soviet Union.**
8. England's captain in that friendly match with the Soviets was Bobby Robson.
9. **The Soviets played six times in the England 1966 finals.**
10. They lost 2-1 to West Germany in the semi-finals.
11. **That was the Soviets' only defeat in the finals of 1966.**
12. The Soviet Union scored 49 goals in all in the World Cup finals up to and including Italy 1990.
13. **Igor Belanov's four goals in the Mexico 1986 finals included two from the penalty spot.**
14. Yugoslavia knocked out Argentina in a penalty shoot-out in the Italy 1990 finals.
15. **This is the last question in the True or False? section.**

ANSWERS: 1.True 2.False - it was 1958 **3.True** 4.True **5.False - it was Tom Finney** 6.False - Billy Wright **7.True** 8.False - Billy Wright again **9.True** 10.True **11.False - they lost the third-place play-off** 12.True **13.True** 14.False - Argentina won 3-2 on penalties **15.It's true, folks!**

The Road to France

England and Scotland's Qualifying Campaigns

Quiz 1 The Road to France

1. **Who were Scotland's first opponents in their qualifying group?**
2. What number group were Scotland in?
3. **In which stadium was their first 1998 World Cup qualifying match played?**
4. Which town was it played in?
5. **What was the score?**
6. Which Premiership striker was in Scotland's attack?
7. **Where was England's first qualifying match?**
8. How many friendlies did England play under Glenn Hoddle before the qualifying tournament began?
9. **How many new caps were there in England's first qualifying tie?**
10. Who were they?
11. **Who scored England's first qualifying goal?**
12. After how many minutes?
13. **What was the final score?**
14. Who became England's 100th captain in that match?
15. **How many survivors from the Euro '96 semi-final played in that game?**

ANSWERS: 1. Austria 2. Four **3. Ernst Happel Stadium** 4. Vienna **5. 0-0** 6. Duncan Ferguson **7. Moldova** 8. None **9. Two** 10. Andy Hinchcliffe, David Beckham **11. Nick Barmby** 12. Twenty-four minutes **13. 3-0 to England** 14. Alan Shearer **15. Six**

Quiz 2

The Road to France

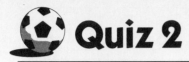

1. **Who scored Scotland's first goal of the qualifying series?**
2. Which club was he playing for at the time?
3. **Who scored his first Scotland goal in the same game?**
4. How many caps had he won before that game?
5. **Which German-based player was in Scotland's midfield for that match?**
6. Who picked up his second booking in that game?
7. **Who were the opponents?**
8. What was the score?
9. **England's first home match of the qualifying series was against whom?**
10. What was the score?
11. **Who scored both goals for England?**
12. Who partnered Alan Shearer in the England attack?
13. **Which team scored first in that game?**
14. What was the name of the first goalscorer?
15. **Who provided the cross for England's first goal?**

ANSWERS: **1. John Collins** 2. Monaco **3. Darren Jackson** 4. Twelve **5. Paul Lambert** 6. Gary McAllister **7. Latvia** 8. 2-0 to Scotland **9. Poland** 10. 2-1 to England **11. Alan Shearer** 12. Les Ferdinand **13. Poland** 14. Marek Citko **15. David Beckham**

Quiz 3

The Road to France

1. **Which players made their first qualifying series appearances in England's third game?**
2. Did Alan Shearer play in that match?
3. **Who were the opponents?**
4. Where was the game played?
5. **What was the score?**
6. Which two players led England's attack in that match?
7. **Who came on for England as a late substitute?**
8. What was the score at half-time?
9. **Who were Scotland's first home opponents?**
10. What was the score in that match?
11. **Where was the game played?**
12. Which stadium was the match played in?
13. **Who was Scotland's goalkeeper for that game?**
14. Who scored for Scotland?
15. **After how many minutes was the goal scored?**

ANSWERS: 1. Tony Adams, Sol Campbell 2. No **3. Georgia** 4. Tbilisi **5. 2-0 to England** 6. Teddy Sheringham, Les Ferdinand **7. Ian Wright** 8. 2-0 **9. Sweden** 10. 1-0 to Scotland **11. Glasgow** 12. Ibrox **13. Jim Leighton** 14. John McGinlay **15. Eight**

Quiz 4

The Road to France

1. **What was strange about Scotland's game in Estonia?**
2. What was the official reason?
3. **Where was the replayed game played?**
4. What was the score?
5. **Who were Scotland's two strikers in that match?**
6. What was the score in the return match, in Scotland?
7. **Where was that game played?**
8. Who scored Scotland's first goal?
9. **Which English club did he used to play for?**
10. Which Premiership striker partnered Darren Jackson up front in that match?
11. **Who was England's first defeat of the qualifying series against?**
12. What month was that game played?
13. **Who was England's captain in that match?**
14. Who was England's goalkeeper for that game?
15. **What was the final score?**

ANSWERS: 1. Estonia didn't turn up 2. Estonia failed to appear because they believed the floodlights were inadequate **3. Monaco** 4. 0-0 **5. Duncan Ferguson, John McGinlay** 6. 2-0 to Scotland **7. Rugby Park, Kilmarnock** 8. Tom Boyd **9. Chelsea** 10. Kevin Gallacher **11. Italy** 12. February **13. Alan Shearer** 14. Ian Walker **15 1-0 to Italy**

Quiz 5

The Road to France

1. **Who scored the only goal of the game between England and Italy?**
2. Which player replaced Steve McManaman with 11 minutes remaining in that game?
3. **Who were beaten 2-0 by Scotland in April 1997?**
4. Where was the game played?
5. **Who scored both goals for Scotland?**
6. Name the Tottenham defender who played in that game.
7. **England unveiled a new home kit against which country?**
8. Who scored England's first goal in their fifth qualifying match?
9. **Who were their opponents?**
10. What was the final score?
11. **Who else scored for England?**
12. Which midfielder made his first World Cup qualifying start in that game?
13. **Who came on as a late substitute for England?**
14. In what minute was England's second goal of that game scored?
15. **Against who did Scotland concede their first goals of the qualifying series?**

ANSWERS: 1. Gianfranco Zola 2. Paul Merson **3. Austria** 4. Parkhead, Glasgow **5. Kevin Gallacher** 6. Colin Calderwood **7. Italy** 8. Teddy Sheringham **9. Georgia** 10. 2-0 **11. Alan Shearer** 12. Robert Lee **13. Jamie Redknapp** 14. Ninetieth **15. Sweden**

Quiz 6

The Road to France

1. **What was the final score in Scotland's away match against Sweden?**
2. Where was the game played?
3. **Who scored for Scotland?**
4. Which Nottingham Forest player made his first appearance of the season in that match?
5. **Who was Scotland's goalkeeper in that game?**
6. Where was England's game in Poland played?
7. **Which England player had to be replaced after just 16 minutes of that match because of injury?**
8. Who replaced him?
9. **What was the final score in that game?**
10. Who scored for England after just six minutes?
11. **Who missed a first-half penalty?**
12. Who scored for England in the final minute of the match?
13. **Scotland had back-to-back matches against which nation in the summer of 1997?**
14. How many goals did they score in those two matches?
15. **In the away match, who scored a penalty for Scotland?**

ANSWERS: 1. 2-1 to Sweden 2. Gothenburg **3. Kevin Gallacher** 4. Scott Gemmill **5. Jim Leighton** 6. Chorzow **7. Paul Gascoigne** 8. David Batty **9. 2-0 to England** 10. Alan Shearer **11. Alan Shearer** 12. Teddy Sheringham **13. Belarus** 14. Five **15. Gary McAllister**

Quizzes about Qualifiers

Quiz 1

Quizzes about Qualifiers

1. **How many matches were played in the first World Cup qualifying round of 1930?**
2. How many qualifying groups were contested in the second World Cup?
3. **How many of the four Home Countries played in the pre-War qualifying competitions?**
4. How many pre-War qualifying rounds did Eire enter?
5. **How many times did Eire play in the pre-War finals?**
6. Against whom did Eire win their first pre-War point in the qualifiers?
7. **Was the score 0-0, 2-2 or 4-4?**
8. Eire were beaten in their other group match by Holland. Was the score 1-0, 4-1 or 5-2?
9. **Two of the three countries in Group 12 of the 1934 finals qualified. Guess which of France, Germany and Luxembourg was eliminated.**
10. Spain and Portugal were the only contestants in Group 6. Spain won the first match 9-0. Who qualified?
11. **Haiti, Cuba, Mexico and USA fought out Group 1 for the single place in the 1934 finals. Who got it?**
12. Hungary, Austria and Bulgaria met in a tough group, only two to qualify. Who went out?
13. **Only one went through from Group 5. Sweden, Lithuania or Estonia?**
14. Twenty-eight countries fought out the 1938 series. Who, as hosts, were exempt from the qualifying round?
15. **Who did Italy, the 1934 hosts, beat in the 1934 qualifying competition?**

ANSWERS: 1.There were no qualifiers 2.Twelve 3.None 4.Two 5.None 6.Belgium 7.4-4 8.5-2 9.Luxembourg 10.Spain 11.USA 12.Bulgaria 13.Sweden 14.France 15.Greece

Quiz 2

Quizzes about Qualifiers

1. **Two of the three in Group 8 went into the finals of 1938. Who was eliminated from Holland, Belgium and Luxembourg?**
2. Two of the four in Group 1 qualified, two years before the start of World War Two. Which of these: Estonia, Finland, Germany, Sweden?
3. **Big scorers in the qualifiers of 1938 were Sweden with a 7-2 win. Who were their victims?**
4. Eire's group contained Norway, Poland and Yugoslavia. Where did Eire finish?
5. **Who did Austria beat in their first qualifying match in October 1937?**
6. Why did Austria then withdraw from the tournament?
7. **Which country turned down FIFA's offer to take Austria's place?**
8. Who were the only qualifiers from South America for the 1938 finals?
9. **Two other non-European countries qualified for the 1938 finals for the only time in their World Cup history. Who were they?**
10. Switzerland and Portugal met in Italy in a single-match qualifying group five weeks before the start of the 1938 finals. Who won?
11. **Hungary beat Greece in a 1938 qualifier - by 5-1, 8-1 or 11-1?**
12. England, Scotland, Wales and Northern Ireland made up Group 1 in the 1950 qualifying competition. Who finished top?
13. **Why did Scotland withdraw after qualifying by finishing second?**
14. Who was the Newcastle player who scored a hat-trick for England against Wales?
15. **Who was the Manchester United player who scored four in England's 9-2 defeat of Northern Ireland?**

ANSWERS: 1.Luxembourg 2.Sweden & Germany **3.Estonia** 4.Bottom **5.Latvia** 6.They were invaded by Germany **7.England** 8.Brazil **9.Cuba & Dutch East Indies** 10.Switzerland 2-1 **11.11-1** 12.England **13.They had vowed to go to Brazil only as British champions** 14.Jackie Milburn **15.Jack Rowley**

Quiz 3

Quizzes about Qualifiers

1. **England beat Scotland 1-0 in their group match for the 1950 finals. Who was the Chelsea player who scored?**
2. Who was England's right-back in that match?
3. **What was the score in Scotland's win over Northern Ireland in the 1950 qualifiers - 4-1, 6-3 or 8-2?**
4. Who was the East Fife centre-forward who got a hat-trick in that game?
5. **Who was the only 'Anglo' in the Scottish side that day?**
6. With which English club did he play?
7. **From which Scottish club was he signed in September 1947?**
8. His transfer fee set a British record at the time. What was it?
9. **Eire played four matches in their 1950 group but still finished second to a country who played only two. Who was it?**
10. Portugal failed to qualify for the third consecutive series. Who beat them in two regional group games?
11. **Who had the biggest win in all the qualifying matches of 1950?**
12. Who won four out of four against USA and Cuba?
13. **Who were exempt from the 1954 qualifying competition?**
14. Eire again finished second and failed to qualify. Which European country headed them with four wins out of four?
15. **Two of the four British Championship teams qualified for the 1954 finals. Who were they?**

ANSWERS: 1.Roy Bentley 2.Alf Ramsey **3.8-2** 4.Henry Morris **5.Billy Steel** 6.Derby County **7.Morton** 8.£15,000 **9.Sweden** 10.Spain **11.England 9-2 v Northern Ireland** 12.Mexico **13.Switzerland (hosts) & Uruguay (holders)** 14.France **15.England & Scotland**

Quiz 4

Quizzes about Qualifiers

1. **England beat Scotland in Glasgow in the 1954 qualifiers - by 3-1, 3-2 or 4-2?**
2. The right-winger was the only England forward not to score in that game. Who was it?
3. **Scotland's goalkeeper won an FA Cup Final medal the previous year. Who was he?**
4. Who were the two Blackpool players in the England side that beat Northern Ireland who also won FA Cup Final medals the previous year?
5. **Who were the two Bolton players in that England side who had won FA Cup losers' medals in the 1953 Final?**
6. Who scored the three England goals against the Irish in that match?
7. **Who was Northern Ireland's famous coach in the 1954 series?**
8. What was the margin of England's victory over Wales in the series?
9. **How many goals did Lofthouse score in that match?**
10. What was the Scotland v Wales result? Was it 1-1, 2-2 or 3-3?
11. **Who wore the No. 9 shirt for Wales in Trevor Ford's absence from that match?**
12. How many goals did he score?
13. **Also a scorer was a Welshman who won 68 caps in 15 years with Swansea, Newcastle and Cardiff. Name him.**
14. Portugal failed to qualify for the fourth consecutive series. Which European side beat them this time?
15. **Who were the highest scorers in one match in the 1954 qualifiers?**

ANSWERS: 1.4-2 2.Tom Finney **3.George Farm (Blackpool)** 4.Harry Johnston & Stanley Matthews **5.Nat Lofthouse & Harold Hassall** 6.Hassall(2) & Lofthouse **7.Peter Doherty** 8.4-1 **9.Two** 10.3-3 **11.John Charles** 12.Two **13.Ivor Allchurch** 14.Austria **15.Austria beat Portugal 9-1**

Quiz 5

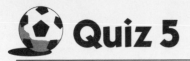

Quizzes about Qualifiers

1. **Turkey played Spain three times in Group 6 of the 1954 qualifiers. Who went through?**
2. Who won three out of three against USA and Haiti?
3. **Two teams only contested the Asian group. Who qualified - Japan or South Korea?**
4. Who were exempt from the qualifying competition for the 1958 finals in Sweden?
5. **England, Scotland, Wales and Northern Ireland were split up for qualifying purposes. How many of them won through to the finals?**
6. Who lost all four ties in England's qualifying group?
7. **Northern Ireland surprisingly headed their three-team group, beating Portugal and who else?**
8. Which other former World Cup winners failed to qualify?
9. **Who was Northern Ireland's captain?**
10. Who was their team manager in 1958?
11. **Who won the last group match between the Irish and Italy?**
12. What was the result of Italy's home match with Northern Ireland?
13. **Who did Brazil beat 2-1 on aggregate in their only two qualifiers?**
14. Who qualified from the South American ABC group of Argentina, Bolivia and Chile?
15. **Who knocked out Uruguay and Colombia?**

ANSWERS: 1.Turkey 2.Mexico **3.South Korea** 4.Sweden (hosts) & West Germany (holders) **5.All four** 6.Denmark **7.Italy** 8.Uruguay **9.Danny Blanchflower** 10.Peter Doherty **11.Ireland 2-1** 12.Italy 1-0 **13.Peru** 14.Argentina **15.Paraguay**

Quiz 6

Quizzes about Qualifiers

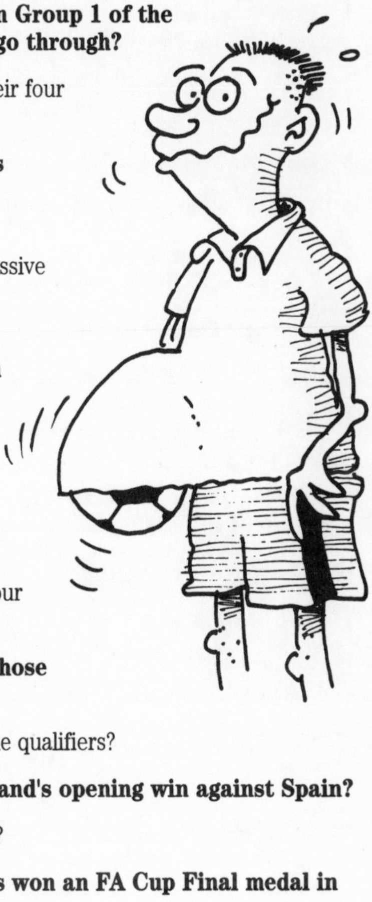

1. **Eire finished second to whom in Group 1 of the 1958 qualifiers, thus failing to go through?**
2. How many did England score in their four group matches?
3. **Club-mates scored all five goals against Denmark. From which English club?**
4. Who scored two hat-tricks in successive qualifying games for England?
5. **Who was his club-mate who scored twice in that first match with Denmark?**
6. Who scored twice for England in their 5-1 home win over Eire?
7. **For which English club did he play?**
8. Who was England's captain in all four qualifying games for 1958?
9. **How many did Taylor score in those qualifying games?**
10. How many did Atyeo score in all the qualifiers?
11. **Who scored a hat-trick in Scotland's opening win against Spain?**
12. Which English club did he play for?
13. **One of his Scotland team-mates won an FA Cup Final medal in 1954. Who was he?**
14. Who captained Scotland in the return match with Spain?
15. **What was the score in that match?**

ANSWERS: 1.England 2.Fifteen **3.Manchester United** 4.Tommy Taylor **5.Duncan Edwards** 6.John Atyeo **7.Bristol City** 8.Billy Wright **9.Eight** 10.Four **11.Jackie Mudie** 12.Blackpool **13.Tommy Docherty** 14.Docherty **15.Spain 4 Scotland 1**

Quiz 7

Quizzes about Qualifiers

1. **How many goalless draws were there in the 89 qualifying round matches for the 1958 finals?**
2. Where did Wales finish in Group 4 in which East Germany and Czechoslovakia also competed?
3. **How did Wales qualify in view of this position?**
4. Who did Wales meet in the two-leg group final?
5. **The score was the same in both legs. Did Wales win each time 1-0, 3-1 or 2-0?**
6. Who beat Finland 10-0 for the highest score of the 1958 qualifiers?
7. **Did USSR or Poland go through to the finals from this group?**
8. Two South American countries were exempt from the 1962 qualifying competition. Who?
9. **Which European country won 9-0 away to record the biggest score of the 1962 qualifiers?**
10. Who were their European victims?
11. **Two hat-tricks were scored in that match. Who got them?**
12. England's right-half against Luxembourg later became a famous manager. Name him.
13. **England dropped one point out of eight in the group. To whom?**
14. Who were the other British countries to reach the 1962 finals?
15. **Scotland went out on a play-off against which country?**

ANSWERS: **1.**Three 2.Second **3.They were elected to play in the Afro-Asian group final after many withdrawals** 4.Israel **5.2-0** 6.USSR **7.USSR** 8.Chile (hosts) & Brazil (holders) **9.England** 10.Luxembourg **11.Bobby Charlton & Jimmy Greaves** 12.Bobby Robson **13.Portugal** 14.None **15.Czechoslovakia**

Quiz 8

Quizzes about Qualifiers

1. **Who failed to win a point from four games in Scotland's 1962 group?**
2. The first match went to Scotland 4-1. Who was the only 'Anglo' in the side who scored two goals?
3. **How many Rangers players were in the Scotland team that day?**
4. Who scored twice for the Scots in the 3-2 defeat of Czechoslovakia?
5. **Who scored the two Scots' goals when the Czechs won the play-off 4-2?**
6. Which Scottish player was sent off in the Czechs' 4-0 victory in their first encounter?
7. **Northern Ireland were second in their group, but who were the qualifiers with four straight wins?**
8. What was the aggregate score over two legs by which Spain eliminated Wales? Was it 3-1, 3-2 or 4-2?
9. **How many matches did England play in the qualifying competition for the 1966 finals?**
10. Who also went directly through to the finals as holders?
11. **Which of the Home Countries qualified for the finals?**
12. How many points did Wales secure from their group matches with USSR, Denmark and Greece?
13. **Where did they finish in the group table?**
14. The Soviets were top with five wins out of six. Who beat them?
15. **Wales beat all three opponents in their group. How many did they lose?**

ANSWERS: **1.Eire** 2.David Herd (Arsenal) **3.Five - Shearer, Caldow, Baxter, Brand, Wilson** 4.Denis Law **5.Ian St John** 6.Pat Crerand **7.West Germany** 8.3-2 **9.None - they were exempt as hosts** 10.Brazil **11.None** 12.Six **13.Second** 14.Wales **15.Three**

Quiz 9

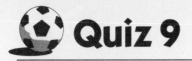

Quizzes about Qualifiers

1. **Eire's 1966 qualifying task involved three matches against Spain. Which country was the neutral venue for the third-match decider?**

2. Spain won the play-off. The score was 1-0, 2-0 or was it 2-1?

3. **Where did Northern Ireland finish in their group containing also Switzerland, Holland and Albania?**

4. Who pipped them to the qualification place by one point?

5. **Which team foiled them in the last group match by drawing 1-1?**

6. Group 8 in 1966 contained Italy, Finland, Poland and Scotland. Who went on to the finals?

7. **Where did Scotland finish in the table?**

8. Italy beat two of their opponents 6-1. Who were they?

9. **Who won both matches when Italy and Scotland met in the last two matches of the group?**

10. Who scored Scotland's only goal in those two games?

11. **Who captained the Scots in that match at Hampden Park?**

12. How many times did he skipper Scotland in World Cup action?

13. **Who was Scotland's manager during those matches?**

14. Who won his first Scottish cap in the Hampden qualifier against Poland?

15. **How old was he at the time?**

ANSWERS: 1.France 2.1-0 **3.Second** 4.Switzerland **5.Albania** 6.Italy **7.Second** 8.Finland & Poland **9.Neither - they won one each** 10.John Greig **11.Jim Baxter** 12.Once **13.Jock Stein** 14.Willie Johnston **15.18**

Quiz 10

Quizzes about Qualifiers

1. **Who did England beat to qualify for Mexico's first finals of 1970?**
2. How many of the other Home Countries joined England in Mexico?
3. **Eire shared a qualifying group with Czechoslovakia, Denmark and Hungary. Where did they finish?**
4. How many of their six matches did they win?
5. **Who did they hold to a draw?**
6. Who shared the top spot in this group on points?
7. **Who won the play-off 4-1 in France?**
8. Who were the top team in Scotland's group above Austria and Cyprus?
9. **Where did Scotland finish in the group table?**
10. Who top-scored in the qualifying series of 1970 by beating Cyprus 12-0?
11. **Against whom did West Germany drop their only group point?**
12. What was the score?
13. **Where was the match played?**
14. What was the estimated attendance at that game - 95,000, 105,000 or 115,000?
15. **Who equalised for Scotland two minutes from time?**

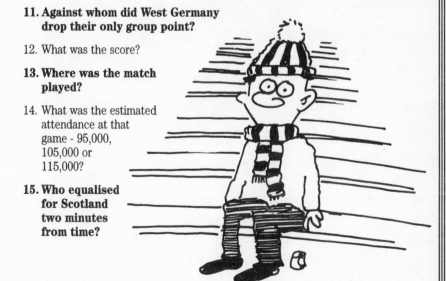

ANSWERS: 1.None - exempt as holders 2.None **3.Bottom** 4.None **5.Denmark 1-1** 6.Czechoslovakia & Hungary **7.Czechoslovakia** 8.West Germany **9.Second** 10.West Germany **11.Scotland** 12.1-1 **13.Hampden Park** 14.115,000 **15.Bobby Murdoch (Celtic)**

Quiz 11

Quizzes about Qualifiers

1. **Who scored West Germany's goal against Scotland at Hampden in the 1970 qualifying game there?**
2. Who saved the Germans from defeat by heading off the line in the last few seconds?
3. **In the return match in Hamburg, who scored West Germany's winning goal nine minutes from time - Muller, Seeler or Libuda?**
4. What was the final score?
5. **Who scored four goals for Scotland against Cyprus?**
6. What was the final score?
7. **Who had last scored four for Scotland in 1929?**
8. Who converted a penalty award for Scotland after Stein had scored four?
9. **How many did Stein score in the 5-0 win in Cyprus?**
10. Who was the Chelsea star playing in his last international at home to Cyprus?
11. **How many World Cup matches did he play for Scotland?**
12. Who scored twice, like Stein, in the match in Cyprus?
13. **Who later played nine World Cup matches for Scotland while with Tottenham?**
14. How many points did Wales take from their four games in Group 3?
15. **Who qualified from that group - Italy or East Germany?**

ANSWERS: 1.Gerd Muller 2.Franz Beckenbauer **3.Libuda** 4.3-2 **5.Colin Stein (Rangers)** 6.8-0 **7.Hughie Gallacher** 8.Tommy Gemmell (Celtic) **9.Two** 10.Eddie McCreadie **11.Eight** 12.Alan Gilzean (Tottenham) **13.Steve Archibald** 14.None **15.Italy**

Quiz 12 Quizzes about Qualifiers

1. Northern Ireland finished second in their three-nation group of the 1970 qualifiers, above Turkey. Who were top?

2. Who played out a goalless draw in that group against USSR?

3. The Soviets had won through from their previous two, or was it three or four, qualifying rounds?

4. How many of the eight European qualifying groups for Mexico were won with 100 per cent records?

5. In how many of the eight groups were countries left without a single point?

6. Which of these point-less teams conceded most goals?

7. Which of the four conceded the fewest goals?

8. Who qualified for their third consecutive finals from Group 8, made up of Bulgaria, Holland, Luxembourg and Poland?

9. Who finished bottom of these four in Group 1: Greece, Portugal, Romania, Switzerland?

10. Who won that group to qualify for their first post-War finals?

11. Are you fed up with answering questions on the 1970 qualifiers?

12. One final 1970 question. Who of Argentina, Brazil and Uruguay failed to qualify?

13. Why did West Germany go directly through to the 1974 finals, although they were only third in the 1970 finals?

14. England and Wales were in a three-team qualifying group for 1974. Who were the third members?

15. Who won the group to qualify for the 1974 finals?

ANSWERS: 1.USSR 2.Northern Ireland **3.Three** 4.None **5.Four - Wales, Turkey, Cyprus, Luxembourg** 6.Cyprus (35) **7.Wales (10)** 8.Bulgaria **9.Portugal** 10.Romania **11.Yes!** 12.Argentina **13.Exempt as hosts** 14.Poland **15.Poland**

Quiz 13

Quizzes about Qualifiers

1. **Who won through as sole representatives of Britain in the 1974 finals in West Germany?**
2. Poland lost one of their four qualifying games. Who beat them?
3. **What was the score - 1-0, 2-0 or 2-1?**
4. Who scored the only goal in England's opening win at Cardiff?
5. **What was the result of the return match at Wembley?**
6. Who stood in for Bobby Moore as captain in England's last group match at Wembley against Poland?
7. **Who scored his first international goal for Scotland against Denmark at Hampden in the 1974 qualifiers?**
8. What was the result?
9. **What was the score in Scotland's win in Denmark - 2-1, 4-1 or 6-1?**
10. In what order did Czechoslovakia and Denmark finish behind Scotland?
11. **Scotland qualified by beating the Czechs 2-1 at Hampden. Who was the 'Anglo' who scored the winning goal after substituting for Dalglish?**
12. Who won the Asian group of 1974 to qualify for the finals for their only time?
13. **Who did they beat in the group final in a play-off?**
14. How many matches did Australia play in the qualifying contest?
15. **Who did Australia beat 3-2 on aggregate in two matches before the group final?**

ANSWERS: 1.Scotland 2.Wales **3.2-0** 4.Colin Bell **5.1-1** 6.Martin Peters **7.Kenny Dalglish** 8.Scotland won 2-0 **9.4-1** 10.Czechs 2nd, Danes 3rd **11.Joe Jordan** 12.Australia **13.South Korea** 14.Eleven **15.Iran**

Quiz 14

Quizzes about Qualifiers

1. **Who qualified for the finals from the African group for the first and only time in 1974?**
2. How many matches did they play in qualifying?
3. **When was the first time England entered for the World Cup but failed to qualify?**
4. When was the second time?
5. **When was the first time for West Germany?**
6. In which World Cup year did the entries first total more than 100?
7. **Why didn't West Germany compete in the qualifying rounds for the 1978 finals in Argentina?**
8. Who were Britain's only qualifiers for the 1978 finals?

9. **Who were their two opponents in qualifying Group 7?**
10. How many players from Scottish clubs were in their first match against Czechoslovakia?
11. **Two of the 'Anglos' were from the same English club. Who were they?**
12. Who captained the Scots in that first match?
13. **Who did Wales beat 3-0 for their only group points?**
14. Were Wales second or third in the final table?
15. **East Germany recorded their biggest World Cup win over a Mediterranean country. Who was it?**

ANSWERS: 1.Zaire 2.Ten **3.1974** 4.1978 **5.Never** 6.1978 **7.Exempt as holders** 8.Scotland **9.Czechoslovakia & Wales** 10.Three **11. Bruce Rioch & Archie Gemmill (Derby County)** 12.Archie Gemmill **13.Czechoslovakia** 14.Third **15.Malta**

Quiz 15

Quizzes about Qualifiers

1. **Which Caribbean country beat fellow-Caribbeans Antigua 11-1 in the 1974 qualifying competition?**
2. Who then beat the 11-goal team to qualify for the only time in their World Cup history?
3. **Haiti finished second after 12 matches in the Central and North America qualifying group. Who beat them to join the 1978 finalists?**
4. The African group was won by a country who were to qualify again for the 1998 finals. Who were they?
5. **In third place in the African 1978 qualifiers were a country who later won through to the 1994 and 1998 finals. Who?**
6. In second place were finalists in Italy in 1934 and 1990. They were?
7. **Who won the group of Belgium, Holland, Iceland and Northern Ireland?**
8. Where did the Irish finish in the group table?
9. **Holland dropped only one point in their six games. To whom?**
10. East Germany crushed Malta 9-0. Who also beat the Maltese by the same margin?
11. **Who won the Asia/Oceania sector to qualify for the first time for the 1978 finals?**
12. When did they next qualify for the World Cup finals?
13. **Who were the third South American country to qualify for the 1978 finals with Argentina (hosts) and Brazil?**
14. Which former champions did Bolivia eliminate to join a final play-off group?
15. **Which East European country beat Bolivia in the play-off 6-0 and 3-2?**

ANSWERS: 1.Trinidad 2.Haiti **3.Mexico** 4.Tunisia **5.Nigeria** 6.Egypt **7.Holland** 8.Third **9.Northern Ireland** 10.Austria **11.Iran** 12.1998 **13.Peru** 14.Uruguay **15.Hungary**

Quiz 16 Quizzes about Qualifiers

1. **How many countries won through the qualifiers to the 1982 finals in Spain?**
2. Who made up the list of finalists as hosts and holders?
3. **How many more were in these finals than the previous series of 1978?**
4. Which of the Home Countries qualified for the 1982 finals?
5. **How many of the qualifiers, including hosts and holders, were from European countries?**
6. How many finals had England failed to reach since the War?
7. **Which were those years?**
8. This was how many times that Scotland had qualified?
9. **For how many finals before 1982 had Northern Ireland qualified?**
10. Which World Cup finals were those?
11. **How many finals places were allocated to Africa?**
12. Who were their 1982 qualifiers?
13. **When had they previously qualified?**
14. Only one country in the seven European groups won eight matches for a 100 per cent record. Who?
15. **One country won four out of four in the only three-team European group. Who?**

ANSWERS: 1. 22 2.Spain & Argentina **3.Eight** 4.England, Scotland, Northern Ireland **5.15** 6.Two **7.1974 & 1978** 8.Five **9.One** 10.Sweden 1958 **11.One** 12.Cameroon **13.Never** 14.West Germany **15.Poland**

Quiz 17

Quizzes about Qualifiers

1. **Wales failed to qualify in a group for the 1982 finals also including USSR, Czechoslovakia, Turkey and Iceland. Where did they finish in the table?**
2. How many points did Wales collect from eight games?
3. **How many points did England earn from their eight group games?**
4. How many points did Scotland win in their group?
5. **Northern Ireland, in the same group as Scotland, finished second with how many points?**
6. England's Group 4 opponents were Hungary, Norway, Romania and Switzerland. Who finished first and second?
7. **Who won the final match in the group - between Hungary and England at Wembley?**
8. Who scored England's goal?
9. **Who won their first match with Hungary in Budapest?**
10. England's captain scored one of the goals in Budapest. Who was he?
11. **England used two goalkeepers in their eight qualifiers. Name them.**
12. Which team won more points in the two matches between Scotland and Northern Ireland?
13. **What were the final scores in those two matches?**
14. Which country inflicted the only group defeat on Scotland - Israel, Portugal or Sweden?
15. **The Irish lost two group matches. To whom?**

ANSWERS: 1.Third 2.Ten **3.Nine** 4.Eleven **5.Nine** 6.Hungary first, England second **7.England 1-0** 8.Paul Mariner **9.England 3-1** 10.Kevin Keegan **11.Clemence & Shilton** 12.Both matches drawn **13.1-1 & 0-0** 14.Portugal 2-1 **15.Portugal & Sweden**

Quiz 18

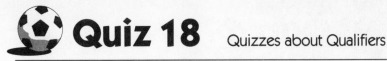

Quizzes about Qualifiers

1. Which European qualifier scored 11 goals more than the second highest scorers in the 1982 European sector?

2. How many did the West Germans total in qualifying - 29, 33 or 39?

3. Who were the second highest qualifying scorers?

4. Who recorded the biggest victory of 8-0 in the European qualifiers?

5. Which of their four rivals suffered this defeat - Albania, Austria, Bulgaria or Finland?

6. Who in that group were beaten 7-1 by West Germany?

7. Which of these three conceded most goals in the European qualifying sector - Cyprus, Finland or Luxembourg?

8. Eire were in Group 2, which also contained Belgium, Cyprus, France and Holland. Who won the group?

9. Eire finished equal on ten points but failed to qualify against which second qualifier?

10. The ultimate World Cup Final winners of 1982 were only second in Group 5. Who were those group runners-up?

11. Who headed the group - Denmark or Yugoslavia?

12. Who were the only country to beat Italy in the group games?

13. Argentina, as holders, and Brazil qualified from the South American qualifying groups. Who were the two others?

14. Which of the South American qualifiers won four out of four?

15. Only one of the nine competing South American teams in the qualifiers failed to win a match. Who were they - Colombia, Ecuador or Venezuela?

ANSWERS: 1.**West Germany** 2.33 3.**Yugoslavia** 4.West Germany 5.**Albania** 6.Finland 7.**Cyprus (29)** 8.Belgium 9.**France** 10.Italy 11.**Yugoslavia** 12.Denmark 3-1 13.**Chile & Peru** 14.Brazil 15.**Colombia**

Quiz 19

Quizzes about Qualifiers

1. Which country in the Asia/Oceania section of the 1982 qualifying competition set up a record in beating Fiji 13-0?

2. Who two days earlier had beaten Fiji 10-0?

3. Fiji gave away in eight qualifying matches how many goals - 35 or 45?

4. The two Central and North American qualifiers for 1982 came from this group of four: Canada, El Salvador, Honduras, Mexico. Who were they?

5. Which of this pair were in their first finals?

6. In how many previous finals had the other qualifier appeared?

7. Which of the four Home Countries failed to qualify for the 1986 World Cup finals in Mexico?

8. What was the finishing order in Group 7 from Iceland, Scotland, Spain and Wales?

9. Who secured three of the four points at stake in the matches between Scotland and Wales?

10. Who did Scotland beat in a play-off over two legs to reach the finals?

11. Another play-off involved group runners-up Holland and Belgium. Who qualified on away goals?

12. Who kept goal for the Scots in all eight qualifiers, conceding only four goals?

13. Who scored in Wales' 1-0 defeat of Scotland at Hampden?

14. Who scored the Welsh goal in the 1-1 return match in Cardiff?

15. Who converted a penalty for Scotland's equaliser nine minutes from time?

ANSWERS: **1.New Zealand** 2.Australia **3.35** 4.El Salvador & Honduras **5.Honduras** 6.One - in 1970 **7.Wales** 8.Spain, Scotland, Wales, Iceland **9.Wales** 10.Australia **11.Belgium** 12.Jim Leighton **13.Ian Rush** 14.Mark Hughes **15.Davie Cooper**

Quiz 20

Quizzes about Qualifiers

1. **Who finished second to England in Group 3 for both to qualify for the 1986 finals?**
2. In what finishing order were the other group members - Romania, Finland, Turkey?
3. **England were unbeaten in their eight group matches. How many did they win?**
4. How many goals were scored in the two matches between England and Northern Ireland?
5. **Who scored for England against the Irish?**
6. How many goals did England score in two games against Turkey? Eleven, 13 or 15?
7. **Who were the hat-trick scorers for England in those matches?**
8. Which country drew both matches with England in the qualifiers?
9. **England conceded only two goals in their eight qualifiers, to Romania and who else?**
10. Group 6 was contested by Denmark, Eire, Norway, Switzerland, USSR. Which two progressed to the finals?
11. **Where did Eire finish in the group table?**
12. Who were the top scorers of the European groups?
13. **How many did they score in eight games?**
14. Who were second highest Europeans to West Germany?
15. **What was their goals total from eight games?**

ANSWERS: **1.Northern Ireland** 2.In that order **3.Four** 4.One **5.Mark Hateley** 6.13 **7.Bryan Robson, Tony Woodcock** 8.Romania **9.Finland** 10.Denmark & USSR **11.Fourth** 12.West Germany **13.22** 14.England **15.21**

Quiz 21

Quizzes about Qualifiers

1. **West Germany were beaten once in their 1986 qualifying group of five teams. Who achieved this of the following: Czechoslovakia, Malta, Portugal, Sweden?**
2. West Germany beat Malta 6-0 at home. What was the score in Malta?
3. **Who scored only nine goals in eight games yet qualified?**
4. Who scored only ten goals in eight games and qualified?
5. **Who scored 16 goals in eight games and finished only third in their group, thus failing to qualify?**
6. Who finished one point above them level on points for both to qualify?
7. **Two of these four bottom teams in the European groups won one point each: Malta, Turkey, Luxembourg, Cyprus. Name them.**
8. Who in Malta's group (see Question 1) were held to a goalless draw on the island pitch?
9. **Canada, Costa Rica and Honduras contested the final qualifying round of the North and Central America sector. Who won it?**
10. How often had these winners appeared in previous World Cup finals?
11. **What happened in the Canada v Jamaica fixture?**
12. Which two of these African group finalists qualified for Mexico - Algeria, Libya, Morocco, Tunisia?
13. **Which of these four eliminated Nigeria 2-1 over two legs?**
14. Which two of these four qualified from the Asian group - Iraq, Japan, South Korea, Syria?
15. **Who won a South American play-off decider to join Brazil, Argentina and Uruguay in the 1986 finals - Paraguay or Chile?**

ANSWERS: 1.Portugal (away 1-0) 2.Malta 2, West Germany 3 **3.Belgium** 4.Scotland **5.East Germany** 6.France & Bulgaria **7.Malta & Turkey** 8.Czechoslovakia **9.Canada** 10.Never **11.Jamaica withdrew** 12.Algeria & Morocco **13.Tunisia** 14.Iraq & South Korea **15.Paraguay**

Quiz 22

Quizzes about Qualifiers

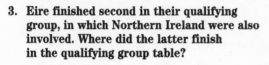

1. **Which country from the British Isles qualified for Italy 1990, their first time in a World Cup finals stage?**
2. Who was their English manager?
3. **Eire finished second in their qualifying group, in which Northern Ireland were also involved. Where did the latter finish in the qualifying group table?**
4. Who won three points out of four in the two all-Irish clashes?
5. **Who finished top of this group - Hungary or Spain?**
6. Spain suffered one defeat in Group 6. Who beat them?
7. **Who were the only European country to fail to win a point in the 1990 qualifiers?**
8. Whom did Malta twice hold to a draw?

9. **Scotland finished second to qualify. Which of these won the group - Cyprus, France, Norway, Yugoslavia?**
10. Scotland lost away twice. Who beat them?
11. **Who kept goal in place of Jim Leighton in one of Scotland's eight qualifying matches?**
12. Who finished above West Germany by one point in Group 4?
13. **West Germany were held to 0-0 draws by two countries. Who were they?**
14. The Germans also drew 1-1. With whom?
15. **How many games did Wales win in the 1990 qualifiers?**

ANSWERS: 1.Eire 2.Jack Charlton **3.Fourth** 4.Eire **5.Spain** 6.Eire 1-0 **7.Albania** 8.Hungary **9.Yugoslavia** 10.Yugoslavia & France **11.Andy Goram** 12.Holland **13.Holland & Wales** 14.Holland **15.None**

Quiz 23

Quizzes about Qualifiers

1. **England qualified from Group 2. Which of Sweden and Poland went through with them to the Italy 1990 finals?**
2. Who finished top of the group?
3. **One of the European countries qualified without conceding a single goal in six matches. Who were they?**
4. What were the results of the two matches between Sweden and England?
5. **Who stood in as captain for Bryan Robson in one of the six qualifiers?**
6. Who came on as a substitute to score against Albania at Wembley?
7. **Who were Africa's two qualifiers from these final four - Algeria, Cameroon, Egypt, Tunisia?**
8. Which of the six Asian group final contestants qualified for the Italy finals - China, North Korea, Qatar, Saudi Arabia, South Korea, United Arab Emirates?
9. **USA qualified for the finals. Was it for their second, third or fourth World Cup tournament?**
10. Costa Rica also qualified from the North/Central America zone. Was it their first or second World Cup finals?
11. **Colombia qualified in a play-off against the Oceania champions. Who were they?**
12. Was this Colombia's first time in the World Cup finals?
13. **Who were South America's other 1990 finalists?**
14. Whose goalkeeper attempted to have the match with Brazil abandoned, feigning blindness from an exploding firework?
15. **FIFA awarded Brazil the tie with what scoreline?**

ANSWERS: **1.Sweden** 2.Sweden **3.England** 4.Both 0-0 **5.Terry Butcher** 6.Paul Gascoigne **7.Cameroon & Egypt** 8.South Korea & United Arab Emirates **9.Fourth** 10.First **11.Israel** 12.No - second **13.Brazil, Uruguay, Argentina (holders)** 14.Chile's **15.2-0**

Quiz 24

Quizzes about Qualifiers

1. **Which of the Home Countries qualified for the 1994 finals in the USA?**
2. Which two nations pushed England into third place in the group - and out of the finals?
3. **Who scored four for England in their last 1994 qualifier?**
4. Who did they beat and what was the score?
5. **Who scored four for England in their first match with San Marino?**
6. Who was England's skipper in that match?
7. **Who was captain in the second San Marino meeting?**
8. Where did Scotland finish in their group of six made up of Estonia, Italy, Malta, Portugal and Switzerland?
9. **From which of those nations did Malta win their only point in ten matches with a 0-0 home draw?**
10. Eire ended their qualifiers level on points with Denmark but went through to the finals again on goals superiority. Where in the table did they finish?
11. **Who finished ahead of them by one point?**
12. Which near neighbour of Eire ended fourth in that group and were eliminated?
13. **Who did West Germany beat to qualify for the 1994 finals?**
14. How many points did the Faroe Islands collect from their ten group matches on their debut in European qualifiers?
15. **Who were the two top-scoring nations in the European groups with 29 goals apiece?**

ANSWERS: 1.None 2.Norway & Holland **3.Ian Wright** 4.San Marino 7-1 **5.David Platt** 6.David Platt **7.Stuart Pearce** 8.Fourth **9.Estonia** 10.Second **11.Spain** 12.Northern Ireland **13.None - exempt as holders** 14.None **15.Holland & Romania**

Quiz 25

Quizzes about Qualifiers

1. **Where did Wales finish in the group headed by Romania in the 1994 qualifying rounds?**
2. Their biggest group win was 6-0 against whom?
3. **Who beat Wales 5-1 for their biggest group defeat?**
4. Who qualified for their first World Cup finals after beating both Hungary and Russia 1-0 in qualifying games?

5. **Who finished second to them to qualify also for the finals?**
6. Who qualified from Group 6 which included Austria, Bulgaria, France and Sweden?
7. **Brazil had to win the last of their eight games to be sure of qualifying for their 15th World Cup finals. Who was this against?**
8. Where did Uruguay finish in their South American group?
9. **Who were second to Brazil to qualify for their third World Cup finals?**
10. Who headed the other South American group to qualify?
11. **Argentina were second and had to meet the Oceania winners in a play-off. Who was that?**
12. Who won that play-off and what was the aggregate for the two matches?
13. **Which two qualified from the Asian sector involving these six: Iran, Iraq, Japan, North Korea, Saudi Arabia, South Korea?**
14. Who were the two African nations qualifying for the third time for the World Cup finals?
15. **Which was the third African country to go to the USA finals, for their first time?**

ANSWERS: 1.Fourth 2.Faroe Islands **3.Romania** 4.Greece **5.Russia** 6.Sweden & Bulgaria **7.Uruguay** 8.Third **9.Bolivia** 10.Colombia **11.Australia** 12.Argentina 2-1 **13.Saudi Arabia & South Korea** 14. Cameroon & Morocco **15.Nigeria**

The Great Europeans

Quiz 1

The Great Europeans
France

1. **France played in the first ever World Cup game. True or false?**
2. Who were their opponents?
3. **Who scored France's first goal - Laurent, Langiller or Maschinot?**
4. In the three group games, France played non-Europeans nations. True or false?
5. **Who were these opponents?**
6. Who beat France 1-0 in the second group game?
7. **Who was captain of France?**
8. How many goals did France score in the 1930 finals?
9. **How many games did France play in Italy 1934?**
10. What was the score in that game?
11. **Who were the opposition?**
12. Who scored a penalty for France in that game - Nicolas or Verriest?
13. **Who did France beat in their first game as hosts in 1938?**
14. What was the score - 2-0, 3-1 or 4-3?
15. **Who scored twice for France in that game - Colaussi, Nicolas or Piola?**

ANSWERS **1. True** 2. Mexico **3. Pierre Laurent** 4. True **5. Mexico, Argentina, Chile** 6. Argentina **7. Alex Villaplane** 8. Four **9. One** 10. France lost 3-2 (after extra time) **11. Austria** 12. Verriest **13. Belgium** 14. 3-1 **15. Jean Nicolas**

Quiz 2

The Great Europeans
France

1. **When was the last time France qualified for the World Cup before hosting the 1998 tournament?**
2. Who beat France in the second round in 1938?
3. **How many World Cup games did France play in 1938?**
4. Who beat them in the first game of the 1954 finals?
5. **Who were beaten 3-2 by France in the second match?**
6. France scored a vital penalty goal in that match, taken by Raymond who?
7. **How many goals did France score in their first World Cup match in 1958? Was it 2, 7 or 9?**
8. Who were their opponents from South America?
9. **Who scored a hat-trick for France in that match?**
10. Which British nation was the first to face France in World Cup finals?
11. **What was the score?**
12. Fontaine scored in every French game in 1958. True or false?
13. **Who inflicted defeat on France in the group stage in 1958?**
14. How many World Cup goals did Fontaine score in that tournament?
15. **Who did France beat in the quarter-finals?**

ANSWERS **1. 1986** 2. Italy **3. Two** 4. Yugoslavia **5. Mexico** 6. Raymond Kopa **7. Seven** 8. Paraguay **9. Just Fontaine** 10. Scotland **11. France won 2-1** 12. True **13. Yugoslavia** 14. Thirteen **15. Northern Ireland**

Quiz 3

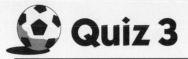

The Great Europeans
France

1. **What was the score in the 1958 France v Northern Ireland quarter-final?**
2. Who did France face in the semi-finals?
3. **What was the score?**
4. The third place play-off produced nine goals. How many did France score?
5. **Who scored four of them?**
6. Who were the opposition?
7. **How many points did France finish with at the 1966 finals?**
8. Who were their first, non-European opponents?
9. **What was the score?**
10. A 2-0 defeat ended France's 1966 tournament. Who beat them?
11. **When was the next time France qualified?**
12. France suffered two 2-1 defeats in Argentina in 1978. By whom?
13. **Who scored for France against Argentina?**
14. Whom did France beat 3-1 in the final group game?
15. **Who were France's opening opponents in 1982?**

ANSWERS 1. 4-0 2. Brazil **3. France lost 5-2** 4. Six **5. Fontaine** 6. West Germany **7. One** 8. Mexico **9. 1-1** 10. England **11. 1978** 12. Italy and Argentina **13. Michel Platini** 14. Hungary **15. England**

Quiz 4

The Great Europeans
France

1. **What was the score in the France v England match in 1982?**
2. Who scored France's goal - Platini, Six or Soler?
3. **Who in their only World Cup finals were beaten 4-1 in France's next match?**
4. Who were the French scorers?
5. **Which Europeans held France 1-1 in the final group match?**
6. Who were France's opponents in the second-round group?
7. **What was France's winning score against Austria?**
8. Who were beaten 4-1 by France in the second stage?
9. **Which two players scored twice in the game?**
10. Who were France's 1982 semi-final opponents?
11. **Who in extra time scored France's third goal?**
12. What was the score after extra time?
13. **What was the score in the penalty shoot-out?**
14. Who were France's opponents in the third place play-off?
15. **Who won the match?**

ANSWERS 1. France lost 3-1 2. Soler **3. Kuwait** 4. Genghini, Platini, Six and Bossis **5. Czechoslovakia** 6. Austria and Northern Ireland **7. 1-0** 8. Northern Ireland **9. Alain Giresse and Dominique Rocheteau** 10. West Germany **11. Alain Giresse** 12. 3-3 **13. West Germany won 5-4** 14. Poland **15. Poland**

Quiz 5

The Great Europeans
France

1. **What was the score in the 1982 play-off?**
2. Who were France's first opponents from across the Atlantic in 1986?
3. **What was the score?**
4. Who scored France's goal?
5. **Which team from Eastern Europe drew 1-1 with France in the second match?**
6. Who were beaten 3-0 by France in the group stages?
7. **Which country, previous World Cup winners, were beaten by France in the second round?**
8. What was the score?
9. **Who scored the first goal?**
10. Who scored against Brazil in the classic 1-1 quarter-final match?
11. **What was the score in the penalty shoot-out?**
12. Who were France's semi-final opponents?
13. **What was the score?**
14. What did France win by in the third place play-off - 2-0, 1-0 or 4-2?
15. **Who were their opponents?**

ANSWERS 1. Poland won 3-2 2. Canada **3. France won 1-0** 4. Jean-Pierre Papin **5. USSR** 6. Hungary **7. Italy** 8. 2-0 **9. Platini** 10. Platini **11. France won 4-3** 12. West Germany **13. France lost 2-0** 14. 4-2 **15. Belgium**

Quiz 6

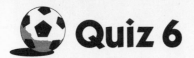

The Great Europeans
Italy

1. **Who were Italy's first ever World Cup opponents?**
2. What year was it?
3. **What was the score?**
4. Who scored a hat-trick?
5. **Which player with a famous surname scored for Italy in the second round against Spain?**
6. What was the score in that game?
7. **What was the score in the replay?**
8. Who did Italy meet in the semi-final?
9. **Who scored the only goal?**
10. Who were their opponents in the Final?
11. **Who scored the winning goal in extra time of the Final?**
12. Who was Italy's captain?
13. **Who were Italy's first opponents in 1938 - Norway or France?**
14. What was the score after extra time in that match?
15. **Which two Italian players scored in both the 1934 and 1938 tournaments?**

ANSWERS 1. USA 2. 1934 **3. Italy won 7-1** 4. Schiavio **5. Ferrari** 6. 1-1 after extra time **7. Italy won 1-0** 8. Austria **9. Guaita** 10. Czechoslovakia **11. Schiavio** 12. Combi **13. Norway** 14. Italy won 2-1 **15. Ferrari and Meazza**

Quiz 7

The Great Europeans
Italy

1. **Whom did Italy beat in the second round in 1938?**
2. Who were Italy's 1938 semi-final opponents?
3. **Which two players both scored twice for Italy in the 1938 Final?**
4. Who were the beaten finalists?
5. **Who were the first team to beat Italy in the World Cup?**
6. Who scored Italy's goals in that 3-2 defeat?
7. **Who did Italy beat in their second game in 1950?**
8. Did Italy qualify for the second round?
9. **Italy suffered another opening defeat in 1954. Was it by Belgium or Switzerland?**
10. Whom did Italy beat in the next game?
11. **What was the score?**
12. Who did Italy face twice in 1954?
13. **Who knocked Italy out of the 1954 finals?**
14. What was the score?
15. **Who scored Italy's consolation goal?**

ANSWERS 1. France 2. Brazil **3. Colaussi and Piola** 4. Hungary **5. Sweden in 1950** 6. Carapallesse and Muccinelli **7. Paraguay** 8. No **9. Switzerland** 10. Belgium **11. 4-1** 12. Switzerland **13. Switzerland** 14. 4-1 **15. Nesti**

Quiz 8

The Great Europeans
Italy

1. **Who were in Italy's group in 1962?**
2. How many wins did Italy pick up in 1962?
3. **Who shared a goalless draw with Italy in the group?**
4. Italy played Switzerland in the group. What was the score?
5. **Which team beat Italy in the 1962 group stage?**
6. Who were Italy's 2-0 opening victims in England in 1966?
7. **How many more goals did Italy score in that tournament?**
8. Who beat Italy in their second game?
9. **Who produced the shock of 1966 by beating Italy in the last group game?**
10. What was the score?
11. **Who were in Italy's group in 1970 alongside Uruguay and Sweden?**
12. Who scored Italy's first goal in 1970?
13. **Who were the opponents?**
14. What was the score?
15. **How many more goals did Italy score in the group stage?**

ANSWERS 1. West Germany, Chile and Switzerland 2. One **3. West Germany** 4. Italy won 3-0 **5. Chile** 6. Chile **7. None** 8. USSR **9. North Korea** 10. 1-0 **11. Israel** 12. Domenghini **13. Sweden** 14. 1-0 **15. None**

Quiz 9

The Great Europeans
Italy

1. **Who held Italy to a shock 0-0 draw in 1970?**
2. Who were beaten 4-1 by Italy in the quarter-final?
3. **Who scored two for Italy in that game?**
4. Who were Italy's opponents in a classic semi-final?
5. **What was the score after extra time?**
6. Who scored the winning goal?
7. **Who scored Italy's goal in the 4-1 Final defeat by Brazil?**
8. Who were Italy's opening victims in 1974?
9. **What was the score?**
10. Italy drew 1-1 against a South American side in the group. Who was it?
11. **Who knocked out Italy by beating them in Stuttgart?**
12. What was the score?
13. **Who scored Italy's consolation goal?**
14. How many goals did Italy score in the 1978 finals?
15. **Which legendary player scored Italy's opening goal in 1978?**

ANSWERS **1. Israel** 2. Mexico **3. Luigi Riva** 4. West Germany **5. Italy won 4-3** 6. Rivera **7. Boninsegna** 8. Haiti **9. 3-1** 10. Argentina **11. Poland** 12. 2-1 **13. Capello** 14. Nine **15. Paolo Rossi**

Quiz 10

The Great Europeans
Italy

1. **Who were beaten 3-1 by Italy in the 1978 group stage - Hungary or Argentina?**
2. What was the score between Italy and Argentina?
3. **Who scored Italy's goal?**
4. Who were Italy's three European opponents in the second-stage group? Name two.
5. **Who was the only Italian player to score in the second stage?**
6. What was the score in Italy's game against Holland?
7. **Who scored Italy's goal?**
8. Who were Italy's opponents in the third place play-off?
9. **Who won?**
10. Who scored for Italy?
11. **How many group games did Italy win in Spain 1982?**
12. Apart from Cameroon, who were Italy's other opponents in the group?
13. **Which two nations each held Italy to a 1-1 draw in the group?**
14. Who did Italy beat 2-1 in the second round group stage?
15. **Who scored a hat-trick for Italy against Brazil in the same stage?**

ANSWERS **1. Hungary** 2. Italy won 1-0 **3. Roberto Bettega** 4. West Germany, Austria and Holland **5. Paolo Rossi** 6. Holland won 2-1 **7. Brandts own goal** 8. Brazil **9. Brazil 2-1** 10. Causio **11. None** 12. Poland and Peru **13. Peru and Cameroon** 14. Argentina **15. Paolo Rossi**

Quiz 11

The Great Europeans
Italy

1. **Who were Italy's 1982 semi-final opponents?**
2. Who scored twice for Italy in that game?
3. **What was the score?**
4. Who scored Italy's final goal against West Germany in the Final?
5. **What was Italy's winning score?**
6. Who scored Italy's first goal in Mexico 1986?
7. **How many scorers did Italy have in the first round in 1986?**
8. How many goals did Alessandro Altobelli score in 1986?
9. **Who scored Italy's third goal in the game against South Korea?**
10. Who knocked out Italy in the second round?
11. **How many goals did Italy concede in the first five games of 1990?**
12. Who were beaten in the opening game - Austria or USA?
13. **Who scored the goals in Italy's 2-0 win over Czechoslovakia?**
14. Who scored Italy's second goal in their 2-0 second-round win - Schillaci or Serena?
15. **Who were their opponents?**

ANSWERS 1. Poland 2. Rossi **3. 2-0** 4. Alessandro Altobelli **5. 3-1** 6. Altobelli **7. One** 8. Four **9. Kwang-rae of South Korea own goal** 10. France **11. None** 12. Austria **13. Toto Schillaci, Roberto Baggio** 14. Aldo Serena **15. Uruguay**

Quiz 12

The Great Europeans
Italy

1. Who beat Italy on penalties in the 1990 semi-final?

2. What was the score after extra time?

3. Who scored a goal each for Italy in the 1990 third place play-off?

4. Who were Italy's opponents in that game?

5. Who were Italy's first opponents in 1994?

6. What was the score?

7. Which Italian player was sent off in the match against Norway?

8. What was the score in that game?

9. Who scored Italy's goal?

10. Who were Italy's second-round opponents?

11. Who scored twice for Italy against them?

12. Who was sent off against Nigeria after coming on as a sub?

13. Both Baggios scored in Italy's quarter-final win over Spain. Who scored first?

14. Whom did Italy beat in the semi-finals?

15. Who missed penalties for Italy in the Final shoot-out?

ANSWERS **1. Argentina** 2. 1-1 **3. Roberto Baggio, Toto Schillaci** 4. England **5. Republic of Ireland** 6. Italy lost 1-0 **7. Gianluca Pagliuca** 8. Italy won 1-0 **9. Dino Baggio** 10. Nigeria **11. Roberto Baggio** 12. Gianfranco Zola **13. Dino** 14. Bulgaria **15. Baresi, Massaro and Roberto Baggio**

Quiz 13

The Great Europeans
Holland

1. **In what year was Holland's first World Cup appearance?**
2. Which European nation were their first opponents?
3. **What was the score?**
4. Who scored Holland's first World Cup goal?
5. **How many games did Holland win in their first World Cup finals?**
6. When was Holland's second World Cup appearance?
7. **How many games did they play in that series?**
8. Who were their opponents in 1938?
9. **What was the score after 90 minutes?**
10. And the score after extra-time?
11. **When did Holland win their first World Cup game?**
12. Which country hosted that tournament?
13. **Who were Holland's first opponents in those finals?**
14. What was the score?
15. **Who scored for Holland?**

ANSWERS: 1. 1934 2. Switzerland **3. 3-2 to Switzerland** 4. Saait **5. None** 6. 1938 **7. One** 8. Czechoslovakia **9. 0-0** 10. Holland lost 3-0 **11. 1974** 12. West Germany **13. Uruguay** 14. 2-0 to Holland **15. Johnny Rep**

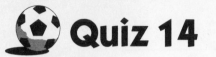

Quiz 14 The Great Europeans Holland

1. Who were Holland's second opponents in 1974?
2. **What was the score?**
3. How many goals did Holland concede in the first round group stage?
4. **How many goals did they score in their final first round match?**
5. Who were their opponents?
6. **What was the final score in that game?**
7. Who scored twice in that match for Holland?
8. **Which other two Dutchmen scored in that game?**
9. Which Dutch player scored an own goal?
10. **Did Holland qualify for the quarter-finals?**
11. Who did Johan Cruyff score his first World Cup goal against?
12. **Who were Holland's first quarter-final group opponents?**
13. What was the final score?
14. **How many goals did Cruyff score in that game?**
15. Who were beaten by Holland in the following match?

ANSWERS: 1. Sweden **2. 0-0** 3. One **4. Four** 5. Bulgaria **6. 4-1** 7. Johan Neeskens **8. Rep, De Jong** 9. Ruud Krol **10. Yes** 11. Argentina **12. Argentina** 13. 4-0 to Holland **14. Two** 15. East Germany

Quiz 15

The Great Europeans
Holland

1. **Who scored for Holland against East Germany in 1974?**
2. How many goals did Holland concede in the 1974 finals?
3. **Who did Holland have to beat to qualify for the 1974 Final?**
4. What was the score in that match?
5. **Who scored for Holland?**
6. Which player captained Holland in the 1974 Final?
7. **Who scored Holland's goal in the Final?**
8. In which minute did he score?
9. **What was the half-time score in the Final?**
10. Who was the Dutch manager in 1974?
11. **Who was Holland's top goalscorer in 1974?**
12. How many did he score?
13. **Who were Holland's first opponents in the 1978 finals?**
14. What was the score?
15. **Who scored a hat-trick in that game?**

ANSWERS: 1. Johan Neeskens, Rob Resenbrink 2. Three **3. Brazil** 4. 2-0 to Holland **5. Johan Neeskens, Johan Cruyff** 6. Johan Cruyff **7. Johan Neeskens** 8. First **9. 2-1 to West Germany** 10. Rinus Michels **11. Johan Neeskens** 12. Five **13. Iran** 14. 3-0 to Holland **15. Rob Rensenbrink**

Quiz 16

The Great Europeans Holland

1. How many of Rensenbrink's goals against Iran in 1978 were penalties?
2. **Who held Holland to a draw in the second match of the first round in 1978?**
3. What was the score?
4. **How many games did Holland win in the group stages?**
5. Who defeated Holland in the final group match?
6. **What was the score?**
7. Before that result, Holland had been unbeaten for how many games?
8. **Who were Holland's first opponents in the second-round group stages?**
9. What was the score in that match?
10. **Who scored twice in that game for Holland?**
11. Which Dutch brothers both scored in the second round stage?
12. **Which brother scored against Austria?**
13. Who were Holland's second opponents in the second round?
14. **What was the score?**
15. Who scored Holland's first goal?

ANSWERS: 1. Two **2. Peru** 3. 0-0 **4. One** 5. Scotland **6. 2-3** 7. Two **8. Austria** 9. 5-1 to Holland **10. Johnny Rep** 11. Willie and Rene Van der Kerkhof **12. Willie** 13. West Germany **14. 2-2** 15. Arie Haan

Quiz 17 The Great Europeans Holland

1. **Which European nation did Holland have to beat to reach the 1978 Final?**
2. What was the score?
3. **Who scored for both teams in that match?**
4. Who scored the winner for Holland?
5. **Which legendary player did not play for Holland in the 1978 finals?**
6. Who scored Holland's equaliser in the 1978 Final?
7. **When was the next time Holland qualified for the finals?**
8. Who scored for Holland in the opening match of the 1990 tournament?
9. **Who were their African opponents in that game?**
10. How many group games did Holland draw in 1990?
11. **Whom did Holland meet in the World Cup for the first time in the second match of the group?**
12. What was the score?
13. **Who were Holland's final group opponents?**
14. Who scored for Holland in that final match?
15. **What was the final score in that game?**

ANSWERS: 1. Italy 2. 2-1 to Holland **3. Brandts** 4. Arie Haan **5. Johan Cruyff** 6. Nanninga **7. 1990** 8. Wim Kieft **9. Egypt** 10. Three **11. England** 12. 0-0 **13. Republic of Ireland** 14. Ruud Gullit **15. 1-1**

Quiz 18

The Great Europeans
Holland

1. Whom did Holland meet in the second round in 1990?

2. Where was that game played?

3. Who scored for Holland in that match?

4. What was the final score in that game?

5. Which two players scored in Holland's opening match of the 1994 finals?

6. Who were their opponents in that game?

7. Who were Holland's opponents in their second match?

8. What was the score?

9. Holland won their final group game 2-1. Who were their scorers?

10. Who were their opponents in that game?

11. Whom did Holland face in the second round?

12. What was the score?

13. Who were the Dutch scorers?

14. Who were Holland's opponents in the quarter-final?

15. What was the score in that game?

ANSWERS: 1. West Germany **2. Milan** 3. Ronald Koeman **4. 2-1 to West Germany** 5. Wim Jonk, Gausten Taument **6. Saudi Arabia** 7. Belgium **8. 1-0 to Belgium** 9. Dennis Bergkamp, Bryan Roy **10. Morocco** 11. Republic of Ireland **12. 2-0 to Holland** 13. Dennis Bergkamp, Wim Jonk **14. Brazil** 15. 3-2 to Brazil

Quiz 19

The Great Europeans
Spain

1. **What year did Spain play their first match in the World Cup?**
2. Who were their opponents?
3. **What was the score?**
4. Who scored twice in that match?
5. **Who were Spain's second round opponents?**
6. What was the score after extra time?
7. **Did the match go to penalties or a replay?**
8. What was the final score in the tie?
9. **Did Spain play in the 1938 finals?**
10. Who did Spain first play in 1950?
11. **Who won?**
12. Who did Spain meet in their second match in 1950?
13. **How many goals did Spain concede in the group stages?**
14. Which Spanish player scored in all three group games?
15. **Who scored the winner for Spain in their final group match?**

ANSWERS **1. 1934** 2. Brazil **3. 3-1 to Spain** 4. Langara **5. Italy** 6. 1-1 **7. Replay** 8. 1-0 to Italy **9. No** 10. USA **11. Spain** 12. Chile **13. 1** 14. Zarra **15. Zarra**

Quiz 20

The Great Europeans
Spain

1. **Who were Spain's opponents in their last group match in 1950?**
2. What was the final score?
3. **Who had scored twice in Spain's opening game?**
4. Who drew with Spain in the first match of the final pool in 1950?
5. **Who scored twice for Spain in that game?**
6. What was the score in Spain's next match?
7. **Which country defeated them?**
8. Who scored for Spain?
9. **Who beat Spain 3-1 in their last match of 1950?**
10. How many goals did Spain score in 1962?
11. **Who were their first opponents?**
12. Who did Spain beat in the second match?
13. **Who then beat Spain and knocked them out of the 1962 tournament?**
14. What was the score?
15. **Who beat Spain in their first match of the 1966 finals?**

ANSWERS **1. England** 2. 1-0 to Spain **3. Basora** 4. Uruguay **5. Basora** 6. They lost 6-1 **7. Brazil** 8. Igoa **9. Sweden** 10. One **11. Czechoslovakia** 12. Mexico **13. Brazil** 14. 3-1 **15. Argentina**

Quiz 21

The Great Europeans Spain

1. What was the score in Spain's defeat by Argentina in 1966?

2. Where was that match played?

3. How many games did Spain lose in 1966?

4. Who else beat Spain in 1966?

5. How many different players scored for Spain in 1966?

6. When was the next time Spain played in the World Cup?

7. Who were their first opponents?

8. What was the score?

9. Who scored for Spain?

10. Who did Spain hold to a draw in the next game?

11. Who were Spain's last group opponents ?

12. What was the score?

13. Did Spain make it to the second round?

14. Did Spain take part in the 1982 finals?

15. What was special for them about this tournament?

ANSWERS 1. 2-1 2. Villa Park **3. Three** 4. Switzerland and West Germany **5. Four** 6. 1978 **7. Austria** 8. Spain lost 2-1 **9. Dani** 10. Brazil **11. Sweden** 12. 1-0 to Spain **13. No** 14. Yes **15. They were hosts**

Quiz 22

The Great Europeans
Spain

1. **Who held Spain to a draw in their opening game in 1982?**
2. Two of Spain's three first round goals were penalties. True or false?
3. **Who were Spain's opponents in their second match in 1982?**
4. Who were their final group opponents?
5. **What was the score of that match?**
6. Who were in the second round group with Spain?
7. **Who beat Spain 2-1 in the second round?**
8. Who scored Spain's only goal in the second round?
9. **Who faced Spain in the first round in both 1982 and 1986?**
10. Who was Spain's opening game against in 1986?
11. **Northern Ireland scored twice against Spain in the 1986 finals. True or false?**
12. What was the score in the game between the two?
13. **Who scored Spain's first goal of the 1986 finals?**
14. Which veteran striker scored for in 1986, 1990 and 1994?
15. **Who did Spain beat in the final group game of 1986?**

ANSWER **1. Honduras** 2. True **3. Yugoslavia** 4. Northern Ireland **5. 1-0 to Northern Ireland** 6. West Germany and England **7. West Germany** 8. Zamora **9. Northern Ireland** 10. Brazil **11. False** 12. 2-1 to Spain **13. Emilio Butragueno** 14. Julio Salinas **15. Algeria**

Quiz 23

The Great Europeans Spain

1. **What was the score in the Spain v Algeria game in 1986?**
2. Who scored twice in that match?
3. **Who were Spain's opponents in the second round?**
4. Who scored four goals for Spain in that game?
5. **What was the final score?**
6. How many penalties were scored in that match?
7. **Who did Spain meet in the quarter-finals in 1986?**
8. What round did they reach that year?
9. **What was the score after extra-time in the quarter-final?**
10. Who scored for Spain?
11. **What was the score on penalties?**
12. Who scored Spain's first goal of the 1990 finals?
13. **Who were their first opponents in 1990?**
14. What was the score in that game?
15. **Who scored a hat-trick in Spain's second match?**

ANSWERS **1. Spain won 3-0** 2. Caldere **3. Denmark** 4. Butragueno **5. Spain won 5-1** 6. Three **7. Belgium** 8. Quarter-finals **9. 1-1** 10. Senor **11. 5-4 to Belgium** 12. Gonzalez **13. Uruguay** 14. 0-0 **15. Gonzalez**

Quiz 24

The Great Europeans
Spain

1. **Who were Spain's second opponents in 1990?**
2. Which European nation did Spain meet in both 1986 and 1990?
3. **What was the score in Spain's final group match of 1990?**
4. Who were their opponents?
5. **In which year did Spain first meet Yugoslavia 1966, 1974 or 1982?**
6. Did they face Yugoslavia in 1990?
7. **Who did Spain take a 2-0 lead against in their first game of 1994?**
8. When was the last time these two countries had met in the World Cup?
9. **What was the final score between the two in 1994 - was it 1-1, 2-0 or 2-2?**
10. Who scored for Spain in two of their three first-round matches?
11. **Which European country were held to a 1-1 draw by Spain in the group stage?**
12. Who were Spain's final group stage opponents?
13. **How many times had these two countries met before in the World Cup?**
14. What was the score?
15. **Who scored twice for Spain in that match?**

ANSWERS **1. South Korea** 2. Belgium **3. Spain won 2-1** 4. Belgium **5. 1982** 6. Yes **7. South Korea** 8. 1990 **9. 2-2** 10. Goikoetxea **11. Germany** 12. Bolivia **13. Never** 14. 3-1 to Spain **15. Jose-Luis Caminero**

Quiz 25

The Great Europeans Spain

1. **Which Spanish player scored a penalty against Bolivia in 1994?**
2. Who were Spain's second-round opponents?
3. **What was the score in that game?**
4. Who scored Spain's second goal?
5. **Which European country did Spain lose to in the quarter-finals?**
6. What was the score?
7. **Who scored for Spain?**
8. Which Spanish player captained the team in 1994?
9. **Who was the top scorer for Spain in 1994?**
10. Which Spanish stadium staged the World Cup Final in 1982?
11. **Three Spanish cities each had two World Cup venues that year. Madrid was one, can you name either of the other two?**
12. Which of these three cities played host to the 1982 semi-finals?
13. **Where did Spain play their first round matches?**
14. Where did they play both their second-stage group games?
15. **What is the traditional venue for Spain's most important international matches?**

ANSWERS **1. Guardiola** 2. Switzerland **3. 3-0 to Spain** 4. Luis Enrique **5. Italy** 6. Italy won 2-1 **7. Caminero** 8. Zubizarreta **9. Caminero** 10. Bernabeu Stadium, Madrid **11. Barcelona, Seville** 12. Barcelona and Seville **13. Valencia** 14. Bernabeu Stadium, Madrid **15. Seville**

Quiz 26

The Great Europeans
USSR

1. What year was USSR or the Soviet Union's first World Cup?

2. Who were the first team they played?

3. What was the final score in that match?

4. Who scored the USSR's second goal in that game?

5. Whom did the USSR meet in a play-off in 1958?

6. How many games did the Soviets play in 1958?

7. What stage did they reach?

8. Who did they play in the quarter-finals?

9. What was the score in that match?

10. Who did the USSR beat for their first World Cup victory?

11. How many games did the Soviets lose in the group stages in 1958?

12. Who were their last opponents in the group stage?

13. What was the score in that game?

14. Who were the USSR's first opponents in their next World Cup?

15. Which year was that?

ANSWERS: 1. 1958 2. England **3. 2-2** 4. Ivanov **5. England** 6. Five **7. Quarter-finals** 8. Sweden **9. 2-0 to Sweden** 10. Austria **11. One** 12. Brazil **13. 2-0 to Brazil** 14. Yugoslavia **15. 1962**

Quiz 27

The Great Europeans USSR

1. **What was the score in the USSR's first game in 1962?**
2. Who scored the second goal in that match?
3. **How many goals were scored in the Soviets' next game?**
4. What was the final score?
5. **Who were their opponents?**
6. Who scored twice in that game for the USSR?
7. **What was the attendance - 8,040 or 10,040?**
8. Who was the top goalscorer for the USSR in 1962?
9. **How many goals did he score?**
10. Who were the USSR's last group opponents in 1962?
11. **Did the Soviets qualify for the quarter-finals?**
12. Who were their final opponents in 1962?
13. **Which round was that game?**
14. Who scored in all three group matches for the USSR?
15. **Who scored the USSR's first goal in the 1966 tournament?**

ANSWERS: 1. They won 2-0 2. Ponedelnik **3. Eight** 4. 4-4 **5. Colombia** 6. Ivanov **7. 8,040** 8. Ivanov **9. Four** 10. Uruguay **11. Yes** 12. Chile **13. Quarter-finals** 14. Ivanov **15. Malafeev**

Quiz 28

The Great Europeans
USSR

1. **Who were the Soviets' opponents in that first match in 1966?**
2. What was the final score?
3. **How many victories did the USSR claim in the group stage?**
4. Who were their second group opponents?
5. **Who scored for the USSR in that match?**
6. What was the final score?
7. **Who scored twice in the USSR's last group game?**
8. Who were their opponents in that match?
9. **What was the score?**
10. Which European nation provided the USSR's quarter-final opposition?
11. **What was the score in that game?**
12. Who was the USSR's goalscorer in that game?
13. **Who was their top goalscorer overall with four in 1966?**
14. Who were their semi-final opponents?
15. **Where was that game played?**

ANSWERS: 1. North Korea 2. 3-0 to the USSR **3. Three** 4. Italy **5. Chislenko** 6. 1-0 **7. Porkujan** 8. Chile **9. The USSR won 2-1** 10. Hungary **11. 2-1 to the USSR** 12. Chislenko **13. Porkujan** 14. West Germany **15. Goodison Park**

Quiz 29

The Great Europeans USSR

1. **What was the half-time score against West Germany in the USSR's 1966 semi-final?**
2. And the final score?
3. **Who scored for the USSR?**
4. Who did the USSR face in the third-place play-off match in 1966?
5. **What was the final score?**
6. Did the USSR score in their first game of the 1970 finals?
7. **Who were their opponents?**
8. What was the score?
9. **What was the recorded attendance - 97,000 or 107,000?**
10. Who was the USSR's first goalscorer in 1970?
11. **Against whom?**
12. Which group game was that?
13. **How many goals did the USSR score in that match?**
14. What was the final score?
15. **Who was their top goalscorer in 1970?**

ANSWERS: 1. 1-0 to West Germany 2. 2-1 to West Germany **3. Porkujan** 4. Portugal **5. 2-1 to Portugal** 6. No **7. Mexico** 8. 0-0 **9. 107,000** 10. Byshovets **11. Belgium** 12. Second **13. Four** 14. 4-1 **15. Byshovets**

Quiz 30

The Great Europeans USSR

1. **Which American country were the USSR's 1970 final group opponents?**
2. What was the score in that game?
3. **Who scored for the USSR?**
4. Who were the USSR's quarter-final opponents?
5. **What was the score?**
6. Which year was the USSR's best World Cup performance?
7. **Which round did they reach?**
8. After 1970, when was the USSR's next World Cup appearance?
9. **Who were their group opponents in that tournament? Name one.**
10. Who did they face in their first match?
11. **What was the final score?**
12. Who scored for the USSR?
13. **How many games did USSR win in the group stage?**
14. Which debutant country were the Soviets' second group opponents in 1982?
15. **What was the final score?**

ANSWERS: 1. El Salvador 2. 2-0 **3. Byshovets** 4. Uruguay **5. 1-0 to Uruguay** 6. 1966 **7. Semi-final** 8. 1982 **9. Scotland, Brazil, New Zealand** 10. Brazil **11. 2-1 to Brazil** 12. Bal **13. One** 14. New Zealand **15. 3-0 to the USSR**

Quiz 31

The Great Europeans
USSR

1. **Who scored the second goal for the USSR against New Zealand in 1982?**
2. How many different goalscorers did the USSR have in 1982?
3. **Which British country did the USSR face in the group stage?**
4. What was the score in that match?
5. **Before 1982, when was the last time the USSR had faced a British nation in the finals?**
6. Who did the USSR meet in the second-round group stage in 1982?
7. **Who were their first opponents?**
8. What was the score in that game?
9. **Who was the goalscorer?**
10. Did the USSR qualify for the semi-finals?
11. **How many goals did the USSR score in their first group match of 1986?**
12. Which European nation were the opposition?
13. **What was the final score?**
14. Who scored twice for the USSR in that game?
15. **Who held the USSR to a draw in their second match?**

ANSWERS: 1. Oleg Blokhin 2. Seven **3. Scotland** 4. 2-2 **5. 1958** 6. Belgium, Poland **7. Belgium** 8. 1-0 to the USSR **9. Oganesian** 10. No **11. Six** 12. Hungary **13. 6-0** 14. Yaremchuck **15. France**

Quiz 32

The Great Europeans
USSR

1. What was the final score in the USSR v France group match in 1986?

2. Who scored for the USSR?

3. Who did the Soviets beat 2-0 in their final group match?

4. Which European country were the USSR's second-round opponents?

5. What was the final score?

6. Who scored a hat-trick for the USSR?

7. How many minutes did the game last?

8. Who was the USSR's first-ever penalty-scorer in the World Cup finals?

9. What year was that?

10. How many finals games did the Soviets win in 1990?

11. Who were their first opponents in 1990?

12. What was the score?

13. Who did the USSR score their first goal against in 1990?

14. Who defeated the USSR in their second group match?

15. Who was the USSR's first goalscorer in 1990?

ANSWERS: 1. 1-1 2. Rats **3. Canada** 4. Belgium **5. 4-3 to Belgium** 6. Igor Belanov **7. 120** 8. Igor Belanov **9. 1986** 10. One **11. Romania** 12. 2-0 to Romania **13. Cameroon** 14. Argentina **15. Oleg Protasov**

Quiz 33

The Great Europeans
West Germany

1. **Who were West Germany's first World Cup opponents?**
2. Who scored their first goal - Morlock or Klodt?
3. **Who defeated West Germany in the second game of the 1954 finals?**
4. What was the score?
5. **Who did West Germany gobble up in a play-off in 1954?**
6. Who scored a hat-trick - Morlock or Klodt?
7. **Who did they beat in the quarter-final - Yugoslavia or Austria?**
8. At which stage of the 1954 finals did West Germany meet Hungary for the second time?
9. **Which two brothers played in the 1954 finals?**
10. Who were West Germany's semi-final opponents in 1954?
11. **Czechoslovakia and Argentina were in West Germany's group in the 1958 first round. Name the fourth country.**
12. Which two teams both drew 2-2 with West Germany in the first round?
13. **West Germany faced Northern Ireland in 1958. Who scored twice for the Irish?**
14. Which legendary German scored his first World Cup goal against Ireland?
15. **Which country did Germany beat in the quarter-finals for the second successive finals?**

ANSWERS **1. Turkey** 2. Klodt **3. Hungary** 4. 8-3 **5. Turkey 7-2** 6. Morlock **7. Yugoslavia** 8. Final **9. Fritz and Otmar Walter** 10. Austria **11. Northern Ireland** 12. Czechoslovakia and Northern Ireland **13. Peter McParland** 14. Uwe Seeler **15. Yugoslavia**

Quiz 34

The Great Europeans West Germany

1. **Who beat West Germany in the 1958 semi-finals?**
2. What was the score?
3. **They were beaten in the third-place play-off as well. By whom?**
4. There were nine goals in that game. What was the score?
5. **West Germany's first game in the 1962 tournament was goalless. Who were the opponents?**
6. Who scored twice for West Germany in their three group matches?
7. **Who beat West Germany in the quarter-finals?**
8. Who were beaten 5-0 in West Germany's first game in England 1966?
9. **Which two players scored twice in that game?**
10. Who else were in West Germany's group?
11. **Which South American country was beaten 4-0 in the quarter-finals?**
12. Name two of the West German scorers.
13. **Who scored West Germany's equaliser in the last minute of normal time in the Final?**
14. How many goals did Gerd Muller score in the 1970 finals?
15. **Muller's tally included two hat-tricks against South American and Eastern European countries. Name them.**

ANSWERS **1. Sweden** 2. 3-1 **3. France** 4. 6-3 **5. Italy** 6. Uwe Seeler **7. Yugoslavia** 8. Switzerland **9. Haller and Beckenbauer** 10. Argentina and Spain **11. Uruguay** 12. Held, Beckenbauer, Seeler and Haller **13. Weber** 14. 10 **15. Bulgaria and Peru.**

Quiz 35

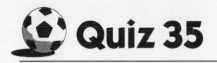

The Great Europeans West Germany

1. How many goals did West Germany score in the three group games?

2. Who scored in their quarter-final defeat of England?

3. Which West German played in the semi-final with a broken collarbone?

4. Who were their opponents in this match?

5. What was the final score in that game?

6. Who did West Germany meet in the third-place play-off?

7. Who scored in that game for West Germany?

8. Who scored the first German goal in the 1974 finals?

9. West Germany's first World Cup meeting with their eastern neighbours was in 1974. True or false?

10. Who beat West Germany in the first round in 1974?

11. West Germany had three opponents in the quarter-finals group. Name one.

12. Which side was beaten 1-0 to guarantee West Germany their place in the Final?

13. Who was the scorer?

14. Who tripped Johan Cruyff to give Holland a first-minute penalty in the 1974 Final?

15. Who equalised for West Germany in the Final?

ANSWERS 1. 10 2. Beckenbauer, Seeler and Muller **3. Beckenbauer** 4. Italy **5. 4-3** 6. Uruguay **7. Wolfgang Overath** 8. Paul Breitner **9. True** 10. East Germany **11. Yugoslavia, Sweden and Poland** 12. Poland **13. Muller** 14. Uli Hoeness **15. Breitner - also a penalty**

Quiz 36

The Great Europeans
West Germany

1. **How many World Cup goals did Gerd Muller score altogether?**
2. Who did West Germany beat 6-0 in the 1978 tournament?
3. **In their next game West Germany were held 0-0 by an African country. Who was it?**
4. Which two European countries did Germany draw with in the second stage of the 1978 tournament?
5. **Who scored an own goal in West Germany's last match of 1978?**
6. Which country beat them in that game?
7. **What was the score?**
8. West Germany suffered defeat by an African nation in their first game of 1982. Who was it?
9. **Which side was beaten 4-0 in West Germany's next game?**
10. Who scored a hat-trick in that match?
11. **Which two other sides were in their second-round group?**
12. Who did they meet in the semi-finals?
13. **What was the score after extra time - 1-1, 2-2 or 3-3?**
14. Who scored the winning penalty in the shoot-out?
15. **Which German has scored in two World Cup Finals?**

ANSWERS **1. 14** 2. Mexico **3. Tunisia** 4. Italy and Holland **5. Berti Vogts** 6. Austria **7. 3-2** 8. Algeria **9. Chile** 10. Karl-Heinz Rummenigge **11. England and Spain** 12. France **13. 3-3** 14. Horst Hrubesch **15. Paul Breitner**

Quiz 37

The Great Europeans
West Germany

1. What was the score in the 1982 Final?

2. Who scored in West Germany's first two group games in 1986?

3. Who beat West Germany in a first group game?

4. Who did West Germany beat in a penalty shoot-out in the quarter-final?

5. What was the score in extra time?

6. Who scored in the semi-final and Final for West Germany?

7. Whom did West Germany beat in the semi-final?

8. Who scored West Germany's first goal in the Final?

9. Who scored twice for West Germany against Yugoslavia in 1990?

10. Who did West Germany beat 5-1 in the group stages?

11. West Germany played their group games in Milan's San Siro stadium. Which three of their team played their club football there at the time?

12. Who was sent off with Holland's Rijkaard in West Germany's second-round match?

13. Who did the Germans beat in the quarter-finals?

14. Who scored a penalty in that game?

15. Who scored West Germany's last World Cup goal in the 1982 tournament?

ANSWERS: 1. Italy 3 West Germany 1 2. Klaus Allofs **3. Denmark** 4. Mexico **5. 0-0** 6. Rudi Voeller **7. France** 8. Karl-Heinz Rummenigge **9. Lother Matthaus** 10. United Arab Emirates **11. Matthaus, Brehme and Klinsmann** 12. Voeller **13. Czechoslovakia** 14. Matthaus **15. Andreas Brehme**

British Isles Challengers

Quiz 1

British Isles Challengers
England

1. **Who were England's first ever opponents in the World Cup finals?**
2. Who in that match became England's first ever goalscorer in the World Cup finals?
3. **In which year was that?**
4. How many victories did England manage in their first finals?
5. **Which European nation beat them 1-0 in their third and last match of the 1950 finals?**
6. Who was England's first World Cup captain?
7. **What was the result of England's high-scoring draw against Belgium in the 1954 finals?**
8. Which two England players scored twice in that game?
9. **Who did England beat in their second match in 1954?**
10. Who did England then face in the quarter-finals?
11. **Which two legendary England players scored in that match?**
12. What was the final score?
13. **England faced which Eastern European country in their first match of the 1958 finals?**
14. Who scored from the penalty spot for England in that match?
15. **What was the final score?**

ANSWERS **1. Chile** 2. Stan Mortensen **3. 1950** 4. One **5. Spain** 6. Billy Wright **7. 4-4** 8. Ivor Broadis, Nat Lofthouse **9. Switzerland** 10. Uruguay **11. Nat Lofthouse, Tom Finney** 12. 4-2 to Uruguay **13. USSR** 14. Tom Finney **15. 2-2**

Quiz 2

British Isles Challengers
England

1. **Which two other countries also drew with England in the 1958 finals?**
2. In the game against Austria, who scored England's opening goal?
3. **Who then eliminated England 1-0 in a play-off?**
4. Which future England manager played in the 1958 side?
5. **One of his team-mates went on to become his assistant with England. Who was that?**
6. Which country did England face first in Chile in 1962?
7. **What was the score?**
8. Which Manchester United player scored for England in their next match, against Argentina?
9. **England scored in all their matches in the 1962 finals. True or false?**
10. Who held them to a draw in the final group match?
11. **Who knocked England out in the quarter-finals, 3-1?**
12. Who scored England's consolation goal?
13. **Where was the game played?**
14. England were the sole British representatives in the 1962 finals. True or false?
15. **They played all their games at Wembley when they hosted the next finals in 1966. Name two other World Cup venues that year.**

ANSWERS: **1. Brazil, Austria** 2. Johnny Haynes **3. USSR** 4. Bobby Robson **5. Don Howe** 6. Hungary **7. England lost 2-1** 8. Bobby Charlton **9. False** 10. Bulgaria **11. Brazil** 12. Gerry Hitchens **13. Vina del Mar** 14. True **15. Old Trafford, Goodison Park, Villa Park, Roker Park, Ayresome Park, Hillsborough, White City**

Quiz 3

British Isles Challengers
England

1. Who were England's first opponents in the 1966 finals?

2. What was the final score in that game?

3. Who scored England's first goal of the finals?

4. Against which country?

5. Who did England face in their last group match?

6. Which Liverpool striker scored twice in that game?

7. Which Tottenham striker suffered an injury against France and never regained his place?

8. Who replaced him for the quarter-finals and scored the winner against Argentina?

9. Who was the German referee of that controversial game?

10. Who man-marked Eusebio in England's semi-final win over Portugal?

11. What was the date of the 1966 World Cup Final?

12. Who scored England's 'other' goal in their 4-2 victory over West Germany, in addition to Geoff Hurst's hat-trick?

13. Against whom did England begin their defence of the trophy four years later in Mexico?

14. Who scored the winner for Brazil in England's next match of the 1970 finals?

15. Who were England's other group opponents?

ANSWERS: **1. Uruguay** 2. 0-0 **3. Bobby Charlton** 4. Mexico **5. France** 6. Roger Hunt **7. Jimmy Greaves** 8. Geoff Hurst **9. Herr Kreitlein** 10. Nobby Stiles **11. 30 July** 12. Martin Peters **13. Romania** 14. Jairzinho **15. Czechoslovakia**

Quiz 4

British Isles Challengers
England

1. Who scored West Germany's winning goal in the 1970 quarter-final against England?

2. Where was that match played?

3. Who replaced Gordon Banks in the England goal for that game?

4. Who came on as a second-half substitute in place of Bobby Charlton?

5. How many years was it before England appeared in the World Cup finals again?

6. When they did so, who were their first opponents in Spain?

7. Where were all of England's first-round group matches played in those 1982 finals?

8. Which two squad members appeared only in Englnd's last match of the 1982 finals as substitutes?

9. Which country progressed from England's second round group, knocking England out?

10. England failed to score in four consecutive World Cup finals matches, against West Germany, Spain, Portugal and which other team?

11. Who broke the sequence with a hat-trick against Poland in 1986?

12. Where were England's group games played in Mexico that year?

13. Who was on target against Paraguay in the second round along with Gary Lineker?

14. Who captained England in the quarter-final against Argentina?

15. Who appeared as a late substitute in that match and set up England's goal?

ANSWERS: 1. Gerd Muller 2. Leon **3. Peter Bonetti** 4. Colin Bell **5. Twelve** 6. France **7. Bilbao** 8. Trevor Brooking, Kevin Keegan **9. West Germany** 10. Morocco **11. Gary Lineker** 12. Monterrey **13. Peter Beardsley** 14. Peter Shilton **15. John Barnes**

Quiz 5

British Isles Challengers
England

1. **In the first game of Italia 90, who equalised for the Republic of Ireland against England?**
2. Where were all England's group matches played that year?
3. **Which England midfielder went off injured against Holland in the second group match and took no further part in the tournament?**
4. Whose last-minute goal from a free-kick was disallowed in that match?
5. **Who scored the winner for England in their last group match?**
6. Who were their opponents?
7. **Who did England then face in the second round?**
8. Who scored England's winner in the last minute of extra time?
9. **Whose free-kick set up that goal?**
10. Who saved England in the quarter-final against Cameroon with an equalising penalty in normal time?
11. **What was the final score in that match after extra time?**
12. Who scored for West Germany against England in the 1990 semi-final?
13. **Who was the German keeper who saved from Stuart Pearce in the penalty shoot-out to decide that match?**
14. Who missed England's fifth and last penalty?
15. **Which country pipped England for third place in 1990, 2-1?**

ANSWERS: 1. Kevin Sheedy 2. Cagliari **3. Bryan Robson** 4. Stuart Pearce **5. Mark Wright** 6. Egypt **7. Belgium** 8. David Platt **9. Paul Gascoigne** 10. Gary Lineker **11. 3-2 to England** 12. Andreas Brehme **13. Bodo Illgner** 14. Chris Waddle **15. Italy**

Quiz 6

British Isles Challengers
Scotland

1. In which year was Scotland's first World Cup finals appearance?

2. Who were their first opponents?

3. How many goals did Scotland concede in their second World Cup match?

4. Who were the opposition in that match?

5. What was the final score?

6. Scotland had to wait until 1958 for their first World Cup point. Against whom did it arrive?

7. Who scored Scotland's first World Cup goal in that match?

8. Who was the Scotland goalkeeper-captain in that match?

9. Which South American nation beat Scotland in their second match in 1958?

10. What was the final score?

11. How many different goalscorers did Scotland have in the 1958 finals?

12. Who defeated Scotland 2-1 in their final group match?

13. When was Scotland's next World Cup finals appearance?

14. Against which African nation was Scotland's first World Cup victory?

15. What was the score in that game?

ANSWERS: 1. 1954 2. Austria **3. Seven** 4. Uruguay **5. 7-0** 6. Yugoslavia **7. Jimmy Murray** 8. Tommy Younger **9. Paraguay** 10. 3-2 to Paraguay **11. Four - Murray, Mudie, Collins, Baird** 12. France **13. 1974** 14. Zaire **15. 2-0**

Quiz 7

British Isles Challengers
Scotland

1. **Who were Scotland's goalscorers against Zaire in 1974?**
2. Who did Scotland hold to a draw in their next match?
3. **What was the score?**
4. Scotland needed to beat which European nation to win their group in 1974?
5. **What was the score in that game?**
6. Who scored for Scotland?
7. **Scotland failed to qualify for the second round on goal difference. Who qualified ahead of them in second place?**
8. Who was Scotland's captain in the 1974 finals?
9. **Which two other countries in their group also had the same number of points as Scotland?**
10. Who were Scotland's first opponents from South American in 1978?
11. **What was the score in that match?**
12. Who scored for Scotland in that game?
13. **Which Asian country then held Scotland to a shock draw?**
14. What was the final score?
15. **Scotland did win in 1978. Against which European nation?**

ANSWERS: 1. Peter Lorimer, Joe Jordan 2. Brazil **3. 0-0** 4. Yugoslavia **5. 1-1** 6. Joe Jordan **7. Brazil** 8. Billy Bremner **9. Yugoslavia and Brazil** 10. Peru **11. 3-1 to Peru** 12. Joe Jordan **13. Iran** 14. 1-1 **15. Holland**

Quiz 8

British Isles Challengers Scotland

1. **Who scored Scotland's opening goal against Holland in 1978?**
2. What was the final score in that match?
3. **How many finals have Scotland qualified for, including 1998?**
4. And how many times have they qualified for the second round?
5. **Who did Scotland beat in 1982 for their biggest World Cup victory?**
6. What was the score?
7. **Who scored twice for Scotland?**
8. Which then-Tottenham striker also scored in that match?
9. **Who opened the scoring for Scotland in their following match?**
10. Who were their opponents?
11. **What was the final score?**
12. Scotland's final group match of 1982 was against which Eastern European opponents?
13. **What was the final score in that game?**
14. Who qualified ahead of Scotland, on the same number of points, in their group?
15. **Who was Scotland's goalkeeper in 1982?**

ANSWERS: **1. Kenny Dalglish** 2. 3-2 to Scotland **3. Eight** 4. None **5. New Zealand** 6. 5-2 **7. John Wark** 8. Steve Archibald **9. David Narey** 10. Brazil **11. 4-1 to Brazil** 12. USSR **13. 2-2** 14. USSR **15. Alan Rough of Partick Thistle**

Quiz 9

British Isles Challengers Scotland

1. **Who scored Scotland's last goal in the 1982 finals?**
2. Who was captain in that match against the USSR?
3. **How many goals did Scotland score in the finals of 1986?**
4. Who was their goalscorer?
5. **Against which European nation did he score?**
6. Who were Scotland's first opponents in the 1986 finals?
7. **What was the score?**
8. Who held Scotland to a goalless draw in their last group match of 1986?
9. **How many points did Scotland win in 1986?**
10. Which Central American nation beat Scotland in their first match in the 1990 finals?
11. **What was the score?**
12. Which European country were beaten 2-1 by Scotland in their second group game?
13. **Who were Scotland's goalscorers?**
14. Who did Scotland then face?
15. **What was the final score in that match?**

ANSWERS: 1. Graeme Souness v USSR 2. Graeme Souness **3. One** 4. Gordon Strachan **5. West Germany** 6. Denmark **7. 1-0 to Denmark** 8. Uruguay **9. One** 10. Costa Rica **11. 1-0** 12. Sweden **13. Stuart McCall, Mo Johnston** 14. Brazil **15. 1-0 to Brazil**

Quiz 10 British Isles Challengers Wales/Republic of Ireland

1. When was Wales' first World Cup finals appearance?

2. Who were their first opponents?

3. Who scored Wales' first World Cup goal?

4. What was the score in their opening match?

5. How many matches did Wales draw in the group stage?

6. Who was their first victory against?

7. That win came in a play-off, 2-1. Who scored Wales' first goal?

8. Wales reached the quarter-finals in 1958. True or false?

9. Who knocked them out of the tournament?

10. When was the last time Wales played in the World Cup finals?

11. The Republic of Ireland reached their first World Cup finals in what year?

12. Who was their English manager?

13. Which British nation were their first World Cup finals opponents?

14. Which then-Swindon Town player was in the Republic's squad?

15. Who was the Republic of Ireland's first World Cup goalscorer?

ANSWERS: 1. 1958 2. Hungary **3. John Charles** 4. 1-1 **5. Three** 6. Hungary **7. Ivor Allchurch** 8. True **9. Brazil** 10. 1958 **11. 1990** 12. Jack Charlton **13. England** 14. Alan McLoughlin **15. Kevin Sheedy**

Quiz 11

British Isles Challengers
Republic of Ireland

1. **What was the final score in the Republic of Ireland's group match against England in 1990?**
2. Who held Ireland to a goalless draw in their second group match?
3. **The Republic faced Holland in their final group game. Where was the game played?**
4. Who scored Ireland's equaliser in that match?
5. **Which European nation were Ireland's second-round opponents?**
6. That match was the first of the 1990 tournament to go to penalties. True or false?
7. **What was the score after extra-time in that game?**
8. Who scored the Republic's winning penalty?
9. **Ireland faced which former World Cup winners in the quarter-finals in 1990?**
10. What was the final score?
11. **In which stadium was that match played?**
12. In which city is the stadium situated?
13. **How many games did the Republic of Ireland win in the 1990 finals?**
14. **Who was their captain in the 1994 finals?**
15. **Who did the Republic defeat for their first World Cup victory?**

ANSWERS: 1. 1-1 2. Egypt **3. Palermo** 4. Niall Quinn **5. Romania** 6. True **7. 0-0** 8. David O'Leary **9. Italy** 10. 1-0 to Italy **11. Olympic Stadium** 12. Rome **13. None** 14. Andy Townsend **15. Italy**

Quiz 12

British Isles Challengers Republic of Ireland/ Northern Ireland

1. Who was the Republic of Ireland's first goalscorer in 1994?

2. Where was that game, against Italy, played?

3. Ireland suffered defeat in their following match against which South American nation?

4. Who scored a valuable goal in that defeat?

5. The Republic qualified after a goalless draw against which European country?

6. In what place in the group did the Republic of Ireland finish?

7. Which World Cup rookie defender from Coventry City played for Ireland in the 1994 finals?

8. Who were the Republic's second round opponents?

9. Where was that game played?

10. Which FA Carling Premiership striker scored Holland's opening goal?

11. What was the final score in that game?

12. Northern Ireland's first World Cup finals appearance was in 1958. Who were their first opponents?

13. Which two World Cup winners, past and future, were also in Northern Ireland's group?

14. Who was Northern Ireland's first defeat against?

15. Which Irish player scored five goals in 1958?

ANSWERS: 1. Ray Houghton 2. New Jersey **3. Mexico** 4. John Aldridge **5. Norway** 6. Second **7. Phil Babb** 8. Holland **9. Orlando** 10. Dennis Bergkamp **11. 2-0 to Holland** 12. Czechoslovakia **13. Argentina, West Germany** 14. Argentina **15. Peter McParland**

Quiz 13 The British Challengers Northern Ireland

1. **Who did Northern Ireland hold to a 2-2 draw in their final match in 1958?**
2. Who then knocked Northern Ireland out in the quarter-finals?
3. **Northern Ireland next qualified for the finals in 1982. Which Central American country held them to a draw in the group stage?**
4. The Irish qualified for the second stage after beating which European nation?
5. **Who scored Northern Ireland's winner in that match?**
6. In their second-stage group, who did Northern Ireland draw 2-2 with?
7. **Who knocked Northern Ireland out in 1982 by defeating them in their next group match?**
8. What was the final score in that game?
9. **Who scored Northern Ireland's consolation goal?**
10. Which African nation held Northern Ireland to a draw in their opening game of the 1986 finals?
11. **Which World Cup record breaker scored for Northern Ireland in that match?**
12. Who did Northern Ireland lose to in their second game?
13. **Who celebrated his 41st birthday playing for Northern Ireland against Brazil?**
14. What was the final score in that game?
15. **Where did Northern Ireland finish in their 1986 group?**

ANSWERS: 1. West Germany 2. France **3. Honduras** 4. Spain **5. Gerry Armstrong** 6. Austria **7. France** 8. 4-1 **9. Gerry Armstrong** 10. Algeria **11. Norman Whiteside** 12. Spain **13. Pat Jennings** 14. 3-0 to Brazil **15. Third**

The South Americans

Quiz 1

The South Americans
Brazil

1. **Brazil's first ever World Cup game was against whom?**
2. Who scored Brazil's first World Cup goal in that match?
3. **What was the full-time score?**
4. Brazil beat whom in their next match?
5. **How many games did Brazil play in the 1934 finals?**
6. Who were their opponents?
7. **In an amazing match, who did Brazil beat 6-5 after extra time in the first round of the 1938 finals?**
8. Which Brazilian scored four goals in that game - Leonidas, Roberto or Romeo?
9. **Brazil needed a replay to progress from round 2 in 1938. Which European country did they beat?**
10. Who then beat Brazil in the semi-finals?
11. **Brazil hosted the 1950 finals. Name one of the three other countries in their first-round group.**
12. How many goals did Brazil score in the those three matches - 4, 8 or 12?
13. **Who held them to a 2-2 draw in the group stages?**
14. In the final pool match, who did Brazil beat 7-1?
15. **Who scored four goals in that game - Chico, Alfredo or Ademir?**

ANSWERS 1. Yugoslavia 2. Neto **3. Yugoslavia 2 Brazil 1** 4. Bolivia **5. One** 6. Spain **7. Poland** 8. Leonidas **9. Czechoslovakia** 10. Italy **11. Mexico, Switzerland and Yugoslavia** 12. Eight **13. Switzerland** 14. Sweden **15. Ademir**

Quiz 2

The South Americans
Brazil

1. **Brazil's next match in 1950 saw a 6-1 win. Over whom?**
2. The final game brought a 2-1 defeat by Uruguay. Who scored Brazil's goal - Friaca or Chico?
3. **Was the attendance for that match more or less than 150,000?**
4. How many games did Brazil play in the 1954 finals?
5. **Who ended their tournament in the quarter-finals?**
6. What was the score?
7. **Brazil faced England for the first time in 1958. What was the score?**
8. Who were Brazil's two other opponents in the group stages?
9. **Pele scored his first World Cup goal in 1958. Against which country?**
10. At which stage of the competition was that?
11. **Who did Brazil beat 5-2 in the semi-finals?**
12. Who scored a hat-trick in that game?
13. **How many goals did Pele score in the 1958 tournament altogether?**
14. Which two Brazilian players scored two goals each in the Final?
15. **Which player scored in Brazil's first game of 1962 and later went on to manage them in the World Cup?**

ANSWERS 1. **Spain** 2. Friaca 3. **More - 199,854** 4. Three 5. **Hungary** 6. 4-2 to Hungary 7. **0-0** 8. Austria and USSR 9. **Wales** 10. Quarter-final 11. **France** 12. Pele 13. **Six** 14. Vava and Pele 15. **Mario Zagalo**

Quiz 3

The South Americans
Brazil

1. **Pele also scored in Brazil's first game of the1962 finals. Who were their opponents?**
2. Who drew 0-0 with Brazil in the group stages?
3. **England were Brazil's opponents in the quarter-finals. Who won?**
4. Who were Brazil's goalscorers?
5. **Which fellow South American team did Brazil beat in the semi-finals?**
6. Who did Brazil beat twice in the 1962 finals?
7. **Which three players scored for Brazil in the Final?**
8. Who were Brazil's first opponents in 1966 - Hungary, Bulgaria or Portugal?
9. **Brazil suffered two defeats to be knocked out in 1966. Who beat them?**
10. What was the score in both games?
11. **Who scored in all of Brazil's 1970 World Cup finals matches?**
12. Czechoslovakia were beaten 4-1 in Brazil's first game of 1970. Name two of the goalscorers.
13. **Who were Brazil's two other opponents in the group stage?**
14. Who scored twice for Brazil against Peru in the quarter-final?
15. **What was the score?**

ANSWERS 1. Mexico 2. Czechoslovakia **3. Brazil 3-1** 4. Garrincha (2), Vava **5. Chile** 6. Czechoslovakia **7. Amarildo, Zito, Vava** 8. Bulgaria **9. Hungary and Portugal** 10. Brazil lost 3-1 **11. Jairzinho** 12. Rivelino, Pele and Jairzinho (2) **13. England and Romania** 14. Tostao **15. 4-2 to Brazil**

Quiz 4

The South Americans
Brazil

1. Which Brazilian defender scored his only goal of the 1970 finals against Uruguay?

2. Who scored Brazil's 100th World Cup goal?

3. Who scored Brazil's second goal in the 1970 Final?

4. Who captained Brazil in 1970?

5. What did Brazil keep after their 1970 success?

6. Brazil's first two games in 1974 ended goalless. Who were their European opponents?

7. Their only win in the group stages came against African opponents. Who were they?

8. Name one of Brazil's three opponents in their second-round group?

9. Who beat Brazil to make it to the 1974 Final?

10. Who scored Brazil's goals against Argentina in the second round?

11. Who beat Brazil in the third place play-off?

12. Which Europeans held Brazil to a 1-1 draw in their opening game of 1978?

13. Who scored the only goal in Brazil's third group game against Austria?

14. Who scored a penalty for Brazil in their opening second stage match against Peru?

15. Argentina were Brazil's next opponents. What was the score?

ANSWERS 1. Clodoaldo 2. Pele **3. Gerson** 4. Carlos Alberto **5. The Jules Rimet trophy** 6. Yugoslavia and Scotland **7. Zaire** 8. East Germany, Argentina and Holland **9. Holland** 10. Rivelino and Jairzinho **11. Poland** 12. Sweden **13. Roberto** 14. Zico **15. 0-0**

Quiz 5

The South Americans
Brazil

1. **Who did Brazil face in the 1978 third/fourth place play-off?**
2. What was the score?
3. **Scotland were in Brazil's group in 1982. Which two other countries were their first-round opponents?**
4. Four players scored for Brazil against Scotland in 1982. Name two.
5. **How many goals did Zico score in the 1982 finals?**
6. What was the score in the classic 1982 match between Brazil and Italy?
7. **Which British country was beaten 3-0 by Brazil in the first round of the 1986 finals?**
8. In the second round, Brazil beat Poland. What was the score?
9. **Name two of the goalscorers.**
10. Who beat Brazil on penalties in the quarter-finals?
11. **Who missed a penalty during that game before the shoot-out?**
12. Who scored in two of Brazil's three first-round matches in 1990?
13. **Scotland were beaten by Brazil in 1990. What was the score?**
14. Brazil and Argentina met in the second stage. Who won?
15. **Where was that match played?**

ANSWERS 1. Italy 2. Brazil won 2-1 **3. USSR and New Zealand** 4. Zico, Oscar, Eder and Falcao **5. Four** 6. Italy 3 Brazil 2 **7. Northern Ireland** 8. 4-0 **9. Socrates, Josimar, Edinho and Careca** 10. France **11. Zico** 12. Muller **13. 1-0** 14. Argentina, 1-0 **15. Turin**

Quiz 6

The South Americans
Brazil

1. **Who captained Brazil in their first game of USA 1994?**
2. Brazil conceded just one goal in the group stages. Against which team?
3. **Who was the scorer?**
4. Who, for Brazil, scored the goal that beat the hosts in 1994?
5. **Who scored the winning goal in Brazil's quarter-final win over Holland?**
6. Who did Brazil beat in the semi-finals?
7. **Which Brazilian failed with his penalty in the shoot-out in the Final?**
8. Who was Brazil's captain for the Final?
9. **Who in the 1994 squad was a cousin of famous Brazilian player Socrates?**
10. Socrates scored Brazil's first goal of the 1982 finals. Who was that against?
11. **What was the final score of that match?**
12. Where was the match played?
13. **Socrates missed a penalty in the quarter-final shoot-out with France in 1986. True or false?**
14. Where was that game played?
15. **The main stadium there is called the Jalisco. True or false?**

ANSWERS **1. Rai** 2. Sweden **3. Kennet Andersson** 4. Bebeto **5. Branco** 6. Sweden **7. Marcio Santos** 8. Dunga **9. Rai** 10. USSR **11. 2-1 to Brazil** 12. Seville **13. True** 14. Guadalajara **15. True**

Quiz 7

The South Americans
Uruguay

1. **In which country did Uruguay play their first World Cup match?**
2. Uruguay's first match was against another South American nation. Who was it?
3. **Uruguay won that first match. The score... 1-0, 2-0 or 2-1?**
4. Their first World Cup goalscorer was definitely not a Cuban. What was his name?
5. **Uruguay won the 1930 World Cup after playing how many games?**
6. How many of those matches did they win?
7. **How many goals did Uruguay score in that first series - 10, 12 or 15?**
8. Which South American country did Uruguay beat in the Final of 1930?
9. **Six goals were scored in that Final. What was the scoreline?**
10. Who scored a hat-trick for Uruguay against Yugoslavia in the 1930 semi-finals?
11. **Uruguay beat Yugoslavia in that match by what score?**
12. When did Uruguay next appear in the World Cup finals?
13. **Their first match of the 1950 finals was against another South American team. Who was it?**
14. Uruguay won that match by a runaway score. Was it 7-0, 8-0 or 9-0?
15. **Who scored four goals in that match?**

ANSWERS: **1.Uruguay** 2.Peru **3.1-0** 4.Castro **5.Four** 6.All of them **7.Fifteen** 8.Argentina **9.4-2** 10.Pedro Cea **11.6-1** 12.1950 **13.Bolivia** 14.8-0 **15.Juan Schiaffino**

Quiz 8

The South Americans
Uruguay

1. **How many goals did Schiaffino score for Uruguay in the 1950 World Cup finals overall?**
2. Omar Miquez and Alcides Ghiggia each scored how many for Uruguay in the 1950 finals?
3. **Uruguay beat Brazil 2-1 in the final pool in 1950 to win the World Cup again. Who scored their goals?**
4. How many of their four matches in the 1950 finals in Brazil did Uruguay lose?
5. **They drew 2-2 with one European country in 1950. Who was it?**
6. In how many World Cup finals series have Uruguay participated?
7. **When was their last appearance in the tournament?**
8. How many spectators were at their 1950 'Final' against Brazil - to the nearest 1,000?
9. **Where did Uruguay finish in the 1954 finals in Switzerland?**
10. Who beat them in the third-place play-off?
11. **What was the score?**
12. Who did Uruguay beat in the quarter-finals that year?
13. **What was the score?**
14. Who did Uruguay beat 7-0 in the 1954 finals?
15. **Who scored a hat-trick in that match?**

ANSWERS: 1.Five 2.Four 3.**Schiaffino & Ghiggia** 4.None 5.**Spain** 6.Nine 7.**1990** 8.200,000 **9.Fourth** 10.Austria **11.3-1** 12.England **13.4-2** 14.Scotland **15.Carlo Borges**

Quiz 9

The South Americans
Uruguay

1. Uruguay failed to qualify for the 1958 finals. Who headed their South American group - Paraguay or Colombia?

2. Paraguay beat Uruguay 5-0 in their first group match. What was the score in the return game?

3. How many games did Uruguay play in the 1962 finals in Chile - 2, 3 or 5?

4. Uruguay were beaten by two Eastern European nations in 1962. Who were they?

5. They defeated a South American team in those finals. Who?

6. How many games did Uruguay play in the 1966 series in England?

7. They had two goalless draws. Against whom?

8. Uruguay's only victory of the 1966 finals was by 2-1 against whom?

9. They were beaten 4-0 in the quarter-finals by whom?

10. How many games did Uruguay play in the 1970 finals in Mexico?

11. How many times were they beaten?

12. Who beat them in the 1970 semi-finals?

13. Who beat them in the play-off for third place?

14. What was Uruguay's total number of goals in the 1970 finals?

15. How many games did they play in the 1974 finals in West Germany?

ANSWERS: 1.Paraguay 2.Uruguay won 2-0 **3.Three** 4.Yugoslavia & Soviet Union **5.Colombia** 6.Four **7.England & Mexico** 8.France **9.West Germany** 10.Six **11.Three** 12.Brazil **13.West Germany** 14.Four **15.Three**

Quiz 10

The South Americans
Uruguay

1. **Uruguay scored only once in West Germany in the 1974 finals. Who got their goal?**
2. Two Uruguayans were sent off in the 1966 finals. Who were they?
3. **Uruguay finished with ten men against Holland in their first finals match of 1974. Who was ordered off?**
4. They qualified for the 1974 finals with a superior goals return over which team in their South American group?
5. **What was the result of Uruguay's home group match against that team?**
6. After 1974, how many years elapsed before Uruguay's next appearance in the finals?
7. **They failed to qualify in 1978, finishing second in their group to whom?**
8. Who beat Uruguay to the qualifying spot in 1982?
9. **How many of their four matches in the 1986 finals did Uruguay win?**
10. How many did they lose?
11. **What was their goals total in the 1986 finals?**
12. Who beat them 6-1 in their 1986 group?
13. **What was the result of their group match with Scotland?**
14. Who was the Uruguayan sent off in that match?
15. **They also finished with ten men against Denmark. Who took the early bath?**

ANSWERS: 1.Pavoni 2.Troche & Silva **3.Julio Montero-Castillo** 4.Colombia **5.Colombia won 1-0** 6.Twelve **7.Bolivia** 8.Peru **9.None** 10.Two **11.Two** 12.Denmark **13.0-0** 14.Jose Batista **15.Miguel Bossio**

Quiz 11

The South Americans
Uruguay

1. **Sixteen players were sent off in total at the 1990 World Cup finals in Italy. How many of them were Uruguayans?**
2. How many games did Uruguay play in Italy?
3. **What was their total of goals in those matches?**
4. Their only win was against whom?
5. **What was the score?**
6. Who eliminated Uruguay in the second round?
7. **What was the score?**
8. Uruguay's qualifying group for the 1994 finals included Bolivia, Brazil, Ecuador and Venezuela. Where did Uruguay finish?
9. **Who finished ahead of them?**
10. Who beat Uruguay 2-0 in their final qualifying match?
11. **Four out of nine South American countries qualified from one group for the 1998 finals. (Brazil were exempt as holders). Where did Uruguay finish?**
12. How many of their 16 qualifying games did they win?
13. **Uruguay's last match at the World Cup finals was against Italy in 1990. At which stadium was the match played?**
14. Who scored the vital opening goal for Italy in that game?
15. **Was that goal scored in the first or second half?**

ANSWERS: **1.**None 2.Four **3.**Two 4.South Korea **5.**1-0 6.Italy **7.**2-0 8.Third **9.**Brazil & Bolivia 10.Brazil **11.**Seventh 12.Six **13.**Stadio Olimpico, Rome 14.Salvatore Schillaci **15.**Second

Quiz 12

The South Americans
Argentina

1. Who were Argentina's first ever opponents in the World Cup finals?

2. What was the score in that match?

3. Who scored Argentina's first goal in the finals - Monti or Stabile?

4. Argentina played two other South American countries in the group stages in 1930. Who were they?

5. Who did Argentina beat 6-1 in the 1930 semi-finals - USA or Yugoslavia?

6. Which two of these players scored twice in that game - Monti, Stabile or Peucelle?

7. Argentina were beaten in the first round in 1934. By whom?

8. Was the score 2-1, 3-1 or 3-2?

9. Name one team of three in Argentina's group for the first round of the 1958 finals?

10. How many goals did Argentina score in those group matches - 4, 5 or 9?

11. Which player scored in all three games - Corbatta or Menendez?

12. Which European team beat Argentina 6-1 in their third and final group match of 1958?

13. Argentina first faced England in the World Cup in 1962. Who won?

14. What was the score?

15. Name any of England's scorers.

ANSWERS 1.France in 1930. 2. 1-0 to Argentina **3. Monti** 4. Mexico and Chile **5.USA** 6. Stabile and Peucelle **7. Sweden** 8. 3-2 **9. West Germany, Northern Ireland and Czechoslovakia** 10. Five **11. Corbatta** 12. Czechoslovakia **13. England** 14. 3-1 **15. Flowers, R. Charlton and Greaves.**

Quiz 13

The South Americans
Argentina

1. **Who was in goal for England against Argentina in 1962?**
2. Who scored Argentina's two goals against Uruguay in the 1930 Final?
3. **Artime scored twice in Argentina's opening game in 1966. True or false?**
4. Who were their Iberian opponents in that match?
5. **What was the score?**
6. Where did Argentina play their group games in 1966?
7. **Which other two teams were in their 1966 group?**
8. Who scored England's goal in the 1966 quarter-final with Argentina at Wembley?
9. **Was the attendance at Wembley that day more or less than 90,000?**
10. All of Argentina's three group matches in 1966 had the same half-time score. What was it?
11. **Argentina suffered defeat in their first match of the 1974 finals. Who were their Eastern European conquerors?**
12. Their first win of 1974 came in their third game, against a team making their only finals appearance. Who were they?
13. **Was the score 2-1, 4-1 or 6-1?**
14. Argentina had three opponents in the second stage. Can you name one of them?
15. **Who were their first opponents in the second stage?**

ANSWERS **1. Ron Springett** 2. Peucelle and Stabile **3. True** 4. Spain **5. 2-1** 6. Villa Park and Hillsborough **7. West Germany and Switzerland** 8. Geoff Hurst **9. More - 90,584** 10. 0-0 **11. Poland** 12. Haiti **13. 4-1** 14. Holland, Brazil and East Germany **15. Holland**

Quiz 14

The South Americans
Argentina

1. What was the score in the Argentina v Holland game in 1974?

2. How many victories did Argentina have in the 1974 second stage?

3. How many points did they win?

4. Where did they finish in the group?

5. Who were the hosts of the 1978 finals?

6. Their first opponents in the 1978 finals were European. Name them.

7. Who scored twice for Argentina in the three group games - Alonso or Luque?

8. Who defeated Argentina in the final group game - Italy, Hungary or France?

9. In the group stages of the second round, who did Argentina beat 2-0?

10. What was the score between Brazil and Argentina in the next match?

11. Was the attendance at that match 46,000 or 64,000?

12. Who did Argentina defeat to qualify for the Final of 1978?

13. How many goals did Mario Kempes score in the 1978 tournament?

14. Who was Argentina's captain in 1978?

15. Who defeated Argentina in the opening game of 1982 - Belgium, Hungary or Italy?

ANSWERS 1.Holland won 4-0 2. None **3. One** 4. Last of four **5. Argentina** 6. Hungary **7. Luque** 8. Italy 1-0 **9. Poland** 10. 0-0 **11. 46,000** 12. Peru 6-0 **13. Six** 14. Daniel Passarella **15. Belgium.**

Quiz 15

The South Americans
Argentina

1. **Where was the 1982 opening match played?**
2. Who scored twice in Argentina's 4-1 defeat of Hungary in 1982?
3. **Which former Tottenham manager also scored in that game?**
4. Who did Argentina beat 2-0 in the third group game?
5. **Who were the two other countries in Argentina's second round group?**
6. What were the two results?
7. **Who was sent off in Argentina's defeat by Brazil?**
8. Who were Argentina's scorers in the second round games?
9. **Who did Park Chang Sun play for in Argentina's 1986 group?**
10. Who scored three goals for Argentina in their three group games?
11. **How many points did Argentina win in the first round?**
12. Who did they beat in their opening game?
13. **In the second round Argentina faced and beat a country they had not played for 56 years in a World Cup finals series. Who?**
14. What was the score - 1-0, 2-0 or 3-0?
15. **Who scored for Argentina in that game?**

ANSWERS **1. Barcelona** 2. Diego Maradona **3. Ossie Ardiles** 4. El Salvador **5. Italy and Brazil** 6. Italy won 2-1, Brazil won 3-1 **7. Maradona** 8. Passarella and Diaz **9. South Korea** 10. Jorge Valdano **11. Five** 12. South Korea 3-1 **13. Uruguay** 14. Argentina won 1-0 **15. Pasculli**

Quiz 16

The South Americans
Argentina

1. **Who scored in 1990 for Argentina in their 2-0 win over the USSR?**
2. Who held Argentina 1-1 in their final group game in 1990?
3. **Who were Argentina's second-round opponents?**
4. What was the score?
5. **Who was Argentina's scorer?**
6. What was the score in Argentina's quarter-final after 120 minutes?
7. **Who were their opponents?**
8. Argentina went on to win on penalties. By what score?
9. **Who scored Argentina's equaliser in the semi-final against Italy?**
10. That game ended 1-1. What was the score after the penalty shoot-out?
11. **Who scored Argentina's two goals in their 1986 quarter-final win over England?**
12. Was the attendance for that match - 114,580, 95,000 or 110,420?
13. **Who were Argentina's opponents in the 1986 semi-finals?**
14. What was the score?
15. **Who scored the opening goal in the 1986 World Cup Final?**

ANSWERS 1. Troglio Burruchaga 2. Romania **3. Brazil** 4. 1-0 to Argentina **5. Claudio Caniggia** 6. 0-0 **7. Yugoslavia** 8. 3-2 **9. Caniggia** 10. 4-3 **11. Maradona** 12. 114,580 **13. Belgium** 14. 2-0 to Argentina **15. Jose-Luis Brown**

Quiz 17

The South Americans
Argentina

1. **Who was Argentina's top goalscorer in 1986?**
2. Which player scored the winning goal in the 1986 Final?
3. **Argentina lost 1-0 in the opening game of 1990. Who to?**
4. Where was the game played?
5. **Argentina won once in their group stages. Who against?**
6. Which Argentine became the first player to be sent off in a World Cup Final?
7. **Who was Argentina's goalkeeper in the 1990 Final?**
8. Who scored a hat-trick in Argentina's first game of 1994?
9. **Who were the opponents?**
10. Which player scored twice for Argentina against Nigeria in 1994?
11. **Argentina suffered defeat in their third game of 1994. Who to?**
12. Which team beat Argentina in the second round?
13. **Who scored Argentina's goals in that game?**
14. Both those goalscorers play their club football in Serie A. True or false?
15. **Can you name Batistuta's club?**

ANSWERS 1. Diego Maradona 2. Jorge Burruchaga **3. Cameroon** 4. Milan **5. USSR** 6. Monzon **7. Goicoechea** 8. Gabriel Batistuta **9. Greece** 10. Caniggia **11. Bulgaria** 12. Romania **13. Batistuta and Balbo** 14. True **15. Fiorentina**

Who said that?

Quiz 1

Who said that?

1. Who was invited by French television to help out with their World Cup presentation because it would 'encourage many more women to watch'?

2. Which Scottish World Cup hopeful said: 'It is difficult to shake off the shadow of my Dad'?

3. Who said: 'Italy never make mistakes on the big occasion'?

4. Who said: 'By the time he arrives in France, I am sure David Beckham will have grown into the new Bobby Charlton'?

5. 'You have to be confident when you play for England... you are only as good as your last game.' Which Manchester United player said that?

6. Which Premiership player said: 'I can't believe we are not going to the World Cup. It's like a bad dream and I am waiting for someone to wake me up'?

7. Who said he refused to cut his hair even though coach Daniel Passarella said he would be banned from the World Cup squad if he didn't?

8. Who said of Andy Cole: 'You can't tell a goalscorer like him what to do. He's a taker, like Gary Lineker was'?

9. Who were the four players named by Alan Shearer when he was asked whom he considered were the world's best strikers?

10. Who said of Ian Wright: 'There are few players who are cast-iron certainties for France. Ian knows he isn't, so he has a lot of work to do'?

ANSWERS: 1.David Ginola 2.Scott Gemmill, son of Archie **3.Gianfranco Zola before the Italy v England qualifying match in Rome** 4.Andy Gray of Sky TV **5.Paul Scholes** 6.Stan Lazaridis (West Ham) after Australia had lost to Iran in the play-offs **7.Fernando Redondo of Argentina** 8.Peter Beardsley **9.Gabriel Batistuta, Dennis Bergkamp, Romario & Ronaldo** 10.Glenn Hoddle

Quiz 2

Who said that?

1. **Who said: 'Only animals are caged'? (He was announcing the dismantling of perimeter fences at all but two of the grounds for World Cup 1998.)**
2. Who was the Italian player who said: 'The English team are getting better but they are lucky'?
3. **Who said: 'We will win when we meet England in the World Cup. I am very optimistic'?**
4. Who warned England after the World Cup draw: 'Don't be thick-headed ... it is important to be humble'?
5. **Who said of England's first match against Tunisia in Marseille: 'On a June afternoon it will be absolutely baking. That will suit the Tunisians - the hotter the better'?**
6. Who said: 'England are the favourites in our group and we must give them lots of respect'?
7. **Which Premiership manager said: 'You can have the best collection of footballers ever, but if there is no-one driving the bus, you'll not get there'?**
8. Which non-footballer said: 'It's a great draw for England. There's no reason why they can't go all the way'?
9. **Who said: 'Brazil will be in the final and if England are also there, it will not look too good for England'?**
10. Which former coach of a World Cup 1998 qualifying country said: 'Players between the ages of 25 and 35 are at their peak. It is their best time because they have both experience and commitment'?

ANSWERS: 1.Sepp Blatter, general secretary of FIFA 2.Filippo Inzaghi **3.Mihai Stoichita, manager of Steaua Bucharest of Romania** 4.Ruud Gullit, Chelsea coach **5.Chris Waddle** 6.Faustino Asprilla of Colombia **7.Alex Ferguson** 8.Prime Minister Tony Blair **9.Pele - after receiving an honorary knighthood** 10.Clive Barker of South Africa

Quiz 3

Who said that?

1. **'The England squad has great self-belief and must have a hell of a good chance of lifting the Cup.' Which England player said that?**

2. 'This may be the last time in my life I get to do something different,' said a German TV commentator and former top-level coach on being offered a job with one of the World Cup qualifiers. Who was it and which country?

3. **Who said: 'We want to show that we can improve on our last World Cup performance'?**

4. Who was the Premiership star who said: 'I must keep learning to be ready for World Cup opponents'?

5. **Who warned footballers playing in England about trying to join the Jamaican team: 'Jamaica is very proud of its team. We don't need people jumping on board just for a holiday in France'?**

6. Who said, on turning down a trial for the Jamaican World Cup squad: 'I was born and bred in Birmingham. I think of myself as English'?

7. **Who is the coach who said, on getting his team into the World Cup for the first time: 'My players said they would never give up. They kept their word. I owe everything to them'?**

8. Who said: 'Our Brazilian coach said three years ago we would qualify. People said he was stupid'?

9. **A possible member of the England 1998 World Cup squad said: 'The fight is on. We've qualified for France but we are all worried whether we will get the trip.' Who was this defender?**

10. Who said: 'Will I be in the World Cup squad? Who knows. I was there in 1990 and it's up to me now to help the youngsters'?

ANSWERS: 1.Alan Shearer 2.Udo Lattek, former Bayern Munich coach, on an offer from Iran **3.Faustino Asprilla, Colombia** 4.Peter Schmeichel, Manchester United & Denmark **5.Robbie Earle of Wimbledon** 6.Dean Sturridge of Derby County **7.Takeshi Okada of Japan** 8.Deon Burton, Derby striker and a member of the Jamaican squad **9.Phil Neville of Manchester United** 10.Paul Gascoigne

Quiz 4

Who said that?

1. **Which national coach said: 'The more I find out about the job, the more I realise that club managership is no apprenticeship for it'?**
2. Who said: 'I am sure that some of those in the stands are faintly amused to see a child on the field in a World Cup match'?
3. **Which national team manager said, following defeat in a World Cup warm-up match: 'They do not judge Pavarotti by how he sings in the shower. They wait until he is on stage'?**
4. Who was the England player who, in reply to four written questions by Italian journalists, wrote 'No, no, yes, no'?
5. **Who said, after West Germany's World Cup win of 1990: 'I think for years Germany will not be beaten. I'm sorry but, for a time to come, we will be invincible'?**
6. Who said of penalty shoot-outs: 'The player who kicks the last penalty either has the key to the hotel or the plane tickets home'?
7. **Who said: 'Nobody beat us, did they? Sad, very sad... but it's time for a new man now'?**
8. Who said: 'French teams don't go out just to make up the numbers anymore, and that is very important. Happiness is winning'?
9. **Who said after the 1970 World Cup finals: 'We all believed we had the best squad in England's history'?**
10. Bobby Robson said before the 1990 finals: 'There are days when he has saved us. He still has a great stature and presence and, for me, he is still our number one. He has never let us down.' Who was he?

ANSWERS: **1.Glenn Hoddle** 2.Pele, on his World Cup debut at 17 **3.Leo Beenhakker, after Holland had lost to Austria in a friendly** 4.Paul Gascoigne **5.Franz Beckenbauer, their coach** 6.Carlos Bilardo, Argentina manager **7.Bobby Robson after the 1990 shoot-out against West Germany** 8.Michel Platini, before Mexico 1986 **9.Bobby Moore** 10.Peter Shilton

Quiz 5

Who said that?

1. **Which famous World Cup coach once said: 'The two best strikers in the world are Rudi Voeller and Gary Lineker'?**
2. Who said: 'The great thing about Jurgen Klinsmann is that he has always been a big game player with a great attitude. He has that aura, that experience and style, too'?
3. **Who said of Teddy Sheringham: 'His greatest strength is his positive attitude. He convinces and pushes everybody'?**
4. Who said: 'We've got some good young players at Manchester United and to win the World Cup you need that mixture of experience and youth. Anyone at United or England should feel confident about playing anyone'?
5. **'I hear England think they will qualify from our group. I am pleased to hear that. In the last World Cup, Pele predicted that Colombia would win, but they played Romania in the first game and lost 3-1.' Who said that?**
6. Who said: 'Have you ever noticed how we only win the World Cup under a Labour government'?
7. **'There are people on the pitch . . . they think it's all over... it is now!' Who said this at the end of the 1966 World Cup Final?**
8. Who described Don Revie's succession to Alf Ramsey as England manager as 'a classic case of poacher turned gamekeeper'?
9. **Who said to the England team before extra time in the 1966 Final: 'You've beaten them once. Now go out and beat them again'?**
10. Who, when asked if he thought World Cup hero Nobby Stiles was a dirty player, said: 'He's never hurt anyone. Mind you, he's frightened a few!'?

ANSWERS: 1.Berti Vogts 2.Alex Ferguson **3.Jurgen Klinsmann** 4.Sir Bobby Charlton **5.Viorel Moldovan of Coventry & Romania** 6.Prime Minister Harold Wilson **7.TV commentator Kenneth Wolstenholme** 8.Alan Hardaker, Football League secretary at the time **9.Alf Ramsey** 10.Matt Busby

Quiz 6

Who said that?

1. **Who said: 'At 29, this may be my last chance to play in the World Cup. Our team is strong and we may beat England again in France'?**
2. Who issued this warning: 'Fans arriving by car at the 80,000-seat Stade de France in Paris will be lucky to see the game before half-time. There are a mere 6,000 parking spaces'?
3. **Who said on winning through to France 1998: 'I am happy to win and I am sad for the losers. God has helped us and our goalkeeper'?**
4. Who said after a vital qualifying match: 'We terrorised them for a lot of the time'?
5. **Who said this of whom: 'He is not just a footballer. I would call him a force of nature who takes the shortest route to the goal'?**
6. Who was the Premiership player who said on being called up by the Scots: 'It is 20 years since I was in Scotland, but my commitment will be there'?
7. **A famous English World Cup star said: 'Now there is a desperation which threatens the game's spirit. The faces of the players are contorted with rage, they snarl and scowl at each other. Even when they celebrate they look angry.' Who was it?**
8. Who was described as 'a lucky dog, symbolising youth, vitality and football fever'?
9. **Who said: 'You have to be selfish as a centre-forward sometimes'?**
10. Who said: 'The great players will agree with me that the World Cup is about achieving success for the side'?

(Editor's note: We believe everything you say, Alan. Now go and win it!)

ANSWERS: 1.Paolo Maldini, captain of Italy 2.Marie-George Duffet, French Sports Minister **3.Valdier Vierra, Iranian coach after the defeat of Australia** 4. Terry Venables, Australia's coach **5.Brazil's coach Mario Zagalo describing Ronaldo** 6.Matt Elliott of Leicester City **7.Bobby Moore** 8.Striker, the official mascot for the 1994 World Cup **9.Alan Shearer** 10.Alan Shearer

Men in Charge

All about managers, coaches, captains… and whistlers

Quiz 1

Men in Charge

1. **Who captained West Germany in the 1974 World Cup Final?**
2. Who was the manager of West Germany's winning team in 1990?
3. **Who was the referee of the 1994 World Cup Final in Los Angeles?**
4. Who was the captain of Scotland in their three World Cup qualifying round matches in 1949 and 1950?
5. **In how many of Scotland's three qualifying matches for the 1954 finals was he captain?**
6. Who who took over in the absence of the first-choice captain in one qualifying match of 1954?
7. **Who took over as captain for Scotland's two finals matches in 1954?**
8. Which English club did he play for at the time?
9. **Who was the Scotland manager who resigned while the 1954 finals were still in progress?**
10. Who took over as Scotland's manager for the 1958 World Cup campaign?
11. **Who was the club manager who agreed to oversee the Scots when they qualified for the finals in Sweden in 1958?**
12. So why were they still managerless for the Sweden finals?
13. **Who was the trainer who took charge for the three games in Sweden?**
14. Who was dropped from the Scotland team for the 1958 finals after skippering them in two qualifying matches?
15. **A goalkeeper assumed the role of captain for two of Scotland's finals matches in Sweden. Who was he?**

ANSWERS: 1. Franz Beckenbauer 2. Beckenbauer **3. Sandor Puhl (Hungary)** 4. George Young **5. Two** 6. Sammy Cox **7. Willie Cunningham** 8. Preston North End **9. Andy Beattie** 10. Nobody was appointed **11. Matt Busby** 12. Busby was too severely injured in the Munich 'plane disaster of February 1958 **13. Dawson Walker** 14. Tommy Docherty **15. Tommy Younger**

Quiz 2

Men in Charge

1. What is the maximum age set by FIFA for a World Cup referee?

2. How many referees officiated in the 1994 World Cup finals in the United States?

3. England had one representative on the referees' list for 1994.Who was he?

4. Who was the last English referee to take charge of a World Cup Final?

5. Where and when was that Final?

6. Who were the finalists?

7. Who was the English referee of the World Cup deciding match in 1950 between Uruguay and Brazil?

8. What was the name of the English referee chosen to officiate in the 1954 World Cup Final?

9. Apart from England, how many other countries have supplied three referees for the Final?

10. Who was presented with the Jules Rimet trophy as captain of the winning team in the 1954 Final?

11. Who, as retiring president of FIFA, made the presentation of the trophy in that Final?

12. Who was the captain of the losing nation in the 1954 Final?

13. Who coached the German squad in that 1954 series?

14. Who was the Welsh referee with the job of linesman in that Final?

15. Who was the Hungarian Deputy Minister of Sport in supremecontrol of the Hungarians in 1954?

ANSWERS: **1. 45** 2. 24 **3. Philip Don** 4. Jack Taylor **5. Munich, 1974** 6. West Germany & Holland **7. George Reader of Southampton** 8. Bill Ling **9. None** 10. Fritz Walter of Germany **11. Jules Rimet** 12. Ferenc Puskas of Hungary **13. Sepp Herberger** 14. Mervyn Griffiths **15. Gustav Sebes**

Quiz 3

Men in Charge

1. Who was coach to the Hungarian Finalists of 1954?

2. Who was captain in England's first-ever World Cup qualifying match in October 1949?

3. Who was England's team manager for the 1950 World Cup finals?

4. Who was the English referee knighted for his services to football in 1949?

5. Who was president of FIFA for 13 years from 1961?

6. Who was team manager of England for four World Cup campaigns?

7. Which former England team manager became FA Director of Coaching and was knighted for his services?

8. England played three qualifying matches and three finals games in the Switzerland 1954 series. Who was captain for all six matches?

9. England played four qualifiers and four finals matches in the 1958 World Cup. Who was captain for all these?

10. In which year did Alf Ramsey become England's manager?

11. Whom did he succeed?

12. What was Ramsey's job before he took over England?

13. Who was England's first World Cup team captain after Billy Wright?

14. That match was in the qualifying round for the 1962 finals in Chile. Who were the opponents?

15. England won that match 9-0. Was the new skipper among the scorers?

ANSWERS: 1. Gyula Mandi 2. Billy Wright **3. Walter Winterbottom** 4. Sir Stanley Rous **5. Sir Stanley Rous** 6. Walter Winterbottom **7. Sir Walter Winterbottom** 8. Billy Wright **9. Billy Wright** 10. 1963 **11. Winterbottom** 12. Ipswich Town manager **13. Johnny Haynes** 14. Luxembourg **15. Yes - once**

Quiz 4 Men in Charge

1. **England had the same captain for seven of their eight matches, qualifiers and finals, in the 1962 series. Who took over just once?**
2. Which club did he play for in the Football League?
3. **That player won 43 England caps. How many times was he skipper in a World Cup match?**
4. In how many qualifying matches was Alf Ramsey the manager of England during the 1966 series?
5. **Who took over as England's captain in May 1964 before the run-up to the 1966 series?**
6. From whom did he take over the captaincy?
7. **Who was the secretary of FIFA at the same time?**
8. Who was the president of FIFA at the same time?
9. **Who was the first captain to be presented with the World Cup in 1930?**
10. The referee for the first World Cup Final was John Langenus. From which country was he?
11. **The 1954 quarter-final match between Hungary and Brazil was called the 'Battle of Berne'. Who was the referee?**
12. How many players were sent off in that match?
13. **Who captained the Austrian team beaten in the 1954 semi-finals by Germany?**
14. Italian players chased referee Mario Viani off the pitch after losing to the Swiss in a 1954 group match. What nationality was he?
15. **Who was the first World Cup captain of France in 1930, later to be executed by the French Resistance for collaborating with the Nazis?**

ANSWERS: **1. Jimmy Armfield** 2. Blackpool **3. Once** 4. None - England qualified as hosts **5. Bobby Moore** 6. Jimmy Armfield **7. Henri Delaunay** 8. Jules Rimet **9. Nasazzi of Uruguay** 10. Belgium **11. Arthur Ellis of England** 12. Three **13. Ernst Ocwirk** 14. Brazilian **15. Alex Villaplane**

Quiz 5

Men in Charge

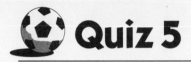

1. **Who, on being appointed a nation's manager, said: 'England will win the World Cup'?**
2. In how many World Cup finals stages was he the manager?
3. **Alf Ramsey named 41 players in his preliminary list for the World Cup of 1966, with seven from each of two clubs. Who were those clubs?**
4. In the 1966 quarter-finals, an English referee sent off two Uruguayans in their match with West Germany. Who was he?
5. **How were those two players punished?**
6. What happened to the Uruguayan player who kicked the ref after the match?
7. **Two British referees officiated in Brazil's group games in 1966 against Bulgaria and Portugal, after which Pele swore never to play in the World Cup again. Who were the refs?**
8. Name the Italian manager who was sacked after his team failed to get beyond the group stage of the 1966 finals.
9. **In how many finals matches was Bobby Moore captain in 1966?**
10. Who in those teams later became a World Cup finals manager?
11. **Who was West Germany's captain in the 1966 World Cup Final?**
12. Who was their team manager in that Final?
13. **Who was West Germany's manager in the next tournament in Mexico?**
14. Who captained the winning Brazilians in Mexico in 1970?
15. **Who was Brazil's team manager in the 1970 finals?**

ANSWERS: 1. Alf Ramsey 2. One **3. Chelsea & Liverpool** 4. Jim Finney **5. Each suspended for three matches** 6. Six matches suspension **7. Jim Finney & George McCabe** 8. Edmondo Fabbri **9. All six** 10. Jack Charlton **11. Uwe Seeler** 12. Helmut Schoen **13. Schoen again** 14. Carlos Alberto **15. Mario Zagalo**

Quiz 6

Men in Charge

1. **In which World Cup finals did Mario Zagalo play for Brazil?**
2. Who was Brazil's captain in 1958 - Bellini or Zagalo?
3. **Who was Brazil's captain in 1962 - Mauro or Zagalo?**
4. From whom did Zagalo take over as manager only three months before the 1970 Mexico finals?
5. **When did Ramsey become Sir Alf?**
6. How many qualifying matches did England play altogether under Ramsey?

7 **How many World Cup finals matches did England play under him?**

8. How many of those matches did England win?
9. **Who was England's trainer under Ramsey?**
10. Who were the opponents at Wembley in Ramsey's last World Cup match?
11. **What was the result?**
12. Who was England's captain in that match?
13. **In what year did Ramsey finish as England manager?**
14. Who were the opponents in Bobby Moore's last match as captain in a World Cup match under Ramsey?
15. **Where was that match and what was the result?**

ANSWERS: 1. 1958 & 1962 2. Bellini **3. Mauro** 4. Joao Saldanha **5. 1967** 6. None - they qualified automatically as holders **7. Ten** 8. Seven **9. Harold Shepherdson** 10. Poland **11. 1-1** 12. Martin Peters **13. 1974** 14. Poland **15. In Chorzow, Poland winning 2-0**

Quiz 7

Men in Charge

1. **Who took over from Ramsey as caretaker-manager of England until the autumn of 1974?**
2. Who took over the permanent post of manager in 1974?
3. **Scotland had four captains for their seven qualifying and finals matches of 1958. Who was the fourth for the last match with France?**
4. Scotland showed some consistency by naming the same skipper for all five qualifying matches in 1961. Who was he?
5. **Which former Scotland manager returned to the job until three weeks before the first qualifying match in 1961?**
6. He decided to put club first and and resigned a second time. Who were that club?
7. **Who at the age of 34 was next to take over as Scotland manager?**
8. How many captains did the Scots have for their six qualifying matches in the 1966 World Cup?
9. **Who captained Scotland in three of those matches?**
10. Ian McColl lost the manager's job after the first qualifier in October 1964, although Finland had been beaten. Who took over as 'caretaker'?
11. **The 'caretaker' had only three months earlier taken up a club managerial appointment. Which was the club?**
12. Who, in 1967, was made the first full-time manager of Scotland?
13. **Which club was he managing before taking the national post?**
14. How many qualifying games did Scotland play without going through to the 1970 finals in Mexico?
15. **One man captained the Scots in all those games. Who was he?**

ANSWERS: **1. Joe Mercer** 2. Don Revie **3. Bobby Evans (Celtic)** 4. Eric Caldow of Rangers **5. Andy Beattie** 6. Nottingham Forest **7. Ian McColl** 8. Four **9. Billy McNeill of Celtic** 10. Jock Stein **11. Celtic** 12. Bobby Brown **13. St Johnstone** 14. Six **15. Billy Bremner of Leeds**

Quiz 8

Men in Charge

1. **When Scotland reached the finals of 1974, after an absence of 16 years, they had the same skipper in three of the four qualifiers. Who was he?**
2. Who stood in for him in the odd match out?
3. **Who was captain of Scotland's finals team of 1974, when they were unbeaten in three games?**
4. How many times did Billy Bremner captain Scotland in World Cup ties, including qualifying matches?
5. **Was this a record?**
6. Who has equalled that record number?
7. **How many times has that player been captain of a World Cup team at the finals stage?**
8. How many times was Bremner the winning captain in World Cup games?
9. **How many times has McAllister been the winning captain in 12 games?**
10. Who captained Scotland in six successive World Cup qualifying matches before McAllister took over on September 8, 1993 at home to Switzerland?
11. **How many times had McStay played for Scotland in World Cup ties?**
12. Who took over as manager of Scotland in 1993 with two World Cup qualifying matches left to play?
13. **From whom had he taken over the managerial post?**
14. What was the role of Craig Brown before taking over Scotland's managership?
15. **Who did Scotland meet in Craig Brown's first World Cup match in charge?**

ANSWERS: 1. Billy Bremner 2. David Hay of Celtic **3. Bremner** 4. Twelve **5. Yes** 6. Gary McAllister **7. None** 8. Seven **9. Eight** 10. Paul McStay of Celtic **11. Seven** 12. Craig Brown **13. Andy Roxburgh** 14. Deputy to Roxburgh **15. Italy**

Quiz 9

Men in Charge

1. **Who was Italy's manager for the match with Scotland in Rome in October 1993?**
2. Why were many Italian fans surprisingly cheering for Scotland in that match?
3. **Scotland had two captains in the three finals matches of 1978, both of them Derby County players. Name them.**
4. Another England-based player, also a midfielder, captained them in one of the 1978 qualifying matches. Who was it?
5. **Which English club was he from?**
6. Who managed Scotland at the start of their 1974 World Cup campaign?
7. **Who was manager at the finals stage of the 1974 campaign?**
8. Why did Tommy Docherty give up the Scotland managerial post?
9. **Did a successor of Docherty at Old Trafford ever have a position with Scotland?**
10. Jock Stein was manager of Scotland in 1978 and again in 1982. He died after a qualifying match in 1985 against whom?
11. **Where was that match played?**
12. What was the result?
13. **Who captained Scotland in nine of their 11 World Cup matches of the 1986 series?**
14. Who was captain in those two other games of the 1986 series?
15. **Who was captain of Scotland in ten of their 11 matches in the 1990 series?**

ANSWERS: 1. Arrigo Sacchi 2. Sacchi had not picked any Roma players **3. Bruce Rioch & Archie Gemmill** 4. Don Masson **5. Queens Park Rangers** 6. Tommy Docherty **7. Willie Ormond** 8. He became Manchester United's manager **9. Yes - Alex Ferguson was coach of Scotland during the 1986 campaign** 10. Wales **11. Cardiff** 12. 1-1 **13. Graeme Souness** 14. Willie Miller of Aberdeen **15. Roy Aitken of Celtic**

Quiz 10 Men in Charge

1. Which Danish World Cup player has captained an English Premiership club?

2. Which Croatian World Cup player has captained an English Premiership club?

3. For which English club does the captain of World Cup 1998 qualifiers South Africa play?

4. How many different captains have England had in the qualifying rounds of the 1998 finals?

5. How many times has Alan Shearer captained England in the World Cup up to the 1998 finals?

6. Who were the other skippers in the 1998 qualifiers?

7. When did Glenn Hoddle become England coach?

8. How many international matches had Hoddle totalled as coach by the end of 1997?

9. How many of these games did England win?

10. Who is France's coach?

11. Who coached World Cup qualifiers Morocco in their unbeaten run of eight matches in 1997?

12. Who was coaching Brazil up to the World Cup finals of 1998?

13. Who coached Paraguay through the qualifying rounds to the finals of 1998?

14. For whom did he play in the World Cup third-place match in West Germany in 1974?

15. Who is George Leeskens?

ANSWERS: 1. Peter Schmeichel (Manchester United) 2. Igor Stimac (Derby County) **3. Leeds United (Lucas Radebe)** 4. Four **5. Five** 6. Tony Adams, David Seaman, Paul Ince **7. June 1996** 8. Fourteen **9. Eleven** 10. Aime Jacquet **11. Henri Michel** 12. Mario Zagalo **13. Paulo Cesar Carpeggiani** 14. Brazil **15. Belgium's coach in the qualifiers for France 1998**

Quiz 11 Men in Charge

1. Who is Cha Bum Kun?

2. Which club did he play for in the Bundesliga as a striker?

3. Who captained Italy in the qualifying rounds of the 1998 series?

4. Who was the Italians' manager on the way to the 1998 finals?

5. Who was Germany's captain on the successful qualifying route to the 1998 finals?

6. Who is Herbert Prohaska?

7. Who is Glenn Hoddle's assistant coach?

8. What is his nationality?

9. Who was Italy's World Cup winning coach in 1982?

10. Who was his deputy at the time?

11. Who was referee of the vital Italy v England closing group match in Rome in 1997?

12. What country does he come from?

13. Who was referee when the Republic of Ireland beat Italy 1-0 at the 1994 World Cup finals?

14. Who was the coach fired by Mexico after getting them through the qualifiers for 1998?

15. Spain's coach since joining them in 1992 experienced only three defeats in 55 matches. Who is he?

ANSWERS: 1. South Korea's successful coach in qualifying for 1998 finals 2. Eintracht Frankfurt **3. Paolo Maldini** 4. Cesare Maldini **5. Matthias Sammer** 6. Austrian coach **7. John Gorman** 8. Scottish **9. Enzo Bearzot** 10. Cesare Maldini **11. Mario van der Ende** 12. Holland **13. Mario van der Ende** 14. Bora Milutinovic **15. Javier Clemente**

Quiz 12 Men in Charge

1. Who is the coach who took Jamaica through the qualifiers in the CONCACAF group to the 1998 finals?

2. What is his nationality?

3. Name the German who was suspended by FIFA because of his refereeing of the World Cup qualifying match between England and Holland in 1993.

4. Italy's team manager had a major problem for the 1970 finals. Who was the manager?

5. His problem was to find a compromise over an outcry when he dropped Gianni Rivera in favour of whom?

6. How did he manage to play them both in the 1970 finals?

7. The manager substituted Mazzola with Rivera in the quarter and semi-finals, but what happened in the Final with Brazil?

8. Did either of them score in those three games?

9. Who managed Italy in the 1974 finals in West Germany?

10. How far did Italy progress in the 1974 finals?

11. Holland's 'Total Football' methods in 1974 were under the control of which manager?

12. Who skippered the Dutch in the 1974 World Cup Final with West Germany?

13. Who was the Germans' winning manager?

14. Which club side did Rinus Michels manage in three consecutive European Cup wins?

15. Which club was he managing when he took Holland to the 1974 Final?

ANSWERS: 1. Rene Simoes 2. Brazilian **3. Karl-Josef Assenmacher** 4. Ferruccio Valcareggi **5. Sandro Mazzola** 6. Substitutes were allowed for the first time **7. Mazzola played throughout, Rivera for the last six minutes** 8. Rivera in quarter and semi-final **9. Valcareggi again** 10. Eliminated in first group matches **11. Rinus Michels** 12. Johan Cruyff **13. Helmut Schoen** 14.Ajax **15. Barcelona**

Quiz 13 Men in Charge

1. **Who was Australia's coach for their only appearance in the World Cup finals?**
2. Which finals year was that?
3. **Who did that same coach take to the previous World Cup finals for the first time?**
4. What was the coach's nationality?
5. **How many matches did those two countries win in the two finals?**
6. How many World Cup qualifying round matches did England play under Don Revie's managership?
7. **How many did they win in the qualifiers with Revie in charge?**
8. Who beat England in the qualifiers under Revie?
9. **Where was that match and what was the score?**
10. Who captained England three times under Revie?
11. **Who else was England's captain under Revie?**
12. Who were the opposition (non-World Cup) for Revie's last match as England manager before resigning?
13. **Where was that match and what was the score?**
14. Who took over as caretaker manager from Revie?
15. **Who were the last two World Cup qualifying opponents for the 1978 finals under the new manager?**

ANSWERS: 1. Rale Rasic 2. 1974 **3. Morocco** 4. Yugoslav **5. None** 6. Four **7. Three** 8. Italy **9. Rome, 0-2** 10. Kevin Keegan **11. Gerry Francis, once** 12. Uruguay **13. Montevideo, 0-0** 14. Ron Greenwood **15. Luxembourg & Italy**

Quiz 14 Men in Charge

1. **What were the results of England's last two qualifying matches for the 1978 finals under the new managership of Ron Greenwood?**
2. Who was the new captain under the Greenwood regime?
3. **Was Kevin Keegan in the England team under Greenwood when the new captain was around?**
4. Who was captain in the absence of Hughes?
5. **Who was Argentina's manager for the 1978 finals in that country?**
6. Who did the new manager appoint as his captain for the finals?
7. **Scotland were the only British representatives in the 1978 finals. Who was their manager?**
8. Who was the first English-born player to captain Scotland?
9. **Who was Holland's new manager for the 1978 finals in Argentina?**
10. What was his nationality?
11. **Who captained Holland in their second consecutive losing World Cup Final in 1978?**
12. The original choice of referee for the 1978 Final was Abraham Klein of Israel. Why was the decision changed?
13. **Who took over as the Final referee?**
14. How many qualifying-round matches did England play under Greenwood leading up to the 1982 finals in Spain?
15. **How many of those games did England win?**

ANSWERS: 1. England won both 2-0 2. Emlyn Hughes **3. Yes** 4. Kevin Keegan **5. Cesar Luis Menotti** 6. Daniel Passarella **7. Ally MacLeod** 8. Bruce Rioch **9. Ernst Happel** 10. Austrian **11. Rudi Krol** 12. Argentina objected to FIFA over their choice **13. Sergio Gonella of Italy** 14. Eight **15. Four**

Quiz 15 Men in Charge

1. **Who of the four captains used by Ron Greenwood in the qualifiers for Spain 1982 was the skipper four times?**
2. In England's five finals matches of 1982, how many times was Keegan the captain?
3. **Who was England's captain in all five finals matches?**
4. Who else of the Home Countries was in the 1982 finals in Spain?
5. **How many times was this that Scotland had qualified for a World Cup finals stage?**
6. How many World Cup finals was this for England?
7. **Who was called up as Greenwood's assistant in the 1982 finals?**
8. What was his club position in England?
9. **Who was Northern Ireland's manager?**
10. Did he ever play in a World Cup finals stage?
11. **How many times have Northern Ireland played in the World Cup finals under the same manager?**
12. Who did Bingham introduce to the Irish World Cup side in 1982 as the youngest ever to play in the finals?
13. **Scotland had three different captains in their eight qualifying games for Spain. Who were they?**
14. They had two different skippers in their three finals games of 1982. Who were they?
15. **Who was Kuwait's coach in the 1982 finals?**

ANSWERS: 1. Kevin Keegan 2. None **3. Mick Mills of Ipswich Town** 4. Scotland & Northern Ireland **5. Five** 6. Seven **7. Don Howe** 8. Arsenal coach **9. Billy Bingham** 10. In 1958 **11. Bingham twice, 1982 & 1986** 12. Norman Whiteside, aged 17 **13. Archie Gemmill, Danny McGrain, Asa Hartford** 14. Danny McGrain & Graeme Souness **15. Carlos Alberto of Brazil**

Quiz 16 Men in Charge

1. **When Kuwait's players threatened to walk off in protest against a referee's decision, the Kuwait FA president persuaded them to stay on. Who was he?**
2. Who was the manager of the French team who reached the last four of the 1982 finals?
3. **Who was Brazil's coach in 1982?**
4. What happened to his 1978 predecessor, Claudio Coutinho?
5. **The Final of 1982 was refereed by a Brazilian, the first time a South American had been in charge. Who was he?**
6. Who was the oldest captain to receive the World Cup trophy?
7. **What was his age on the Final day?**
8. Who was the captain of the losing Finalists of 1982?
9. **Name the manager of the West Germany runners-up team in the Mexico 1986 Final.**
10. A doctor and former international was the manager of the winning team of 1986. Who was he?
11. **Who was the Scottish manager who described the Uruguayan team as 'a disgrace' after a 0-0 draw meant elimination at the 1986 group stage?**
12. Who was the Uruguayan manager on the receiving end?
13. **England qualified for the 1986 Mexico finals under a new manager. Who was he?**
14. In which year did he take over from Greenwood?
15. **Did he have any previous coaching experience at England level?**

ANSWERS: 1. Prince Fahid 2. Michel Hidalgo **3. Carlos Alberto Parreira** 4. Died from drowning **5. Arnold Cesar Coelho** 6. Dino Zoff of Italy **7. Forty** 8. Karl-Heinz Rummenigge **9. Franz Beckenbauer** 10. Carlos Bilardo of Argentina **11. Alex Ferguson** 12. Omar Borras **13. Bobby Robson** 14. 1982 **15. Yes - as England 'B' manager**

Quiz 17 Men in Charge

1. **How many times did Bobby Robson play for England?**
2. How many matches, in the qualifiers and the finals, did England play in the World Cup under Bobby Robson?
3. **How many of these were finals matches in 1986 and 1990?**
4. How many times were England beaten in World Cup qualifying matches under Robson's management?
5. **How many times were England beaten in finals matches under Robson in 1986 and 1990?**
6. Who was the World Cup winning captain of 1986?
7. **Who in the role of captain picked up World Cup Final runners-up medals in consecutive finals?**
8. Which years and for which country was he playing?
9. **Who was West Germany's manager in that 1982 runners-up year?**
10. Robson's first World Cup captain was a familiar name. Who?
11. **How many times was he a World Cup captain - qualifiers and finals?**
12. Who was an ever-present for England in 13 World Cup matches of the 1986 series?
13. **Who was captain in that last match of 1986?**
14. Who played in all 26 World Cup matches during Bobby Robson's management?
15. **Who was stand-in captain for Bryan Robson in two of the eight qualifying matches in the 1986 series?**

ANSWERS: 1. 20 2. 26 **3. 12** 4. None **5. Four, including a penalty shoot-out** 6. Diego Maradona **7. Karl-Heinz Rummenigge** 8. West Germany, 1982 & 1986 **9. Jupp Derwall** 10. Robson (Bryan of that ilk) **11. 15** 12. Peter Shilton **13. Shilton** 14. Shilton **15. Ray Wilkins**

Quiz 18 Men in Charge

1. In how many World Cup matches was Peter Shilton captain of England?

2. How many times did Ray Clemence captain England in the World Cup?

3. How many times did Clemence play in the World Cup - qualifying or finals?

4. Has any other goalkeeper skippered England in a World Cup match?

5. How many times?

6. Whose decision was that?

7. How many goals did Bryan Robson score for England as captain in the 1986 series?

8. Against whom did he record a hat-trick in the 1986 qualifiers?

9. How many goals did Bryan Robson score as World Cup skipper during the 1990 series?

10. England played how many matches, qualifying or in the finals, in the 1990 World Cup series?

11. How many captains did England have during the 1990 series?

12. Who was captain four times for England in the 1990 series?

13. How many times did Shilton wear the captain's armband during the 1990 series?

14. With which club was Butcher playing during his England captaincy?

15. How many goals did Diego Maradona score as captain of Argentina in their seven finals matches of 1986?

ANSWERS: 1. Five 2. None **3. Twelve** 4. David Seaman **5. Once** 6. Glenn Hoddle **7. Five** 8. Turkey **9. One** 10. 13 **11. Three** 12. Terry Butcher **13. Twice** 14. Glasgow Rangers **15. Five**

Quiz 19 Men in Charge

1. How did Diego Maradona describe his method of heading a goal against England in 1986 in Mexico?

2. Maradona was second to whom as top goalscorer of the 1986 finals?

3. Who was Argentina's captain in the World Cup Final of 1990?

4. England topped the group in which Holland were eliminated in the 1990 finals. Who was Holland's manager?

5. In how many World Cup series did Bryan Robson skipper England?

6. Who was the Republic of Ireland's manager in the 1990 and 1994 World Cup finals?

7. How many English clubs did he manage before taking the Ireland job?

8. Who were they?

9. United Arab Emirates were in their first finals in Italy in 1990. Who was their Brazilian manager?

10. From whom did he take over the post - also a Brazilian?

11. What was the result of England's last World Cup match under Bobby Robson?

12. At what stage of the finals was this?

13. From which country was the 1990 Final referee E.Codesal?

14. Who was the England manager after Bobby Robson?

15. With whom was he manager when he got the England appointment?

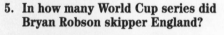

ANSWERS: 1. Assisted by 'the hand of God' 2. Gary Lineker scored six **3. Diego Maradona** 4. Leo Beenhakker **5. Three** 6. Jack Charlton **7. Three** 8. Middlesbrough, Sheffield Wednesday & Newcastle United **9. Carlos Alberto Parreira** 10. Mario Zagalo **11. Italy 2 England 1** 12. Third-place play-off **13. Mexico** 14. Graham Taylor **15. Aston Villa**

Quiz 20 Men in Charge

1. **How many of the ten matches did England win with Graham Taylor as manager?**
2. Name the two teams who beat England in those qualifying games.
3. **Only two players captained England in those qualifiers. Name them.**
4. Who captained Italy in the 1994 Final and missed a penalty in the shoot-out?
5. **Who was the president of the USA soccer administration for the 1994 World Cup finals?**
6. Who was the new manager of Italy who took them to the 1994 Final?
7. **Who was manager of England from 1994 to 1996?**
8. How many World Cup matches did England play under his managership?
9. **Who did he take to within one match of the 1998 finals?**
10. When did Glenn Hoddle take over as coach of England?
11. **How many World Cup qualifying matches did England play under Hoddle in the run-up to France 1998?**
12. Who captained the first World Cup match with Hoddle in charge?
13. **How many of the eight qualifiers did England lose?**
14. How many times has Shearer captained England in the 1998 qualifiers?
15. **Who was England's captain in their last World Cup match before the arrival of Hoddle and Shearer?**

ANSWERS: 1. Five 2. Norway & Holland **3. David Platt & Stuart Pearce** 4. Franco Baresi **5. Alan Rothenberg** 6. Arrigo Sacchi **7. Terry Venables** 8.None **9. Australia** 10. 1996 **11. Eight** 12. Alan Shearer **13. One - 1-0 to Italy** 14. Five **15. Stuart Pearce**

Fill the Gaps

Quiz 1

Fill the Gaps

1. 19?? - First round - Hungary 6 0

2. 1930 - Pool 1 - Argentina 6 3

3. 1990 - Final - West Germany (?) 1 Argentina (0) 0

4. 1994 - Group ? - Russia 6 Cameroon 1

5. 1958 - Final - ...... (2) 5 Sweden (?) 2

6. 1970 - Quarter-final - West Germany ? England 2

7. 1962 - ....-..... - Chile 2 USSR 1

8. 1934 - First round - Spain 3 1

9. 1994 - Group D - Argentina 0 2

10. 1966 - Quarter-final - Portugal ? North Korea ?

ANSWERS 1. 38, Dutch East Indies 2. Mexico 3. 0 4. B **5. Brazil, 1** 6. 3 **7. Quarter-final** 8. Brazil **9. Bulgaria** 10. 5, 3

Quiz 2

Fill the Gaps

1. 1954 - Pool 4 - England ? Belgium 4

2. 1934 - Final - Italy (0) ? Czechoslovakia (0) 1

3. 1982 - Group ? - England 1 0

4. 1954 - Semi-final - Hungary 2

5. 1970 - Semi-final - Brazil ? Uruguay ?

6. 1950 - Final Pool - ...... 7 Sweden 1

7. 1978 - Group 2

Final Table

Country	P	W	D	L	F	A	Pts
......	3	2	1	0	4	1	5
West Germany	3	1	2	0	6	0	4
Tunisia	3	1	1	1	3	2	3
Mexico	3	0	0	3	2	12	0

8. 1938 - Second round - Sweden 8 Cuba ?

9. 1970 - Final - Brazil (1) 4 ..... (1) 1

10. 1950 - Pool 2

Final Table

Country	P	W	D	L	F	A	Pts
Spain	3	3	0	0	6	1	6
England	3	1	0	2	?	?	2
Chile	3	1	0	2	5	6	2
...	3	1	0	2	4	8	2

ANSWERS 1. 4 2. 2 **3. 4, Kuwait** 4. 4, Uruguay **5. 3, 1** 6. Brazil **7. Poland** 8. 0 **9. Italy** 10. 2, 2, USA

Quiz 3

Fill the Gaps

1. 1930 - Final - Uruguay (1) 4 Argentina (?) 2

2. 1974 - Third-place match - …… 1 Brazil 0

3. 1982 - Group 2 - ……. 2 West Germany 1

4. 1954 - Quarter-final - Austria ? Switzerland ?

5. 1974 - Group 1 - …. Germany 1 …. Germany 0

6. 1958 - Pool 1

Final Table

Country	P	W	D	L	F	A	Pts
West Germany	3	1	2	0	7	5	4
Czechoslovakia	3	1	1	1	8	4	3
…….. …….	3	1	1	1	4	5	3
Argentina	3	1	0	2	5	10	2

7. 1950 - Pool 4 - Uruguay ? Bolivia 0

8. 1974 - Group ? - East Germany ? Australia 0

9. 1966 - Group ? - ….. ….. 1 Italy 0

10. 1962 - Quarter-final - …… 3 England 1

ANSWERS 1. 2 2. Poland 3. **Algeria** 4. 7, 5 5. **East, West** 6. Northern Ireland 7. 8 8. 1, 2 9. 4, **North Korea** 10. Brazil

Quiz 4

Fill the Gaps

1. 1994 - Semi-final - Italy 2 1

2. 1950 - Pool 2 - England ? Chile 0

3. 1974 - Group ? - Holland ? Argentina 0

4. 1950 - Final Pool

Final Table

Country	P	W	D	L	F	A	Pts
Uruguay	3	2	1	0	7	5	5
......	3	2	0	1	14	4	4
Sweden	3	1	0	2	6	11	2
.....	3	0	1	2	4	11	1

5. 1930 - Pool 1 - France ? Mexico 1

6. 1958 - Quarter-final - .... Wales 0

7. 1974 - Final - West Germany (2) ? Holland (?) 1

8. 1966 - Third-place match - Portugal 2 1

9. 1994 - Group A - Romania 1 4

10. 1934 - Third-place match - Germany 2

ANSWERS 1. Bulgaria 2. 2 **3. A, 4** 4. Brazil, Spain **5. 4** 6. Brazil, 1 **7. 2, 1** 8. USSR **9. Switzerland** 10. 3, Austria

Quiz 5 Fill the Gaps

1. 1974 - Group 4 - Poland 7 0

2. 1958 - Pool 1 - Northern Ireland ? Czechoslovakia 0

3. 1970 - ....-..... - Italy 4 Mexico 1

4. 1966 - Final - England (?) 4 West Germany (1) 2

5. 1994 - Second round - .... 1 Sweden 3

6. 1962 - Group 4 - Hungary ? England 1

7. 1954 - Pool 3

Final Table

Country	**P**	**W**	**D**	**L**	**F**	**A**	**Pts**
Uruguay	2	2	0	0	9	0	4
Austria	2	2	0	0	6	0	4
Czechoslovakia	2	0	0	2	0	7	0
....	2	0	0	2	?	?	0

8. 1978 - Group B - .... 6 Peru 0

9. 1982 - Group ? - Italy 1 1

10. 1934 - Second round - Germany ? Sweden 1

ANSWERS 1. Haiti 2. 1 **3. Quarter-final** 4. 1 **5. Saudi Arabia** 6. 2 **7. Scotland, 0, 8**
8. Argentina **9. 1, Cameroon** 10. 2

Quiz 6

Fill the Gaps

1. 1978 - Third-place match - ...... 2 Italy 1

2. 1930 - Pool 2

Final Table

Country	P	W	D	L	F	A	Pts
....	2	2	0	0	6	1	?
Brazil	2	1	0	1	5	2	2
Bolivia	2	0	0	2	0	8	0

3. 1958 - Pool 4 - England ? Brazil ?

4. 1966 - Group 2 - West Germany ? Switzerland 0

5. 1962 - Group ? - West Germany ? Italy ?

6. 1986 - Group C - USSR ? Hungary 0

7. 1966 - Group 3 - .... 3 Brazil 1

8. 1982 - Group B -

Final Table

Country	P	W	D	L	F	A	Pts
West Germany	2	1	1	0	2	1	3
England	2	?	?	0	0	0	2
.....	2	0	1	1	1	2	1

9. 1958 - Pool 4 play-off - .... 1 England 0

10. 1986 - Second round - Spain 5 Denmark ?

ANSWERS 1. Brazil 2. Yugoslavia, 4 **3.** 0, 0 **4.** 5 **5.** 2, 0, 0 **6.** 6 **7. Hungary** **8.** 0, 2, Spain **9. USSR** 10. 1

Quiz 7

Fill the Gaps

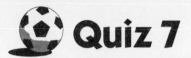

1. 1990 - Second round - West Germany 2 1

2. 1962 - Group 3 - ...... 3 Czechoslovakia 1

3. 1938 - Second round - 3 1

4. 1986 - Quarter-final - France 1 Brazil 1 (...... won ?-? on penalties)

5. 1986 - Third-place match - France 4 2

6. 1954 - Final - West Germany (2) ? Hungary (2) 2

7. 1990 - Group ? - Cameroon ? Argentina 0

8. 1970 - Group 1 - Belgium 3 0

9. 1978 - Group A

Final Table

Country	P	W	D	L	F	A	Pts
....	3	2	1	0	?	4	5
Italy	3	1	1	1	2	2	3
....	3	0	2	1	4	5	2
Austria	3	1	0	2	4	8	2

10. 1962 - Group 1 - England 0 Uruguay ?

ANSWERS 1. Holland 2. Mexico **3. Italy, France** 4. France, 4, 3 **5. Belgium** 6. 3 **7. B, 1** 8. El Salvador **9. Holland, 9, West Germany** 10. 0

Quiz 8

Fill the Gaps

1. **1990 - Group C - .... 2 Sweden 1**
2. 1966 - Semi-final - England ? Portugal 1
3. **1934 - Semi-final - .... 3 Germany 1**
4. 1970 - Group ? - England 1 0
5. **1958 - Quarter-final - France 4 Northern Ireland ?**
6. 1990 - Quarter-final - ..... 1 Republic of Ireland 0
7. **1978 - Group ? - Scotland 1 Iran 1**
8. 1966 - Quarter-final - West Germany 4 0
9. **1950 - Deciding match - Uruguay (0) 2 Brazil (0) ?**
10. 1990 - Semi-final - Argentina 1 Italy 1 (Argentina won ?-? on penalties)

ANSWERS 1. Scotland 2. 2 **3. Czechoslovakia** 4. 3, Romania **5. 0** 6. Italy **7. 4** 8. Uruguay **9. 1** 10. 4, 3

Quiz 9

Fill the Gaps

1. 1930 - Semi-final - .... 6 USA 1

2. 1958 - Third place match - France ? West Germany 3

3. 1982 - Semi-final - .... 3 France 3 (5-4 on penalties)

4. 1986 - Group E - Scotland 0 0

5. 1962 - Final - Brazil (1) ? Czechoslovakia (1) 1

6. 1990 - Group F - England ? Republic of Ireland ?

7. 1966 - Group 1

Final Table

Country	P	W	D	L	F	A	Pts
....	3	2	?	?	4	0	5
Uruguay	3	1	2	0	2	1	4
Mexico	3	0	2	1	1	3	2
France	3	0	1	2	2	5	1

8. 1938 - Semi-final - .... 5 Sweden 1

9. 1970 - Group 4 - .... 5 Bulgaria 2

10. 1994 - Group E

Final Table

Country	P	W	D	L	F	A	Pts
......	3	1	1	1	3	3	4
Ireland	3	1	1	1	2	2	4
.....	3	1	1	1	?	?	4
Norway	3	1	1	1	1	1	4

ANSWERS 1. Argentina 2. 6 **3. West Germany** 4. Uruguay **5.** 3 **6.** 1, 1 **7. England, 1, 0**
8. Hungary **9. West Germany** 10. Mexico, Italy, 2, 2

Quiz 10 Fill the Gaps

1. 1938 - Final - Italy (3) ? Hungary (1) 2

2. 1954 - Pool 2 play-off - West Germany ? Turkey 2

3. 1990 - Third-place match - Italy ? England ?

4. 1962 - Third-place match - ..... 1 Yugoslavia 0

5. 1974 - Group B - West Germany ? Sweden 2

6. 1958 - Semi-final - ...... 3 West Germany 1

7. 1954 - Third-place match - .... 3 Uruguay 1

8. 1978 - Group 3 - .... 2 Spain 1

9. 1994 - Final - Brazil (0) 0 Italy (0) 0 (Brazil won ?-? on penalties)

10. 1962 - Group 4

Final Table

Country	P	W	D	L	F	A	Pts
....	3	2	1	0	8	2	5
England	3	?	1	?	4	3	3
Argentina	3	1	1	1	2	3	3
Bulgaria	3	0	1	2	1	7	1

ANSWERS 1.4 2.7 **3.2,1** 4.Chile **5.4** 6.Sweden **7.Austria** 8.Austria **9.3,2**
10.Hungary, 1, 1

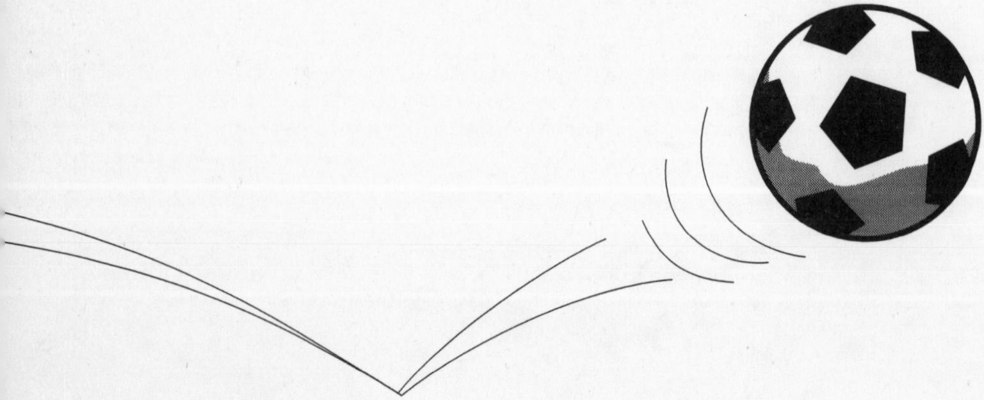

The Outsiders

Quiz 1

The Outsiders

1. **Which African country beat West Germany in their first ever World Cup match?**
2. What was the score?
3. **Who scored the winner?**
4. What year was it?
5. **Who else did they beat in the group?**
6. Algeria qualified for the 1986 finals. How many games did they win in the tournament?
7. **Which European country beat them 3-0 in their final group match?**
8. Who were drawn against East and West Germany in their first finals appearance?
9. **Austria made their World Cup debut in which year?**
10. What round did they reach?
11. **Who knocked them out of the competition?**
12. How long was the gap before Austria's next World Cup appearance?
13. **Which British nation were in their group in 1954?**
14. What was the score?
15. **Whom did Austria thump 5-0 in the following match?**

ANSWERS: 1. Algeria 2. 2-1 **3. Belloumi** 4. 1982 **5. Chile** 6. None **7. Spain** 8. Australia **9. 1934** 10. Semi-finals **11. Italy** 12. 20 years **13. Scotland** 14. Austria won 1-0 **15. Czechoslovakia**

Quiz 2

The Outsiders

1. **Who scored a hat-trick for Austria in their 5-0 group win in 1954?**
2. In the quarter-final, how many goals were scored?
3. **What was the score?**
4. Who scored three goals for Austria in that match?
5. **Who beat Austria in the semi-final?**
6. What was the score?
7. **How many goals did Austria score in the 1954 tournament?**
8. Who did Austria draw with in 1958?
9. **Who else were in the group?**
10. Which year did they next make an appearance?
11. **Which European nation did they beat in their first group match?**
12. Austria qualified for the quarter-final group stage, but were beaten 5-1 by whom?
13. **Who else beat them?**
14. Austria did win one group match. Against whom?
15. **What was the score?**

ANSWERS: 1. Probst 2. 12 **3. 7-5** 4. Wagner **5. West Germany** 6. 1-6 **7. 14** 8. England **9. Brazil, USSR** 10. 1978 **11. Spain** 12. Holland **13. Italy** 14. West Germany **15. 3-2**

Quiz 3 The Outsiders

1. **Who scored twice for Austria against West Germany in 1978?**
2. Austria won two of their three group games in 1982. Name one of the non-European nations they beat.
3. **Did Austria qualify for the quarter-final stage in 1982?**
4. Austria suffered two 1-0 defeats in 1990. Who were the European victors?
5. **They did win one game in 1990. Against whom?**
6. What was the score?
7. **Bulgaria have appeared in how many World Cup tournaments?**
8. When was their first appearance?
9. **Who were their first World Cup finals opponents?**
10. Who scored Bulgaria's first World Cup goal?
11. **Who beat them 6-1 in their second match?**
12. How many goals did Bulgaria concede in 1966?
13. **How many of them were own goals?**
14. Who scored their only goal in 1966?
15. **How many games did it take Bulgaria to win their first point?**

ANSWERS: 1. Hans Krankl 2. Chile and Algeria **3. Yes** 4. Italy and Czechoslovakia **5. USA** 6. 2-1 **7. Six up to 1994** 8. 1962 **9. Argentina** 10. Sokolov **11. Hungary** 12. Eight **13. Two** 14. Asparoukhov **15. Three**

Quiz 4 — The Outsiders

1. **Who were the opponents in Bulgaria's 0-0 draw of 1962?**
2. Who captained the opposition on that day?
3. **Who beat Bulgaria 5-2 in the 1970 group stage?**
4. Who beat Bulgaria 4-1 in 1974 on their way to the Final?
5. **How many goals did Bulgaria score in 1974?**
6. Who held Bulgaria to a draw in the second match of 1986?
7. **What was the score?**
8. When was the first time Bulgaria qualified for the second round?
9. **Who were their opponents?**
10. Bulgaria lost to whom in their opening match of 1994?
11. **Who scored Bulgaria's first World Cup penalty?**
12. Who did Bulgaria beat in their final group game of 1994?
13. **What was the score?**
14. Who did Bulgaria meet in the second round?
15. **What was the score after extra-time?**

ANSWERS: 1. England 2. Johnny Haynes **3. West Germany** 4. Holland **5. Two** 6. South Korea **7. 1-1** 8. 1986 **9. Mexico** 10. Nigeria **11. Hristo Stoichkov** 12. Argentina **13. 2-0** 14. Mexico **15. 1-1**

Quiz 5

The Outsiders

1. **Bulgaria came from behind to beat whom in the 1994 quarter-finals?**
2. Who scored their winning goal?
3. **Who scored a penalty for Bulgaria in the semi-final?**
4. Who did Bulgaria face in the third place play-off?
5. **What was the score?**
6. Cameroon made their first World Cup finals appearance in what year?
7. **Who were their first opponents?**
8. How many goals did they score in their first tournament?
9. **Did Cameroon lose a game in their maiden finals?**
10. Which World Cup-winning nation were Cameroon's 1982 final group match opponents?
11. **What was the score?**
12. Who scored Cameroon's only goal in 1982?
13. **Who were the opponents?**
14. Who qualified for the second stage ahead of Cameroon only on goal difference?
15. **When was the next time Cameroon qualified?**

ANSWERS: 1. Germany 2. Iordan Letchkov **3. Hristo Stoichkov** 4. Sweden **5. Sweden 4 Bulgaria 0** 6. 1982 **7. Peru** 8. One **9. No** 10. Italy **11. 1-1** 12. M'Bida **13. Italy** 14. Italy **15. 1990**

Quiz 6 The Outsiders

1. **Who were Cameroon's first opponents in 1990?**
2. Cameroon produced the shock result of the first round when they beat which former winners?
3. **What was the score?**
4. Who scored for Cameroon?
5. **What was the name of the brothers in Cameroon's squad?**
6. Who did they beat in their second game?
7. **What was the score?**
8. Who scored twice for Cameroon?
9. **Who were Cameroon's final group opponents?**
10. Which South American nation were their second-round opponents?
11. **What was the score after 90 minutes?**
12. What was the final score?
13. **Who scored Cameroon's goals?**
14. Who beat Cameroon in the quarter-finals?
15. **Who scored an equalising penalty for Cameroon?**

ANSWERS: 1. Argentina 2. Argentina **3. 1-0** 4. François Omam-Biyick **5. Omam and Kana Biyick** 6. Romania **7. 2-1** 8. Roger Milla **9. USSR** 10. Colombia **11. 0-0** 12. 2-1 **13. Roger Milla** 14. England **15. Kunde**

Quiz 7

The Outsiders

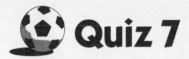

1. **Cameroon took a 2-1 lead against England through whose goal?**
2. What was the final score?
3. **Who scored Cameroon's first goal of 1994?**
4. Who were their first opponents?
5. **What was the score?**
6. Who defeated Cameroon 3-0 in their second group match?
7. **Who set an individual goalscoring record against Cameroon in 1994?**
8. Who was he playing for?
9. **Who became the oldest player to score in a World Cup match, against Russia?**
10. What was the final score?
11. **Who is Cameroon's top World Cup goalscorer?**
12. How many goals has he scored?
13. **The 1986 finals was the debut year for which North American country?**
14. How many games did they win?
15. **How many goals did they score?**

ANSWERS: **1. Ekeke** 2. Cameroon lost 3-2 **3. Embe** 4. Sweden **5. 2-2** 6. Brazil **7. Oleg Salenko** 8. Russia **9. Roger Milla** 10. 1-6 **11. Roger Milla** 12. Five **13. Canada** 14. None **15. None**

Quiz 8

The Outsiders

1. Chile were in the original World Cup. True or false?

2. Who were their first opponents?

3. What was the score?

4. What was the attendance - 500, 5,000 or 50,000?

5. Which other South American nation did Chile face in their first finals?

6. Which player scored in all three of Chile's matches?

7. In 1950, Chile met England or Scotland in the group stage?

8. Who were Chile beaten by in their first match of 1950?

9. What was the score?

10. Chile failed to reach the second round in 1950, despite beating which nation 5-2?

11. Who scored a hat-trick in that match?

12. Have Chile ever played in a World Cup finals out of their continent?

13. Chile hosted the 1962 World Cup. Who were their first opponents?

14. What was the score?

15. Who else did they beat in the first round?

ANSWERS: **1. True** 2. Mexico **3. 3-0** 4. 500 **5. Argentina** 6. Subiabre **7. England** 8. England **9. 2-0** 10. USA **11. Cremaschi** 12. Yes **13. Switzerland** 14. 3-1 to Chile **15. Italy**

Quiz 9 The Outsiders

1. Chile were beaten in their final group game of 1962. By whom?

2. What was the score?

3. Whom did Chile beat in the quarter-final?

4. What was the score?

5. Who scored the winner?

6. Whom did Chile face in the semi-final?

7. What was the score?

8. Who scored a penalty for Chile?

9. Chile finished third by beating which European nation?

10. Who scored the only goal?

11. How many games did Chile win in 1966?

12. With whom did they draw 1-1?

13. Who was their only scorer in 1966?

14. Which European teams beat Chile in 1966?

15. Chile drew two of their three games in 1974. Who beat them?

ANSWERS: 1. West Germany 2. Chile lost 2-0 **3. USSR** 4. Chile 2 USSR 1 **5. Rojas** 6. Brazil **7. Brazil 4 Chile 2** 8. L. Sanchez **9. Yugoslavia** 10. Rojas **11. None** 12. North Korea **13. Marcos** 14. Italy, USSR **15. West Germany**

Quiz 10 The Outsiders

1. **Who held Chile to a goalless draw in 1974?**
2. Chile faced West Germany in 1982. What was the score?
3. **Who beat Chile in their opening game?**
4. Who else beat Chile in 1982? It's a country beginning with A!
5. **What was the score?**
6. Costa Rica made their World Cup debut in 1986. True or false?
7. **Whom did they beat in their first World Cup game?**
8. To whom did they lose narrowly in their second match?
9. **What was the final score?**
10. Sweden were the opponents in Costa Rica's third game. What was the score?
11. **Who scored their winning goal - Flores or Medford?**
12. Costa Rica met whom in the second round?
13. **What was the score?**
14. When was Cuba's only World Cup appearance?
15. **Whom did they beat in a first round replay?**

ANSWERS: **1. Australia** 2. West Germany 4 Chile 1 **3. Austria** 4. Algeria **5. 3-2** 6. False - 1990 **7. Scotland** 8. Brazil **9. 1-0** 10. Costa Rica 2 Sweden 1 **11. Medford** 12. Czechoslovakia **13. 1-4** 14. 1938 **15. Romania**

Quiz 11

The Outsiders

1. **What was the score in Cuba's first World Cup match?**
2. What was the score in the replay?
3. **Who scored for Cuba in both games - Maquina or Socorro?**
4. Who were their second-round opponents?
5. **What was the score?**
6. When was Denmark's first World Cup?
7. **Who scored their first World Cup goal?**
8. Who were the opponents?
9. **What was the score?**
10. Which former winners did Denmark beat 6-1 in their second match?
11. **Who scored a hat-trick?**
12. Which former Manchester United player scored in that match?
13. **Denmark beat another former winner in their following match. Who were they?**
14. What was the score?
15. **Who scored a penalty in that match?**

ANSWERS: 1. 3-3 2. Cuba won 2-1 **3. Maquina** 4. Sweden **5. Chile lost 8-0** 6. 1986 **7. Preben Elkjaer** 8. Scotland **9. 1-0** 10. Uruguay **11. Preben Elkjaer** 12. Jesper Olsen **13. West Germany** 14. 2-0 **15. Jesper Olsen**

Quiz 12 The Outsiders

1. **Who gave Denmark their first World Cup defeat?**
2. What was the score?
3. **Who scored in three consecutive matches for Denmark in 1986?**
4. How many penalties did he score?
5. **Which round did Denmark reach in 1986?**
6. The Dutch East Indies played one World Cup match. What year was it?
7. **Who were the opponents?**
8. What was the score?
9. **East Germany's first World Cup finals was in what year?**
10. They remained unbeaten in the first round. True or false?
11. **Who did they beat in their first game?**
12. What was the score?
13. **Who held them to a 1-1 draw in their opening group match?**
14. In their only finals meeting, who won the East-West Germany clash?
15. **What was the score?**

ANSWERS: 1. Spain 2. 5-1 **3. Jesper Olsen** 4. Two **5. Second round** 6. 1938 **7. Hungary** 8. Hungary 6 Dutch East Indies 0 **9. 1974** 10. True **11. Australia** 12. 2-0 **13. Chile** 14. East Germany **15. 1-0**

Quiz 13 The Outsiders

1. Who scored for East Germany against West Germany in 1974?

2. Who were East Germany beaten by in the quarter-final group stage?

3. East Germany won one point in the quarter-final group stage. Against whom?

4. What was the score?

5. Who scored for East Germany - Streich or Hoffman?

6. Egypt played once in 1934. Who were the opponents?

7. What was the score?

8. Who scored twice for Egypt?

9. When was the next time Egypt played in the finals?

10. Have Egypt ever faced England in the World Cup?

11. Who were Egypt's first opponents in 1990?

12. What was the score?

13. Who scored a penalty for Egypt?

14. Who were their next opponents?

15. Did Egypt score?

ANSWERS: 1. Jurgen Sparwasser 2. Brazil, Holland **3. Argentina** 4. 1-1 **5. Streich** 6. Hungary **7. Hungary 4 Egypt 2** 8. Fawzi **9. 1990** 10. Yes **11. Holland** 12. 1-1 **13. Abdel-Ghani** 14. Republic of Ireland **15. No**

Quiz 14 The Outsiders

1. **Egypt lost their second game in 1990. True or false?**
2. What was the score?
3. **Who did Egypt face in their final group match?**
4. What was the score?
5. **Egypt finished third in the group. True or false?**
6. When was El Salvador's first World Cup finals appearance?
7. **Which European nation were their first opponents?**
8. What was the score?
9. **El Salvador also lost to the host nation in their first finals. Who were they?**
10. What was the score in that match?
11. **What was the attendance for that match - 53,000 or 103,000?**
12. El Salvador scored their first World Cup goal in 1982 against whom?
13. **How many did the opposition score?**
14. What was the score at half-time?
15. **How many goals have El Salvador scored in two World Cup finals?**

ANSWERS: 1. False 2. 0-0 **3. England** 4. England 1 Egypt 0 **5. False - fourth** 6. 1970 **7. Belgium** 8. Belgium 3 El Salvador 0 **9. Mexico** 10. 4-0 **11. 103,000** 12. Hungary **13. 10** 14. 3-0 **15. One**

Quiz 15

The Outsiders

1 **Haiti's only World Cup finals appearance was when?**

2. How many goals did they concede in the group stage?

3. **Who scored twice for Haiti in the finals?**

4. Who beat Haiti 7-0 in their second game?

5. **How many goals have Haiti scored in the finals?**

6. Whom did Honduras hold to a draw in their first World Cup finals match?

7. **What was the score?**

8. Honduras also drew their second game. Against which British nation?

9. **To which team did Honduras in their last finals match?**

10. What was the score?

11. **Iran have won one World Cup finals point. Against whom?**

12. What was the score in that game?

13. **In their only World Cup finals, Iran were beaten by which eventual finalists?**

14. Which year was it?

15. **Who else beat Iran in the finals?**

ANSWERS: 1. 1974 2. 14 **3. Sanon** 4. Poland **5. Two** 6. Spain **7. 1-1** 8. Northern Ireland **9. Yugoslavia** 10. 1-0 **11. Scotland** 12. 1-1 **13. Holland** 14. 1978 **15. Peru**

Quiz 16 The Outsiders

1. **What was the score in Iran's third match of the 1978 finals?**
2. Iraq have also made one appearance in the finals. Which year was it?
3. **Which South American country beat Iraq in their first match?**
4. What was the score?
5. **Against whom did Iraq score their only World Cup goal?**
6. Who is the only World Cup scorer in Iraq's history?
7. **Who were Israel's first opponents in a finals match?**
8. What was the score?
9. **Israel drew with Italy in 1970. True or false?**
10. What was the score between the two nations?
11. **Who scored Israel's only World Cup goal?**
12. Kuwait made their first appearance in 1982. Who were their first opponents?
13. **What was the score?**
14. Who scored for Kuwait?
15. **Who beat them 4-1 in their next game?**

ANSWERS: 1. Peru 4 Iran 1 2. 1986 **3. Paraguay** 4. 1-0 **5. Belgium** 6. Rahdi **7. Uruguay** 8. Uruguay 2 Israel 0 **9. True** 10. 0-0 **11. Spiegler** 12. Czechoslovakia **13. 1-1** 14. Al Dakheel **15. France**

Quiz 17 The Outsiders

1. Which British nation beat Kuwait in the final group match in 1982?

2. What was the score?

3. Morocco's first finals were in 1970. Who were their opening opponents?

4. What was the score?

5. Who were the first country not to beat Morocco in a finals match?

6. What year was it?

7. Morocco next played in the 1986 finals. Who were their first opponents?

8. What was the score?

9. Morocco drew in their second match of the tournament. Who were their British opposition?

10. Who did Morocco beat in their final 1986 group match?

11. What was the score?

12. Who scored twice for Morocco?

13. Who did Morocco face in the second round?

14. What was the score?

15. Morocco were also in the 1994 finals. Who were their first opponents?

ANSWERS: 1. England 2. 1-0 **3. West Germany** 4. West Germany 2 Morocco 1 **5. Bulgaria** 6. 1970 **7. Poland** 8. 0-0 **9. England** 10. Portugal **11. 3-1** 12. Khairi **13. West Germany** 14. West Germany 1 Morocco 0 **15. Belgium**

Quiz 18 The Outsiders

1. **What was the score in Morocco's first finals match of 1994?**
2. They then suffered two 2-1 defeats. Who were the first team to beat them them by that score?
3. **Who scored for Morocco - Chaouchi or Nader?**
4. Who were their final group opponents?
5. **What was the score?**
6. How many goals did New Zealand score in their first World Cup match?
7. **What year was it?**
8. Who were the opposition?
9. **What was the final score?**
10. Who was New Zealand's first World Cup goalscorer?
11. **How many goals did they score for the rest of the tournament?**
12. Who were their second opponents?
13. **What was the score?**
14. New Zealand were beaten 4-0 by whom in their final match?
15. **Nigeria's first opponents in 1994 were Romania. True or false?**

ANSWERS: 1. Lost 1-0 2. Saudi Arabia **3. Chaouchi** 4. Holland **5. Holland 2 Morocco 1**
6. Two **7. 1982** 8. Scotland **9. Scotland 5 New Zealand 2** 10. Sumner **11. None** 12. USSR
13. USSR 3 New Zealand 0 14. Brazil **15. False - Bulgaria**

Quiz 19 The Outsiders

1. **What was the score in Nigeria's first World Cup finals match?**
2. Who was their first goalscorer - Rashidi Yekini or Daniel Amokachi?
3. **Which eventual semi-finalists were beaten by Nigeria in the group stage?**
4. Who beat Nigeria in the second group match?
5. **What was the score?**
6. Who did Nigeria need to beat to qualify for the second round?
7. **What was the final score?**
8. Who scored for Nigeria?
9. **Whom did Nigeria meet in the second round?**
10. Which country took the lead?
11. **Who scored for Nigeria?**
12. Was North Korea's only World Cup finals appearance in Mexico?
13. **Who were North Korea's first World Cup final opponents?**
14. What was the score?
15. **Who was North Korea's first World Cup goalscorer - Pak Seung Jin or Li Dong Woon?**

ANSWERS: 1. 3-0 to Nigeria 2. Yekini **3. Bulgaria** 4. Argentina **5. 2-1** 6. Greece **7. Nigeria 2 Greece 0** 8. Finidi George, Daniel Amokachi **9. Italy** 10. Nigeria **11. Emmanuel Amunike** 12. No - they also appeared in England in 1966 **13. USSR** 14. USSR 3 North Korea 0 **15. Pak Seung Jin**

Quiz 20 The Outsiders

1. **Who were North Korea's opponents in their second match of the 1966 finals?**
2. What was the final score?
3. **Whom did North Korea beat to qualify for the quarter-finals?**
4. Whom did they lead 3-0 in the quarter-finals?
5. **What was the final score?**
6. When was Norway's first World Cup appearance?
7. **Who were their opponents?**
8. What was the score?
9. **The next time Norway appeared was in 1994. Who were their first opponents?**
10. Who scored for Norway?
11. **What was the final score?**
12. Which country have Norway played in both their World Cup final appearances?
13. **How many goals did Norway score in 1994?**
14. With whom did they draw in their final group game?
15. **Where did they finish in the group?**

ANSWERS: 1. Chile 2. 1-1 **3. Italy** 4. Portugal **5. Portugal 5 North Korea 3** 6. 1938 **7. Italy** 8. Italy 2 Norway 1 **9. Mexico** 10. Rekdal **11. 1-0** 12. Italy **13. One** 14. Republic of Ireland **15. Fourth**

Quiz 21 The Outsiders

1. **Portugal have made two World Cup appearances. True or false?**
2. Whom did they face in each of their first two World Cup finals?
3. **Portugal's first appearance was in 1966. Whom did they beat in their first match?**
4. What was the score?
5. **In their first four matches, how many times did Portugal score three or more goals?**
6. Who scored in each of their first two matches?
7. **Whom did they beat in their second game?**
8. Which favourites did Portugal beat in the final group match?
9. **What was the score?**
10. Who scored twice for Portugal in that match?
11. **Against whom did Portugal come from 3-0 down to win in the quarter-final?**
12. Who scored four goals in that match?
13. **How many penalties did that include?**
14. What was the final score?
15. **Who were Portugal's semi-final opponents?**

ANSWERS: 1. True 2. England **3. Hungary** 4. 3-1 **5. Four times** 6. Torres **7. Bulgaria** 8. Brazil **9. 3-1** 10. Eusebio **11. North Korea** 12. Eusebio **13. Two** 14. Portugal 5 North Korea 3 **15. England**

Quiz 22 The Outsiders

1. **What was the result of England v Portugal in 1966?**
2. Whom did Portugal beat to claim third place?
3. **How many goals did Eusebio score in the 1966 finals?**
4. How many of those were penalties?
5. **Whom did Portugal beat in their first game of the 1986 finals?**
6. Who scored for Portugal?
7. **What was the score?**
8. How many games did Portugal lose in 1986?
9. **Poland beat Portugal 2-0 in their second match. True or false?**
10. Who beat Portugal in their final group match?
11. **What was the score?**
12. Who scored Saudi Arabia's first World Cup finals goal - Amin or Owairan?
13. **What year was it?**
14. Who were Saudi Arabia's first World Cup finals opponents?
15. **Who were the first nation to be beaten by Saudi Arabia?**

ANSWERS: **1. England won 2-1** 2. USSR **3. Nine** 4. Four **5. England** 6. Carlos Manuel **7. 1-0** 8. Two **9. False - it was 1-0** 10. Morocco **11. 3-1 to Morocco** 12. Amin **13. 1994** 14. Holland **15. Morocco**

Quiz 23 The Outsiders

1. **What was the score in Saudi Arabia's first finals win?**
2. Who scored a penalty for Saudi in that game?
3. **Which European nation were also beaten in the group stage by Saudi Arabia?**
4. Who scored the winning goal?
5. **Who did they meet in the second round?**
6. Who scored for Saudi Arabia?
7. **What was the final score?**
8. Tunisia's first World Cup finals appearance was when?
9. **What was Tunisia's winning score in their first game?**
10. Who were the opponents?
11. **Who scored Tunisia's first World Cup goal - Dhoib or Kaabi?**
12. In their second match, to whom did Tunisia lose by a single goal?
13. **Which World Cup giants were their final opponents?**
14. What was the score?
15. **When was the last time Turkey played in the finals?**

ANSWERS: 1. 2-1 2. Al Jaber **3. Belgium** 4. Saieed Owairan **5. Sweden** 6. Al Ghesheyan **7. Sweden 3 Saudi Arabia 1** 8. 1978 **9. 3-1** 10. Mexico **11. Kaabi** 12. Poland **13. West Germany** 14. 0-0 **15. 1954**

Quiz 24 The Outsiders

1. **Who scored Turkey's first finals goal in 1954 - Suat or Burhan?**
2. Who beat them 4-1 in their first game?
3. **Which team were defeated by Turkey in the following match?**
4. What was the score?
5. **Who scored a hat-trick for Turkey in that game?**
6. Who beat them in the play-off?
7. **What was the score?**
8. In how many of their 1990 finals matches did the United Arab Emirates score a goal?
9. **When was their first appearance?**
10. Who were their first opponents?
11. **Against whom did United Arab Emirates score their first goal?**
12. Who was the goalscorer?
13. **What was the score?**
14. Who beat the United Arab Emirates in their final match?
15. **What was the score?**

ANSWERS: 1. Suat 2. West Germany **3. South Korea** 4. 7-0 **5. Burhan** 6. West Germany **7. West Germany 7 Turkey 2** 8. Two **9. 1990** 10. Colombia **11. West Germany** 12. Mubarek **13. West Germany 5 United Arab Emirates 1** 14. Yugoslavia **15. 4-1**

Quiz 25 The Outsiders

1. **When was Zaire's first World Cup finals appearance?**
2. Who beat them in their first game?
3. **What was the score?**
4. How many goals did Zaire score in the tournament?
5. **Who were their second opponents?**
6. What was the final score?
7. **What was the score at half-time?**
8. Who beat them in the final game?
9. **When was Zaire's last World Cup appearance?**
10. Czechoslovakia's first World Cup was in 1934. Who were their first opponents?
11. **Who scored Czechoslovakia's first World Cup finals goal - Puc or Nejedly?**
12. Who were Czechoslovakia's second opponents?
13. **Who scored twice for Czechoslovakia in the semi-final - Puc or Nejedly?**
14. What was the score in the semi-final?
15. **Whom did they beat?**

ANSWERS: 1. 1974 2. Scotland **3. Scotland 2 Zaire 0** 4. None **5. Yugoslavia** 6. Yugoslavia 9 Zaire 0 **7. 6-0** 8. Brazil **9. 1974** 10. Romania **11. Puc** 12. Switzerland **13. Nejedly** 14. 3-1 to Czechoslovakia **15. Germany**

Quiz 26 The Outsiders

1. **Who beat Czechoslovakia in the World Cup Final of 1934?**
2. Holland were the Czechs' first opponents in 1938. What was the score?
3. **Whom did Czechoslovakia face in the second round?**
4. What was the score after extra-time?
5. **What was the score in the replay?**
6. How many goals did Czechoslovakia score in 1954?
7. **Who beat them 5-0 in their final match of 1954?**
8. Name one of the other countries in Czechoslovakia's group in 1958.
9. **Whom did they beat 6-1 in the final group match?**
10. Which two players scored twice in that game?
11. **Who defeated the Czechs in the play-off?**
12. What was the score?
13. **How many World Cup Finals have Czechoslovakia played in?**
14. Who were their first opponents in 1962?
15. **Whom did they hold to a goalless draw in the group stage?**

ANSWERS: 1. Italy 2. Czechoslovakia 3 Holland 0 **3. Brazil** 4. 1-1 **5. Brazil 2 Czechoslovakia 1** 6. None **7. Austria** 8. Northern Ireland, West Germany, Argentina **9. Argentina** 10. Zikan, Hovorka **11. Northern Ireland** 12. 2-1 **13. Two** 14. Spain **15. Brazil**

Quiz 27 The Outsiders

1. **Whom did Czechoslovakia beat in a quarter-final in 1962?**
2. What was the score?
3. **Whom did Czechoslovakia meet in the semi-final?**
4. Who scored Czechoslovakia's goal in the Final?
5. **What was the first post-war year Czechoslovakia failed to play in the finals?**
6. Who beat them in their first game of 1970?
7. **What was the score?**
8. Who scored both of Czechoslovakia's goals in the 1970 games?
9. **Which British nation faced Czechoslovakia in the 1 970 finals?**
10. What was the score?
11. **Who held Czechoslovakia to a 1-1 draw in 1982?**
12. Which famous Czech player scored a penalty against France in 1982?
13. **What was the final score in that match?**
14. Who were beaten 5-1 by Czechoslovakia in their opening game of 1990?
15. **Who scored twice for Czechoslovakia?**

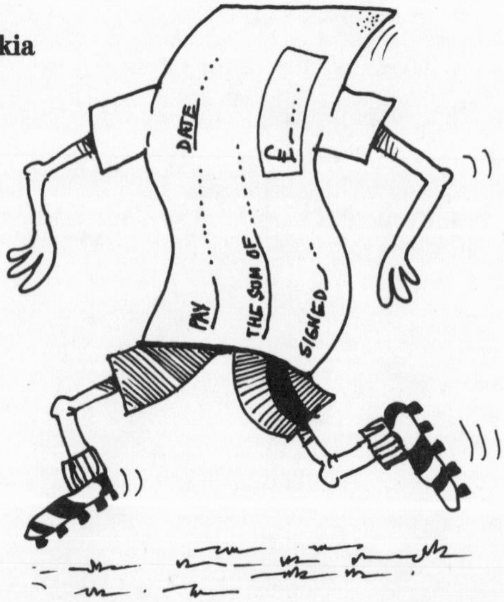

ANSWERS: 1. Hungary 2. 1-0 **3. Yugoslavia** 4. Josef Masopust **5. 1950** 6. Brazil **7. 4-1** 8. Petras **9. England** 10. England 1 Czechoslovakia 0 **11. Kuwait** 12. Antonin Panenka **13. 1-1** 14. USA **15. Tomas Skuhravy**

Quiz 28 The Outsiders

1. **Who was the only team to beat the Czechs in the 1990 group stage?**
2. Who were their second-round opponents?
3. **What was the score?**
4. Who scored a hat-trick in that game?
5. **Who knocked Czechoslovakia out in the quarter-final?**
6. When was Colombia's first World Cup finals?
7. **Who were their first opponents?**
8. How many goals did Czechoslovakia score in their second game?
9. **What was the final score?**
10. Who were their opponents?
11. **Who beat Colombia in their final game of 1962?**
12. What was the score?
13. **Colombia didn't qualify again until 1990. Who were their first opponents?**
14. Who scored Colombia's second goal in that match?
15. **With whom did Colombia draw in their final group match?**

ANSWERS: 1. Italy 2. Costa Rica **3. Czechoslovakia 4 Costa Rica 1** 4. Tomas Skuhravy **5. West Germany** 6. 1962 **7. Uruguay** 8. Four **9. 4-4** 10. USSR **11. Yugoslavia** 12. 5-0 **13. United Arab Emirates** 14. Carlos Valderrama **15. West Germany**

Quiz 29 The Outsiders

1. **What was the score between Colombia and West Germany in 1990?**
2. Who scored for Colombia?
3. **Who were Colombia's opponents in the second round?**
4. What was the score?
5. **Who scored Colombia's first goal in 1994?**
6. Who were the opponents?
7. **What was the score?**
8. Who did Colombia beat in 1994?
9. **What was the score?**
10. Did Colombia qualify for the second round?
11. **When was Mexico's first World Cup appearance?**
12. How many goals did they concede in their first finals?
13. **How many games did Mexico consecutively lose, beginning with their first World Cup series of 1930?**
14. Who were the first British nation to face Mexico in the finals?
15. **Which year was it?**

ANSWERS: 1. 1-1 2. Freddy Rincon **3. Cameroon** 4. Cameroon 2 Colombia 1 **5. Aldolfo Valencia** 6. Romania **7. Romania 3 Colombia 1** 8. Switzerland **9. 2-0** 10. No **11. 1930** 12. 13 **13. Nine** 14. Wales **15. 1958**

Quiz 30 The Outsiders

1. **Mexico were in England's group in 1966. True or false?**
2. When was the first time Mexico qualified from the first stage of the finals?
3. **Who were Mexico's quarter-finals opponents in 1970?**
4. Mexico qualified for seven of the eight tournaments from 1950. Which was the odd one out?
5. **Who amazingly beat Mexico in their first game in 1978?**
6. Mexico also lost 6-0 in 1978. To whom?
7. **Which famous player scored Mexico's winner against Belgium in 1986?**
8. Whom did Mexico beat to qualify for the second round in 1986?
9. **Whom did Mexico meet in the second round in 1986 and 1994?**
10. Who beat Mexico on penalties in 1986?
11. **What was the score after extra-time?**
12. Against whom did Mexico notch up their solitary victory in the 1994 finals?
13. **What was the score?**
14. Who scored twice for Mexico in that game?
15. **Who knocked Mexico out of the 1994 finals?**

ANSWERS: 1. True 2. 1970 **3. Italy** 4. 1974 **5. Tunisia** 6. West Germany **7. Hugo Sanchez** 8. Iraq **9. Bulgaria** 10. West Germany **11. 0-0** 12. Republic of Ireland **13. 2-1** 14. Luis Garcia **15. Bulgaria**

Quiz 31 The Outsiders

1. Which European nation were the first team to be beaten by Paraguay in the World Cup finals?

2. Which year was it?

3. Paraguay's next World Cup victory came in 1958. Against whom?

4. Who beat Paraguay 7-3 in 1958?

5. When was the only time Paraguay qualified from the first round?

6. Who were their second-round opponents in those finals?

7. What was the score in that game?

8. Which European nation were Peru's first World Cup opponents?

9. What year was it?

10. How many years elapsed before Peru's next finals?

11. Which European country were the first to be beaten in the World Cup by Peru?

12. Which legendary player scored in all four of Peru's 1970 World Cup matches?

13. How many goals did he score?

14. Who beat Peru in the 1970 quarter-final?

15. Which British nation were beaten by Peru in their opening game in 1978?

ANSWERS: 1. Belgium 2. 1930 **3. Scotland** 4. France **5. 1986** 6. England **7. England 3 Peru 0** 8. Romania **9. 1930** 10. 40 **11. Bulgaria** 12. Teofilo Cubillas **13. Five** 14. Brazil **15. Scotland**

Quiz 32

The Outsiders

1. **Whom did Peru hold to a goalless draw in 1978?**
2. Whom did they beat 4-1 in the group stages?
3. **Who scored a hat-trick in that match?**
4. How many of those were penalties?
5. **How many games did Peru lose in the quarter-final group stage?**
6. Who beat them 6-0 in their final match?
7. **How many games did Peru draw in the 1982 group stage?**
8. With whom did they share a 1-1 draw in 1982?
9. **Who defeated Peru 5-1 in the final group match?**
10. Who were Poland's first World Cup finals opponents?
11. **What year was it?**
12. What was the remarkable final score?
13. **How many goals did Ernest Wilimowski score in that match?**
14. How many group games did Poland win in 1974?
15. **Whom did they beat 7-0 in their second match?**

ANSWERS: **1. Holland** 2. Iran **3. Cubillas** 4. Two **5. Three** 6. Argentina **7. Two** 8. Italy **9. Poland** 10. Brazil **11. 1938** 12. Brazil 6 Peru 5 **13. Four** 14. Three **15. Haiti**

Quiz 33 The Outsiders

1. **Whose 1-0 victory denied Poland a place in the 1974 Final?**
2. Whom did Poland face in the third place play-off?
3. **What was the score?**
4. Who scored for Poland in that match?
5. **Who were Poland's first opponents in 1978?**
6. Who beat Poland in their opening quarter-final group game?
7. **Who else defeated Poland in the quarter-final stage?**
8. Whom did Poland beat 5-1 in 1982?
9. **How many different goalscorers were in that match?**
10. Which two European nations were in Poland's quarter-final group in 1982?
11. **Who beat Poland in the 1982 semi-final?**
12. What was the score?
13. **What year did Romania first play in the World Cup finals?**
14. Who were their South American first opponents?
15. **Who beat Romania in a replay in 1938?**

ANSWERS: 1. West Germany 2. Brazil **3. Poland 1 Brazil 0** 4. Lato **5. West Germany** 6. Argentina **7. Brazil** 8. Peru **9. Six** 10. Belgium, USSR **11. Italy** 12. 2-0 **13. 1930** 14. Peru **15. Cuba**

Quiz 34 The Outsiders

1. **Which British nation beat Romania in the 1970 finals?**
2. How many games did Romania win in 1970?
3. **Romania won only once in their first six finals games. When did they win their second?**
4. Who were Romania's opponents in their final 1990 group match?
5. **Who beat Romania in a penalty shoot-out in the 1990 second round?**
6. What was the score on penalties?
7. **Who beat Romania 4-1 in 1994?**
8. Who scored twice for Romania in their 3-1 win over Colombia?
9. **Whom did Romania beat in the second round?**
10. Who scored twice for Romania in that game?
11. **Who knocked Romania out of the 1994 World Cup on a shoot-out?**
12. What was the score after extra-time?
13. **When did South Korea first appear in the World Cup finals?**
14. Who beat them 9-0 in their first game?
15. **Turkey also beat them in 1954. What was the score?**

ANSWERS: 1. England 2. One **3. 1970** 4. Argentina **5. Republic of Ireland** 6. 5-4 **7. Switzerland** 8. Florin Raducioiu **9. Argentina** 10. Ilie Dumitrescu **11. Sweden** 12. 2-2 **13. 1954** 14. Hungary **15. 7-0**

Quiz 35 The Outsiders

1. **South Korea's first finals draw was in 1986. Who was it against?**
2. Which World Cup winning nations beat them in their 1986 group?
3. **How many goals did South Korea score in 1990?**
4. With whom did South Korea draw 2-2 in 1994, despite having been two goals down?
5. **Which South American nation shared a goalless draw with South Korea in 1994?**
6. Sweden's first World Cup game was against whom in 1934?
7. **What was Sweden's winning score?**
8. Who knocked Sweden out in 1934?
9. **Sweden beat which South American nation 8-0 in 1938?**
10. Who beat Sweden in the semi-final?
11. **Sweden qualified for the 1950 final pool by beating which European nation?**
12. Who beat Sweden 7-1 in the final pool?
13. **Whom did Sweden beat in their final pool match?**
14. Which British nation held Sweden in 1958?
15. **What was the score?**

ANSWERS: 1. Bulgaria 2. Argentina, Italy **3. One** 4. Spain **5. Bolivia** 6. Argentina **7. 3-2** 8. Germany **9. Cuba** 10. Hungary **11. Italy** 12. Brazil **13. Spain** 14. Wales **15. 0-0**

Quiz 36 The Outsiders

1. **Whom did Sweden beat in the semi-final in 1958?**
2. Which side scored first in the 1958 Final?
3. **Who held Sweden to a 1-1 draw in 1970?**
4. Sweden failed to qualify from the first round in 1970 despite beating which South American nation?
5. **Which South American nation were beaten by Sweden in their 1974 group?**
6. How many wins did Sweden collect in the 1974 quarter-final group stage?
7. **Which World Cup winning nation were held 1-1 by Sweden in 1978?**
8. How many goals did Sweden score altogether in 1978?
9. **Sweden lost two of their three group games in 1978 to European countries. Who were their victors?**
10. How many of the three games did Sweden lose in 1990?
11. **Sweden's defeats were all by the same scoreline. What was it?**
12. Whom did Sweden beat for their only group win in 1994?
13. **Whom did Sweden meet twice in the 1994 World Cup?**
14. Who were beaten by Sweden in the 1994 second round?
15. **Whom did Sweden beat to claim third place in 1994?**

ANSWERS: 1. **West Germany** 2. Sweden 3. **Israel** 4. Uruguay 5. **Uruguay** 6. One 7. **Brazil** 8. One 9. **Austria, Spain** 10. Three 11. **2-1** 12. Russia 13. **Brazil** 14. Saudi Arabia 15. **Bulgaria**

Quiz 37 The Outsiders

1. **What was Sweden's winning score in the 1994 third-place match?**
2. Both of Switzerland's games in 1934 had the same scoreline. What was it?
3. **Which European nation were Switzerland's first opponents?**
4. Who knocked Switzerland out of the 1938 finals?
5. **Whom did Switzerland hold 2-2 in 1950?**
6. Switzerland hosted the 1954 finals. Who were their first opponents?
7. **Who beat them in their second game?**
8. Whom did Switzerland beat 4-1 in a 1954 play-off?
9. **Who defeated Switzerland in the quarter-final?**
10. **What was the mammoth final score?**
11. **How many games did Switzerland win in 1962?**
12. Who beat Switzerland 5-0 in their opening game of 1966?
13. **Which South American nation beat Switzerland in their final game in 1966?**
14. Whom did Switzerland beat 4-1 in the first round of 1994?
15. **Who was the English manager of the Swiss in 1994?**

ANSWERS: 1. 4-0 2. 3-2 **3. Holland** 4. Hungary **5. Brazil** 6. Italy **7. England** 8. Italy **9. Austria** 10. 7-5 **11. None** 12. West Germany **13. Argentina** 14. Romania **15. Roy Hodgson**

Quiz 38 The Outsiders

1. **Who knocked Switzerland out of the 1994 World Cup?**
2. USA made their first World Cup appearance in what year?
3. **Which European nation were their first opponents?**
4. Who beat the USA 6-1 in the semi-final?
5. **A World Cup winning nation went one better four years later. Who were they?**
6. Which South American nation beat the USA 5-2 in 1950?
7. **How many goals did the USA score in the 1990 finals?**
8. How many games did the USA draw in 1990?
9. **Who were the USA's first opponents in 1994?**
10. What was the score?
11. **Who defeated the USA in their final group match in 1994?**
12. On which historic date did USA play their second-round match?
13. **Who were their opponents?**
14. Whom did Yugoslavia beat in their first World Cup finals match?
15. **What year was it?**

ANSWERS: 1. Spain 2. 1930 **3. Belgium** 4. Argentina **5. Italy beat them 7-1** 6. Chile **7. Two** 8. None **9. Switzerland** 10. 1-1 **11. Romania** 12. July 4 **13. Brazil** 14. Brazil **15. 1930**

Quiz 39 The Outsiders

1. **Who beat Yugoslavia in the quarter-final in 1954?**
2. Which British nation drew 1-1 with Yugoslavia in 1958?
3. **Who knocked Yugoslavia out of the 1958 finals in the second round?**
4. Whom did Yugoslavia beat 5-0 in the group stage of 1962?
5. **Who beat Yugoslavia in the 1962 semi-final?**
6. Who did Yugoslavia face in the opening match of the 1974 finals?
7. **What was the final score?**
8. Who did Yugoslavia beat 9-0 in their next match in 1974?
9. **Who scored for Yugoslavia against Scotland in their last 1974 group match?**
10. What was the final score?
11. **Where was the match played?**
12. Yugoslavia drew with another British side in 1982. Who was it?
13. **Yugoslavia won only once in 1982. Against whom?**
14. Who scored twice for Yugoslavia in their 4-1 win over United Arab Emirates in 1994?
15. **Who knocked Yugoslavia out of the 1990 finals after a penalty shoot-out?**

ANSWERS: 1. West Germany 2. Scotland **3. West Germany** 4. Colombia **5. Czechoslovakia** 6. Brazil **7. 0-0** 8. Zaire **9. Karasi** 10. 1-1 **11. Frankfurt** 12. Northern Ireland **13. Honduras** 14. Darko Pancev **15. Argentina**

Great Players

Quiz 1

Great Players

1. Who is the only player to have scored in successive World Cup Finals?

2. Who was World Cup star Edwaldo Izidio Neto better known as?

3. In how many series of World Cup finals did Pele appear?

4. How many times did Pele appear in the World Cup Final?

5. Who was the centre-forward who played in four World Cup tournaments from 1958 to 1970?

6. How many matches did he play in those four finals?

7. Whose penalty in 1978 was the 1,000th goal in World Cup history?

8. Who were the opposition on that historic occasion?

9. Who captained Scotland a record 12 times in the World Cup qualifiers and finals of the 1974 tournament?

10. How many of those matches did Scotland lose under his captaincy?

11. Who also captained Scotland 12 times in World Cup matches but only in qualifiers?

12. Who is the only player to score a hat-trick in a World Cup Final?

13. Who was the oldest captain of a World Cup winning team?

14. When and where was this achieved?

15. Who was known as 'The Galloping Major'?

ANSWERS: 1.Vava - in 1958 & 1962 2.Vava **3.Four** 4.Twice **5.Uwe Seeler** 6.Twenty-one **7.Robbie Rensenbrink (Holland)** 8.Scotland **9.Billy Bremner** 10.Two **11.Gary McAllister** 12.Geoff Hurst (England) **13.Dino Zoff** 14.Spain, 1982 **15.Ferenc Puskas**

Quiz 2 Great Players

1. Who had made most World Cup appearances for Scotland in the 1950-94 period?

2. How many was that?

3. Who overtook that figure when being brought on as a substitute in the qualifying home match against Austria in 1997?

4. Who scored the only goal of Wales' first World Cup finals match?

5. In which country and year was that?

6. With which Italian club was he playing when he appeared in those finals?

7. What was he known as - and why?

8. Who was the very first hat-trick scorer in a World Cup match in 1930?

9. He headed the list of goalscorers in those finals with how many?

10. Who scored England's first World Cup goal in a qualifying match?

11. Who scored the first hat-trick for England in a qualifier?

12. Who scored the first England goal in the World Cup finals?

13. Who is the only player to have appeared in five World Cup finals series?

14. What position did he play?

15. Who was the first person to play for and later manage a World Cup winning team?

ANSWERS: 1.Kenny Dalglish 2.Twenty-six **3.Paul McStay** 4.John Charles **5.Sweden, 1958** 6.Juventus **7.The Gentle Giant - because he was never sent off or even cautioned** 8.Guillermo Stabile of Argentina **9.Eight** 10.Stan Mortensen **11.Jackie Milburn** 12.Stan Mortensen **13.Antonio Carbajal of Mexico** 14.Goalkeeper **15.Mario Zagalo**

Quiz 3

Great Players

1. **Who was Jair Ventura Filho better known as?**
2. What was his record feat in the 1970 Mexico finals?
3. **How many goals did he score in that series?**
4. Who was the leading scorer in the Argentina finals of 1978?
5. **How many did he score in that series?**
6. He also played in the 1974 and 1982 World Cup finals. How many more did he score in those finals?
7. **Who was voted Player of the Tournament when Argentina won the World Cup in 1986?**
8. He first played for Argentina at what age?
9. **In how many World Cup finals series did he play for Argentina?**
10. How many goals did he score altogether in the World Cup finals?
11. **The first World Cup Final penalty was awarded in 1974. Who scored from it?**
12. Who also scored from the penalty spot in that Final?
13. **Who was the losing side's captain that day?**
14. How many times was he European Footballer of the Year?
15. **How many times was Franz Beckenbauer the European Footballer of the Year?**

ANSWERS: 1.Jairzinho 2.He scored in every game of Brazil's six-match triumph **3.Seven** 4.Mario Kempes **5.Six** 6.None **7.Diego Maradona** 8.Sixteen **9.Four** 10.Eight **11.Johan Neeskens** 12.Paul Breitner **13.Johan Cruyff (Holland)** 14.Three **15.Twice**

Quiz 4

Great Players

1. **Who was known as 'The Kaiser'?**
2. In how many World Cup finals series did he play?
3. **For which club did he play in the United States in the closing stages of his career?**
4. How many European Cup winning medals did he secure?
5. **With which club did he gain these?**
6. Which German player was known as 'Der Bomber'?
7. **How many European Cup winning medals did he collect?**
8. With which club did he win these?
9. **In which year and where did he score most World Cup finals goals?**
10. How many goals did he score in those finals?
11. **How many caps did Bobby Moore earn under manager Alf Ramsey for England?**
12. How old was Moore when he captained England to victory in the 1966 World Cup Final?
13. **How many times did Moore captain England before the 1966 finals?**
14. How many times did Bobby Charlton play for England in World Cup qualifying rounds and finals?
15. **How many goals did he score in his first World Cup match for England?**

ANSWERS: 1.**Franz Beckenbauer** 2.Three 3.**New York Cosmos** 4.Three 5.**Bayern Munich** 6.Gerd Muller 7.**Three** 8.Bayern Munich 9.**Mexico, 1970** 10.Ten 11.**100** 12.Twenty-five 13.**Twenty-four** 14.Eighteen 15.**Three (v Luxembourg)**

Quiz 5

Great Players

1. How old was Bobby Charlton when he played his first World Cup match for England?

2. How many goals did he score in the 1966 finals?

3. When was he knighted?

4. How old was Stanley Matthews when he played his last World Cup match for England?

5. How many times did Matthews play in World Cup matches, qualifiers or finals?

6. When was he knighted?

7. How many times did Tom Finney play for England in World Cup matches?

8. How many World Cup goals did he score?

9. How many did he score altogether for England?

10. When was he knighted?

11. How many times did Gary Lineker score in all his World Cup matches for England?

12. How many times did he play in the World Cup, qualifiers or finals?

13. How many World Cup hat-tricks did he score?

14. How many times did he captain England in the World Cup?

15. In how many World Cup matches, qualifiers and finals, did Bryan Robson play for England?

ANSWERS: **1.Twenty-three years 8 days** 2.Three **3.1994** 4.Forty-two **5.Seven** 6.1965 **7.Sixteen** 8.Two **9.Thirty** 10.1998 **11.Fifteen** 12.Twenty-two **13.Two** 14.None **15.Twenty-five**

Quiz 6

Great Players

1. **How many World Cup goals did Bryan Robson score for England?**
2. How many did he score altogether for England?
3. **Who holds the record for the most goals scored in a World Cup finals series?**
4. Which series was that?
5. **In which country was Fontaine born?**
6. Fontaine played only 20 games for France. How many goals did he score?
7. **Who was nicknamed the 'Black Panther'?**
8. What was his full name?
9. **In which African country was he born?**
10. He was top scorer in the 1966 World Cup finals with how many goals?
11. **How many of those were scored from penalties?**
12. Who was the youngest-ever player to appear in a World Cup Final?
13. **Which Final was that and against whom?**
14. How many goals did Pele score in that match?
15. **What governmental appointment did Pele receive in Brazil in 1994?**

ANSWERS: **1.Nine** 2.26 **3.Just Fontaine of France** 4.1958 **5.Morocco** 6.Twenty-seven **7.Eusebio** 8.Eusebio da Silva Ferreira **9.Mozambique** 10.Nine **11.Four** 12.Pele at 17 **13.1958 v Sweden** 14.Two **15.Minister for Sport**

Quiz 7

Great Players

1. **Pele came out of retirement to play for which American club?**
2. How many goals did he score in World Cup finals matches?
3. **How many first-class goals did he score in his career?**
4. How old was Ferenc Puskas when he first played for Hungary?
5. **Puskas captained Hungary in the World Cup Final of which year?**
6. Hungary scored twice in the first ten minutes in that match. Who got the first goal?
7. **How many goals did Puskas score in the 1954 finals?**
8. Puskas played in another World Cup series. In what year?
9. **Which country did he play for then?**
10. How many goals did he score in the 1962 finals?
11. **Who was the Hungarian nicknamed 'Golden Head'?**
12. He top-scored in the 1954 World Cup finals with how many goals?
13. **How many goals did Kocsis score in his 68 matches for Hungary?**
14. Who was Poland's leading scorer with seven goals in the 1974 World Cup finals?
15. **How many goals did he score in Poland's six finals games of 1978?**

ANSWERS: **1.New York Cosmos** 2.Twelve **3.1,283** 4.Eighteen **5.1954** 6.Puskas **7.Five** 8.1962 **9.Spain** 10.None **11.Sandor Kocsis** 12.Eleven **13.Seventy-five** 14.Grzegorz Lato **15.Two**

Quiz 8

Great Players

1. **Who was West Germany's captain in their victorious World Cup Final of 1990?**
2. Who won the Player of the Tournament in the 1990 World Cup series?
3. **Who was Waldir Pereira?**
4. In how many World Cup Finals did he appear for Brazil?
5. **Whose World Cup squad did he manage after retiring as a player?**
6. Who captained Italy in the 1970 Final against Brazil?
7. **Who scored Italy's only goal in that match?**
8. How many times did Facchetti play for Italy in all internationals?
9. **When was Carlos Bledorn Verri presented with the World Cup Trophy?**
10. What was he better known as?
11. **Who was the Spaniard known as 'The Vulture'?**
12. Spain's biggest World Cup finals win was by 5-1 against Denmark in 1986. Who scored four goals in that match?
13. **Who was nicknamed 'Dracula' by the England players in 1966?**
14. Why was he jokingly called this?
15. **Name Egypt's goalkeeper in the 1934 World Cup who 'got the hump'.**

ANSWERS: **1.Lothar Matthaus** 2.Matthaus **3.Didi** 4.Two **5.Peru** 6.Giacinto Facchetti **7.Boninsegna** 8.Ninety-four **9.1994** 10.Dunga of Brazil **11.Emilio Butragueno** 12.Butragueno **13.West Germany's goalkeeper Tilkowski** 14.He didn't like crosses! **15.Moustafa Kamel**

All about Numbers

Quiz 1

All about Numbers

1. How many nations took part in the first World Cup finals - 10, 13 or 16?

2. How many towns and cities staged the 1930 finals - 1,3 or 4?

3. How many people watched the first World Cup Final - 85,000 or 90,000?

4. How many goals did top scorer Guillermo Stabile of Argentina record in the finals - 7, 8 or 10?

5. How many finals matches did Uruguay play in winning the 1930 tournament - 4, 5 or 6?

6. Argentina were beaten in the 1930 Final although they scored most goals in the series. How many - 14, 15 or 18?

7. What was Argentina's winning score against the USA in the 1930 semi-finals - 6-1, 6-2 or 7-2?

8. Uruguay beat Argentina in the 1930 Final… by 4-1, 5-1 or 4-2?

9. How many games were played in the 1930 qualifying competition?

10. How many nations took part in the 1934 finals - 12, 16 or 18?

11. How many venues were nominated for the Italian finals of 1934 - 5, 7 or 8?

12. The leading scorer for Italy was Schiavio… with 4, 6 or 7?

13. How many did Schiavio score in the first match of the 1934 finals?

14. That match was against the USA. What was the score - 5-1, 6-1 or 7-1?

15. How many of their five finals matches of 1934 did Italy draw?

ANSWERS: 1. Thirteen 2. One - all games in Montevideo **3. 90,000** 4. Eight **5. Four** 6. Eighteen **7. 6-1** 8. 4-2 **9. None** 10. Sixteen **11. Eight** 12. Four **13. Three** 14. 7-1 **15. One - with Spain**

Quiz 2

All about Numbers

1. **How many times have Brazil won the World Cup - 3, 4 or 5?**
2. How many times have Germany/West Germany finished in the first three - 5, 7 or 8?
3. **How many times have Germany/West Germany been beaten in a World Cup Final - 1, 2 or 3?**
4. How many times have Italy won the World Cup - 1, 2 or 3?
5. **How many times have Italy lost in a World Cup Final - 1, 2 or 3?**
6. How many third-place play-offs have Italy won - 1, 2 or 3?
7. **How many times have England finished in the first three - 1, 2 or 3?**
8. How many times did England play at Wembley in the 1966 finals - 5, 6 or 7?
9. **Buenos Aires was the venue of the World Cup Final in...1974, 1978 or 1982?**
10. How many times have Poland finished in the first three - 2, 3 or 4?
11. **Argentina have appeared in a World Cup Final how many times - 2, 3 or 4?**
12. How many times have Holland appeared in the World Cup Final - 1, 2 or 4?
13. **The first time France were hosts for the finals was in... 1934, 1938 or 1950?**
14. How many World Cup Finals have gone into extra time - 2, 4 or 6?
15. **How many World Cup Finals have been decided on a penalty shoot-out - 1 or 2?**

ANSWERS: 1. Four 2. Eight 3. Three 4. Three 5. Two 6. One 7. One 8. Six 9. 1978 10. Two 11. Four 12. Two 13. 1938 14. Four 15. One

Quiz 3

All about Numbers

1. How many of the three finals before the Second World War were won by Europeans - 1, 2 or 3?

2. Brazilian Leonidas was the leading scorer in the 1938 series with 7, 8 or 10?

3. How many years did Italy hold the World Cup before losing it to Uruguay - 4, 8 or 16?

4. How many games did Italy play in the 1950 finals in Brazil - 2, 4 or 5?

5. How many matches did Uruguay play in winning the 1950 tournament - 4, 5 or 6?

6. How many matches did Brazil play in the 1950 series - 4, 5 or 6?

7. Uruguay recorded the biggest win in the 1950 finals, beating Bolivia by... 7-0, 8-0 or 10-0?

8. Brazilian Ademir was the leading scorer in the 1950 series with... 5, 6 or 7?

9. England scored how many goals in their three group matches of 1950 - 2, 4 or 5?

10. England's humiliating defeat by USA in Brazil in 1950 was watched by a crowd of - 10,151 or 30,151?

11. England's 1-0 defeat by Spain in their last match in the 1950 finals was watched by - 29,703 or 74,462?

12. Uruguay's deciding match with Brazil in 1950 in the Maracana Stadium, Rio de Janeiro, was watched by... 189,850 or 199,850?

13. Uruguay were the winners by... 2-0, 2-1 or 3-1?

14. Brazil scored first in which minute - 37th, 47th or 57th?

15. How many countries contested the 1954 finals in Switzerland - 14, 15 or 16?

ANSWERS: 1.Two 2. Eight **3. Sixteen - from 1934 to 1950** 4. Two **5. Four** 6. Six **7. 8-0**
8. Seven **9. Two** 10. 10,151 **11. 74,462** 12. 199,850 **13. 2-1** 14. 47th **15. Sixteen**

Quiz 4

All about Numbers

1. The biggest win in a World Cup qualifying round was by Iran against The Maldives in Damascus in 1997. The score... 15-2 or 17-0?

2. Fiji were beaten twice in 48 hours during August 1981, by Australia and New Zealand, conceding a total of… 21, 22 or 23 goals?

3. Fiji replied with a total of... 0, 1 or 3?

4. New Zealand top-scored in those two matches by 10-0, 12-0 or 13-0?

5. The biggest win in a finals match was by Hungary against El Salvador in 1982. The score - 10-0, 10-1 or 10-2?

6. The previous highest finals score was registered by Hungary (v South Korea) and Yugoslavia (v Zaire). That score was… 9-0, 9-1 or 9-2?

7. The first World Cup match on artificial turf was between Canada and the USA in Vancouver. In what year - 1966, 1976 or 1986?

8. The first indoors, USA v Canada in Seattle, was in… 1966, 1976 or 1986?

9. The first indoor match of a World Cup finals series was USA v Switzerland. The year... 1978, 1990 or 1994?

10. Pickles the pooch found the stolen Jules Rimet Trophy in a garden how many months before the 1966 World Cup finals… 2, 4 or 6?

11. The trophy was insured for how much - £20,000, £30,000 or £50,000?

12. How many times has the World Cup been won by a European country outside Europe - 0, 1 or 2?

13. How many times has the World Cup been won in Europe by a South American country - 0, 1 or 2?

14. How many World Cup Finals have been won by South American countries - 6, 7 or 8?

15. How many have been won by Europeans - 6, 7 or 8?

ANSWERS: 1. 17-0 2. Twenty-three **3. Nil** 4. 13-0 **5. 10-1** 6. 9-0 **7. 1976** 8. 1976 **9. 1994** 10. Four **11. £30,000** 12. None **13. One** 14. Eight **15. Seven**

Quiz 5

All about Numbers

1. Hungary were runners-up in the 1954 finals. Was it their first, second or third World Cup Final?

2. Was 1954 the third, fourth or fifth finals appearance for Hungary?

3. Hungary played how many games in the 1954 finals... 4, 5 or 6?

4. How many goals did the Hungarians score in their first match of the 1954 finals against South Korea - 3, 6 or 9?

5. How many in their second match of 1954 against Germany - 2, 4, 6 or 8?

6. How many did the Germans score in that match - 1, 3 or 5?

7. The Hungarians scored how many goals altogether in the 1954 finals - 21, 24 or 27?

8. Germany scored how many in winning the 1954 tournament - 22, 25 or 28?

9. How many goals did Sandor Kocsis score for Hungary in their first meeting with Germany in 1954 - 2, 3 or 4?

10. How many did Ferenc Puskas score in that match - 1, 2 or 3?

11. How many goals did Kocsis score in the final with Germany - 0, 1 or 2?

12. How many did Puskas score in the Final - 0, 1 or 2?

13. Helmut Rahn scored four in Germany's six finals matches of 1954. How many in the Final - 0, 1 or 2?

14. The top scorer in the Switzerland finals was Kocsis with... 7, 9 or 11 goals?

15. England's opening match of 1954 against Belgium ended in a draw. The score... 0-0, 2-2 or 4-4?

ANSWERS: 1. Second 2. Third **3. Five** 4. Nine **5. Eight** 6. Three **7. Twenty-seven** 8. Twenty-five **9. Four** 10. One **11. None** 12. One **13. Two** 14. Eleven **15. 4-4**

Quiz 6

All about Numbers

1. **Vittorio Pozzo was manager of how many of Italy's World Cup winning teams - 1 or 2?**

2. Mario Zagalo was manager of Brazil in how many of their World Cup winning years - 1 or 2?

3. **How many times was Franz Beckenbauer manager of West Germany's World Cup winning teams - 1 or 2?**

4. Walter Winterbottom was manager of England in how many World Cups - 2, 3 or 4?

5. **Jack Charlton managed the Republic of Ireland in how many World Cup finals - 1, 2 or 3?**

6. For how many finals have Eire qualified - 1, 2 or 3?

7. **Eire's only win over 90 minutes in nine finals matches was against Italy. The score was... 1-0, 2-0 or 3-1?**

8. Of their nine finals matches, Eire drew how many - 2, 3 or 5?

9. **What was the score in Eire's heaviest World Cup finals defeat, by Holland, in 1994 - 1-0, 2-0 or 3-1?**

10. Northern Ireland have played in how many World Cup finals tournaments - 1, 2 or 3?

11. **How many games have Northern Ireland played in the World Cup finals - 8, 10 or 13?**

12. Their first finals saw them reach the quarter-finals stage. What year was that - 1954, 1958 or 1986?

13. **Northern Ireland were beaten in that quarter-final by France by what score - 2-0, 3-1 or 4-0?**

14. Northern Ireland's last match in the World Cup finals was against Brazil. In what year?

15. **Brazil were the winners of that match by... 2-0, 3-0 or 5-0?**

ANSWERS: 1. Two 2. One **3. One** 4. Four **5. Two** 6. Two **7. 1-0** 8. Five **9. 2-0** 10. Three
11. Thirteen 12. 1958 **13. 4-0** 14. 1986 **15. 3-0**

Quiz 7

All about Numbers

1. In which year did Sweden host the World Cup finals - 1958 or 1962?

2. How many times have Sweden played in the finals - 7, 9 or 11?

3. How many times have they reached the World Cup Final - 0, 1 or 2?

4. How many times have the Swedes reached the semi-finals - 2, 3 or 4?

5. How many times have they won a third-place play-off - 0, 1 or 2?

6. Sweden's biggest win in finals matches was against Cuba in 1938. The score was... 6-0, 8-0 or 9-0?

7. Their heaviest defeat, at the hands of Brazil in 1950, was... 7-1, 8-1 or 9-1?

8. Ademir was Brazil's main scorer in that match with... 3, 4 or 5 goals?

9. France have twice finished third in the World Cup - in 1958 and what other year?

10. Just Fontaine of France was top scorer in the 1958 finals with 13 goals. How many hat-tricks did that include?

11. Pele was top scorer for Brazil in the 1958 finals. How many did he get - 4, 6 or 8?

12. How many did he score in Brazil's 5-2 win over Sweden?

13. How many did his team-mate Vava score in that Final - 1, 2 or 3?

14. West Germany played how many games in the 1958 finals - 3, 5 or 6?

15. How many did Fontaine score against West Germany in the match for third place - 2, 3 or 4?

ANSWERS: 1. 1958 2. Nine **3. One** 4. Three **5. One** 6. 8-0 **7. 7-1** 8. Four **9. 1986** 10. Two
11. Six 12. Two **13. Two** 14. Six **15. Four**

Quiz 8

All about Numbers

1. What was the score in the France play-off win over West Germany in the 1958 finals - 4-1, 5-2 or 6-3?

2. West Germany played how many games in the 1962 finals in Chile - 3, 4 or 5?

3. They were beaten in the quarter-finals by Yugoslavia. The score... 1-0, 2-0 or 2-1?

4. How many matches did Chile play in their host year of 1962 - 3, 4, 5 or 6?

5. Chile lost to Brazil in a 1962 semi-final by...3-1, 4-1 or 4-2?

6. Brazil went on to win the 1962 Final. Was it their first or second World Cup triumph?

7. How many were in the Santiago ground for the Brazil v Czechoslovakia Final of 1962 - 48,679 or 68,679?

8. Czechoslovakia's semi-final with Yugoslavia at Vina del Mar attracted a smaller crowd. Was it 5,890 or 15,890 or 25,890?

9. How many times have the Czechs qualified for the World Cup finals - 6, 8 or 10?

10. How many times have they reached the Final itself - 1, 2 or 3?

11. West Germany played how many games in the 1966 finals - 4, 5 or 6?

12. How many games did they win in the 1966 finals - 3, 4 or 5?

13. How many did England win in the 1966 finals - 4, 5 or 6?

14. How many goals did England score in the 1966 finals - 9, 11 or 14?

15. How many did West Germany score in the 1966 finals - 11, 13 or 15?

ANSWERS: 1. 6-3 2. Four **3. 1-0** 4. Six **5. 4-2** 6. Second **7. 68,679** 8. 5,890 **9. Eight** 10. Two
11. Six 12. Four **13. Five** 14. Eleven **15. Fifteen**

Quiz 9

All about Numbers

1. **How many times have Argentina qualified for the World Cup finals stage, including 1998 - 9, 11 or 12?**

2. How many qualifications by Cameroon - 2, 3, 4 or 5?

3. **Bulgaria qualified for 1998 after how many previous finals - 6, 7 or 8?**

4. How many times have Denmark qualified for the finals - 1, 2 or 4?

5. **How many times for Iran - 1, 2 or 3?**

6. And how many times for Tunisia?

7. **Paraguay appeared in how many finals before 1998 - 2, 4 or 6?**

8. How many countries qualified for the 1998 finals for the first time - 2, 3, 4 or 5?

9. **How many countries qualified for 1998 for their second finals - 2, 3, 4 or 5?**

10. Portugal v North Korea produced the most goals in all the 1966 finals matches. Portugal were the winners by… 6-2, 5-2 or 5-3?

11. **How many goals were scored in the first half of the 1966 Final - 2, 3 or 4?**

12. Eusebio was the top scorer of the 1966 finals with… 8, 9 or 10 goals?

13. **The 1966 finals were staged on how many English grounds - 6, 7 or 8?**

14. How many venues were used for the 1970 finals in Mexico - 5, 7 or 9?

15. **The World Cup Final in Mexico City in 1970 was attended by how many spectators - 57,412 or 87,412 or 107,412?**

ANSWERS: 1. Twelve 2. Four **3. Six** 4. Two **5. Two** 6. Two **7. Four** 8. Four **9. Five** 10. 5-3 **11. Two** 12. Nine **13. Eight** 14. Five **15. 107,412**

Quiz 10

All about Numbers

1. How many goals did Pele score in the 1970 World Cup Final, Brazil v Italy? Was it 0, 1 or 2?

2. How many did Jairzinho score in that Final - 0, 1 or 2?

3. What was Brazil's winning score - 4-0, 4-1 or 4-2?

4. Gerd Muller was the leading scorer in the 1970 finals with... 8, 10 or 11 goals?

5. West Germany were third-placed in 1970 after beating Uruguay in the play-off. The score was... 1-0, 2-0 or 2-1?

6. That match was West Germany's fifth, sixth or seventh game in the 1970 finals?

7. Morocco played in the 1970 finals, making their first or second appearance?

8. The referee of the 1974 World Cup Final was an Englishman, Jack Taylor. Was he the first, second or third English referee to control a Final?

9. How many penalties were converted in the 1974 Final - 0, 1 or 2?

10. The 1974 Final result was 2-1 to West Germany. What was the half-time score - 1-0, 1-1 or 2-1?

11. Scotland's appearance in the 1974 finals was their second, third or fifth?

12. How many of the other Home Countries were in those finals - 0, 1 or 2?

13. Yugoslavia, Brazil and Scotland all won four points in Group 2 of the 1974 finals. Where did the Scots finish - first, second or third?

14. Brazil scored how many goals in their group games - 1, 3 or 6?

15. Scotland scored how many in their group games - 1, 3 or 5?

ANSWERS: 1. One 2. One **3. 4-1** 4. Ten **5. 1-0** 6. Sixth **7. First** 8. Third **9. Two** 10. 2-1
11. Third 12. None **13. Third** 14. Three **15. Three**

Quiz 11

All about Numbers

1. **Yugoslavia recorded the biggest win of the 1974 finals against Zaire. The score was... 8-0, 9-0 or 9-1?**
2. Poland had the second biggest win of 1974, beating Haiti by... 6-0, 7-0 or 8-0?
3. **How many goals did Haiti concede in three games in their only finals appearance - 14, 16 or 18?**
4. How many goals did Haiti score altogether - 0, 1 or 2?
5. **What was Zaire's goals total in their three finals games - 0, 1 or 3?**
6. How many goals did Zaire concede in those three games - 14, 16 or 18?
7. **How many British Isles nations were represented in the 1978 World Cup finals - 1, 2 or 3?**
8. How many countries competed in the 1978 finals - 16 or 24?
9. **The 1978 Final between Argentina and Holland went to extra time. Was it the first, second or third time this had been necessary?**
10. When was the previous Final that extra time was called for?
11. **How many goals were scored in extra time of the 1978 Final - 1, 2 or 3?**
12. What was the score after 90 minutes in the 1978 Final between Argentina and Holland - 0-0, 1-1 or 2-2?
13. **How many points did Scotland win in their three group matches of 1978 - 1, 2 or 3?**
14. Holland finished above Scotland to qualify for the next stage with... 3, 4 or 5 points?
15. **Mario Kempes of Argentina was the top scorer in the 1978 finals with... 6, 7 or 8 goals?**

ANSWERS: 1. 9-0 2. 7-0 **3. Fourteen** 4. Two **5. None** 6. Fourteen **7. One** 8. Sixteen **9. Third** 10. 1966 **11. Two** 12. 1-1 **13. Three** 14. Three **15. Six**

Quiz 12

All about Numbers

1. By winning the 1978 Final in Buenos Aires, Argentina became the third, fourth or fifth host nation to do so?

2. How many more times did this happen after 1978 - never, once or twice?

3. How many times has the host nation finished runners-up... never, once or twice?

4. How many times has the host nation finished in third place - never, once or twice?

5. How many times has the host nation failed to finish in the first three - 3, 6 or 9?

6. Mexico have won through to the quarter-finals as hosts… never, once or twice?

7. Spain, the 1982 host nation, played how many finals matches that year - 4, 5 or 6?

8. How many times did they lose in 1982 - 1, 2 or 3?

9. Spain were beaten in the second round by West Germany by... 2-1, 3-1 or 2-0?

10. How many countries competed in the 1982 finals - 16 or 24?

11. How many British teams competed in the Spanish finals - 1, 2 or 3?

12. How many British teams won through to the second round - 1, 2 or 3?

13. How many of those won through to the semi-finals - 0, 1 or 2?

14. How many goals did England score in their two second-round matches of 1982 against West Germany and Spain - 0, 2 or 3?

15. Paolo Rossi was Italy's top scorer in their winning campaign of 1982. How many did he score in the tournament - 6, 7 or 9?

ANSWERS: 1. Fifth 2. Never **3. Twice** 4. Twice **5. Six** 6. Twice **7. Five** 8. Two **9. 2-1** 10. Twenty-four **11. Three** 12. Two **13. None** 14 None **15. Six**

Quiz 13

All about Numbers

1. New Zealand's only finals appearance was in 1982 - or was it in 1986?

2. How many did New Zealand score in their three matches - 0, 1 or 2?

3. Their defeat against Scotland was by...4-1, 6-1 or 5-2?

4. How many goals did New Zealand concede in the 1982 finals - 11, 12 or 14?

5. The first round of the 1982 finals consisted of how many groups - 4, 5 or 6?

6. Kuwait made their only appearance in World Cup finals in 1982, winning how many points from their three games?

7. How many goals did Kuwait's defence concede in those games - 6, 9 or 12?

8. England were Kuwait's last opponents in the World Cup finals. The winners were England by… 1-0, 2-0 or 3-1?

9. Cameroon made their World Cup finals debut in 1982, losing how many of their three group games - 0, 1 or 2?

10. How many did they win - 0, 2 or 3?

11. In their three games, Cameroon gave away... 1, 2 or 3 goals?

12. How many goals did Paolo Rossi score in the 1982 Final against West Germany - 0, 1 or 2?

13. How many goals were scored in the first half of that Final - 0, 1 or 3?

14. West Germany qualified for the 1982 Final by beating France in a penalty shoot-out. The penalties margin was 4-3, 5-3 or 5-4?

15. Rossi scored how many goals in the last three of Italy's seven games in the 1982 finals. Was it 3, 4 or 6?

ANSWERS: **1.** 1982 **2.** Two **3.** 5-2 **4.** Twelve **5.** Six **6.** One **7.** Six **8.** 1-0 **9.** None **10.** None **11.** One **12.** One **13.** None **14.** 5-4 **15.** Six

Quiz 14

All about Numbers

1. **How many qualifying games did New Zealand play before the 1982 finals - 10, 13 or 15?**

2. Kuwait qualified from the same Asia/Oceania zone after playing how many games - 9, 11 or 13?

3. **Canada made their only finals appearance in 1986 in Mexico. How many points did they earn from their three matches - 0, 1 or 2?**

4. How many goals did they score in those games - 0, 1 or 2?

5. **How many goals did they concede in those games - 5, 8 or 10?**

6. How many British teams went to Mexico 1986 - 1, 2 or 3?

7. **How many of them won through to the second round - 0, 1 or 2?**

8. England beat Paraguay in the second round by… 1-0, 2-0 or 3-0?

9. **How many of the 1986 quarter-finals were decided by penalty shoot-outs - 1, 2 or 3?**

10. England went out to the eventual tournament winners Argentina by… 1-0, 3-1 or 2-1?

11. **Gary Lineker was the leading scorer of the 1986 finals with how many goals - 6, 7 or 8?**

12. Argentina beat West Germany in the 1986 Final by… 3-1, 3-2 or 4-2?

13. **The same two nations contested the 1990 World Cup Final in Italy. What was the Germans' winning score - 1-0, 2-0 or 3-0?**

14. Two players were sent off in this Final. How many were Argentine - 0, 1 or 2?

15. **The Final in Rome was watched by how many spectators - 73,603 or 98,603?**

ANSWERS: 1. Fifteen 2. Nine 3. None 4. None 5. Five 6. Three 7. One 8. 3-0 9. Three 10. 2-1 11. Six 12. 3-2 13. 1-0 14. Two 15. 73,603

Quiz 15

All about Numbers

1. **How many venues staged the 1990 finals in Italy - 8, 10 or 12?**

2. How many matches did England play in the Italy finals - 5, 6 or 7?

3. **How many of England's games went to extra time - 1, 2 or 3?**

4. England were knocked out at the semi-final stage by West Germany after a penalty shoot- out, which ended at... 3-2, 4-2 or 4-3?

5. **Scotland went out in the first round of the 1990 finals. How many times has this happened - 5, 7 or 8?**

6. Italy, hosting the finals of 1990, also went out at the semi-final stage on a penalty shoot-out. Argentina won the shoot-out by... 3-2, 4-2 or 4-3?

7. **Colombia played ten finals matches altogether up to and including the 1994 series. How many did they win - 2, 3 or 4?**

8. How many of those ten games did they lose - 3, 5 or 6?

9. **One of their draws was against West Germany in 1990. The score was... 0-0, 1-1 or 2-2?**

10. In which minute did Andy Brehme score the only goal from the penalty spot in the 1990 Final - 74th, 85th or 89th?

11. **Costa Rica's four games in their only finals, in Italy 1990, resulted in how many wins for them - 0, 1 or 2?**

12. What was their result v Scotland - won 1-0, drew 1-1 or lost 1-0?

13. **United Arab Emirates were 1990 debutants. The highest of their three defeats was against West Germany...by 7-0, 6-1 or 5-1?**

14. Egypt lost only one match in the 1990 finals - to England. The score was... 1-0, 2-0 or 3-0?

15. **How many goals did Egypt concede in those three games - 2, 4 or 5?**

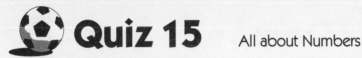

ANSWERS: 1. Twelve 2. Seven 3. Three 4. 4-3 5. Eight 6. 4-3 7. Two 8. Six 9. 1-1 10. 85th 11. Two 12. Won 1-0 13. 5-1 14. 1-0 15. Two

Quiz 16

All about Numbers

1. **Eire met Egypt in the 1990 finals in a match that produced... 0, 2 or 3 goals?**
2. How many games did Cameroon play in those finals - 3, 4 or 5?
3. **How many goals did Roger Milla score in those matches - 3, 4 or 5?**
4. Cameroon played extra time how many times in those finals - 0, 1 or 2?
5. **What was the record number of entries for the 1994 World Cup finals in the USA - 138, 144 or 150?**
6. How many countries took part in the finals - 16, 24 or 32?
7. **Germany were eliminated in the 1994 finals after... 4, 5 or 6 matches?**
8. How many of these matches did Germany win - 2, 3 or 4?
9. **The Germans were finally beaten by Bulgaria. The score was... 1-0, 2-1 or 3-1?**
10. Jurgen Klinsmann scored in how many of Germany's 1994 finals matches - 2, 3 or 4?
11. **Greece were first-time finalists in 1994, winning how many points from their three matches - 0, 1 or 3?**
12. The Greeks scored how many goals in those matches - 0, 1 or 2?
13. **They were beaten 4-0 in their first finals match by Argentina. How many did Maradona score - 1, 2 or 3?**
14. How many did Batistuta score - 1, 2 or 3?
15. **Brazil won the Final, having scored how many goals in the 1994 matches in the States - 11, 14 or 17?**

ANSWERS: 1. None 2. Five **3. Four** 4. Two **5. 144** 6. Twenty-four **7. Five** 8. Three **9. 2-1**
10. Four **11. None** 12. None **13. One** 14. Three **15. Eleven**

Quiz 17 All about Numbers

1. **What was the number of African finalists in USA 1994? Was it 2, 3 or 4?**
2. Italy were beaten in the Final of 1994, having scored how many goals on the way there - 8, 11 or 14?
3. **Roberto Baggio was Italy's top scorer in the 1994 finals with how many goals - 4, 5 or 6?**
4. Italy beat Bulgaria 2-1 in the semi-finals. How many did Roberto Baggio score - 0, 1 or 2?
5. **Argentina were eliminated at the second stage by Romania 3-2. How many goals for Romania did Ilie Dumitrescu score - 1, 2 or 3?**
6. The Romanians went out in the quarter-finals to Sweden in a penalty shoot-out. By what score - 3-2, 4-3 or 5-4?
7. **The biggest win of the USA finals was recorded by Russia against Cameroon. The score was... 7-0, 7-1 or 6-1?**
8. Nigeria played four matches on their finals debut in 1994. How many goals did they total - 4, 6 or 7?
9. **Saudi Arabia also played four matches on their debut. Their goals total was... 3, 4 or 5?**
10. Saudi Arabia won how many games in the finals - 1, 2 or 3?
11. **Eire played four times in the 1994 finals, scoring... 2, 3 or 4 goals?**
12. Salenko (Russia) and Stoichkov (Bulgaria) were top scorers in the 1994 finals, each with... 6, 7 or 9 goals?
13. **How many penalty shoot-outs were there in the 1994 finals - 2, 3 or 4?**
14. How many of the 1994 finals matches went into extra time - 3, 4 or 5?
15. **Europe were beaten by the Rest of the World on the day of the 1998 World Cup draw in Marseille. What was the score - 4-2, 5-2 or 5-3?**

ANSWERS: **1.** Three **2.** Eight **3.** Five **4.** Two **5.** Two **6.** 5-4 **7.** 6-1 **8.** Seven **9.** Five **10.** Two **11.** Two **12.** Six **13.** Three **14.** Four **15.** 5-2

Mixed Bag

Quiz 1

Mixed Bag

1. **Which player has appeared in five World Cup tournaments?**
2. Who called the Polish keeper Jan Tomaszewski a 'clown' before the England v Poland World Cup qualifier in 1973?
3. **Who were the first team to qualify for the 1994 World Cup?**
4. Which African country qualified for both World Cup finals held in Mexico?
5. **Spain entered the 1938 World Cup - why did they not compete?**
6. Which three teams did Cameroon beat to reach the World Cup quarter-finals in 1990?
7. **Prior to the 1994 World Cup, which team had appeared in five tournaments but failed to win a game?**
8. How many times have Mexico played in the World Cup finals?
9. **In the 1938 World Cup, which country received a bye through to the second round due to Germany's invasion of Austria?**
10. Which was the first African country to reach a World Cup quarter-final?
11. **In the 1994 qualifiers, San Marino lost nine games and drew one. Who was the draw against?**
12. Why did India withdraw from the 1950 World Cup?
13. **Why were Nigeria disqualified from the 1974 World Cup?**
14. Who finished third in the 1982 World Cup?
15. **North Korea beat which team to progress to the quarter-finals in the 1966 World Cup?**

ANSWERS: 1. The Mexican goalkeeper Antonio Carbajal (1950 World Cup through to 1966) 2. Brian Clough **3. Mexico** 4. Morocco **5. Because of the Spanish Civil War** 6. Argentina, Romania and Colombia **7. Bulgaria** 8. Ten **9. Sweden** 10. Cameroon **11. Turkey** 12. They were not allowed to play barefoot **13. Crowd trouble at a home fixture against Ghana which led to the match being abandoned** 14. Poland **15. Italy.**

Quiz 2

Mixed Bag

1. In which World Cup finals did Zaire make their only appearance?

2. Which country finished third in the 1974 World Cup?

3. Before playing in 1994, when was Norway's last appearance in the World Cup finals?

4. Which nation played a World Cup match only two days after the country had been devastated by an earthquake?

5. Which nation qualified for five finals series between 1962 and 1986 yet failed to win any of their sixteen matches?

6. Which goalkeeper played in a record five World Cups yet appeared on the winning side only once?

7. Which nation did not qualify for the finals between 1938 and 1974 then reached the next four, finishing third twice?

8. Which nation holds the highest goals-per game average in the World Cup matches?

9. Which is the only nation to lose 32 successive World Cup matches?

10. Which nation won 47 of 48 internationals between 1950 and 1956 yet failed to win the World Cup?

11. Which was the first Asian team to play in the World Cup?

12. Which nation's only appearance in the finals resulted in a 6-0 defeat?

13. Who finished ahead of Brazil in the group stages of the 1978 World Cup finals?

14. Who conceded twelve goals in their three group matches in the 1978 World Cup finals?

15. Who beat West Germany in the group stages of the 1974 World Cup?

ANSWERS: 1. 1974 2. Poland **3. 1938** 4. Peru in 1970 **5. Bulgaria** 6. Antonio Carbajal - Mexico **7. Poland** 8. Turkey average 3.33 goals **9. Luxembourg 1974 - 1990** 10. Hungary **11. Indonesia 1938** 12. Indonesia by Hungary in 1938 **13. Austria** 14. Mexico **15. East Germany**

Quiz 3

Mixed Bag

1. **Which Polish star scored a hat-trick against Belgium in the 1982 World Cup?**
2. Who did Sweden beat 8-0 in the second round of the 1938 finals?
3. **Who beat South Korea 9-0 in the group stage of the 1954 World Cup?**
4. Which team scored 17 goals in two group matches in the 1954 tournament?
5. **This Colombian player scored an own goal when playing the United States in the 1994 World Cup. What was his name?**
6. Which two past winners failed to qualify for the 1994 World Cup finals?
7. **Altogether there were 52 games played in the 1990 World Cup - how many players were sent off?**
8. Which captain has twice led the losing team in the World Cup Final?
9. **Who was the top goalscorer in the 1990 World Cup?**
10. In the 1990 World Cup, who won the Fair Play award?
11. **Who became the first man to captain and manage a World Cup winning side?**
12. How many players were there left on the pitch at the end of the 1990 World Cup Final?
13. **What nationality was the referee in the England v Argentina 'Hand of God' 1986 quarter-final?**
14. Who returned from a two-year suspension to become the top goalscorer in the 1982 World Cup?
15. **What was used for the first time in the 1974 World Cup finals?**

ANSWERS: 1. Zbigniew Boniek 2. Cuba **3. Hungary** 4. Hungary **5. Andres Escobar** 6. England and Uruguay **7. Sixteen** 8. Karl-Heinz Rummenigge **9. Salvatore Schillaci** 10. England **11. Franz Beckenbauer** 12. Twenty **13. Tunisian** 14. Paulo Rossi **15. New FIFA World Cup trophy**

Quiz 4

Mixed Bag

1. **England, Wales, Scotland and Northern Ireland were not eligible to participate in the first World Cup in Uruguay in 1930 - why?**
2. Which country has withdrawn from the World Cup the most often?
3. **In 1966 which team was pelted with rotten fruit on their return home?**
4. What was the name of the dog that found the Jules Rimet trophy in 1966?
5. **Who was the first person to score a goal in the World Cup?**
6. What was stolen from the Olympic Stadium in Rome on 8th July after the 1990 World Cup?

7. **What was the name of the Italian 1990 World Cup mascot?**
8. What fruit was the 1982 Spanish World Cup mascot based on?
9. **In 1974 West Germany had two World Cup mascots. What were their names?**
10. How many times has the host nation won the World Cup?
11. **Why did Uruguay refuse to defend their World Cup title in Italy in 1934?**
12. Which team has held the World Cup the longest?
13. **In which World Cup was Britain represented by all four home counties?**
14. Who were the first country to hold both the European Championship and the World Cup titles at the same time?
15. **What has been the highest score in a World Cup tournament?**

ANSWERS 1. Withdrew from FIFA in 1928 2. Egypt in 1938, 1950, 1962 and 1966 **3. Italy** 4. Pickles **5. Pedro Cea of Uruguay** 6. The reinforced centre spot **7. Ciao** 8. Orange **9. Tip and Tap** 10. Five **11. Because so few had bothered to take part in Uruguay in 1930** 12. Italy **13. Sweden 1958** 14. West Germany **15. 9-0 Yugoslavia v Zaire in 1974 and 9-0 Hungary v South Korea in 1954**

Quiz 5

Mixed Bag

1. Who was the top goalscorer in the 1970 tournament?

2. Who holds the individual goalscoring record in a World Cup tournament?

3. The 1986 World Cup Final was held in which stadium?

4. Who won the Most Exciting Team award at the 1994 World Cup?

5. Who won the Fair Play award at the 1994 World Cup?

6. How many countries will be playing in the 1998 World Cup?

7. Where did the draw for the 1994 World Cup finals take place?

8. What was unusual about all the 15 penalties awarded in open play in the 1994 World Cup?

9. In the 1994 World Cup, the referees' and linesmen's kit came in which three colours?

10. Which is the only country to have played in every World Cup tournament?

11. For the first time in the World Cup finals, what was awarded for a win in a group match in 1994?

12. The 1994 'Striker' mascot was a dog created by whom?

13. Who won the Golden Ball award for the best player in the 1994 World Cup?

14. Who scored the 1,000th World Cup goal?

15. Why did the English referee Jack Taylor delay the start of the 1974 World Cup Final?

ANSWERS 1. Gerd Muller 2. Just Fontaine **3. Azteca Stadium** 4. Brazil **5. Brazil** 6. Thirty two **7. Caesars Palace, Las Vegas** 8. All were converted **9. Silver, gold and pink on a black check background** 10. Brazil **11. Three points** 12. Warner Brothers **13. Romario, Brazil** 14. Robbie Rensenbrink (Holland) **15. All the midfield and corner flags had gone missing**

Quiz 6

Mixed Bag

1. **Who are the only two players to have scored in two different World Cup Finals?**
2. Who is the oldest player to have won a World Cup winner's medal?
3. **What could Argentina and Uruguay not agree on before the start of the 1930 World Cup Final?**
4. Which World Cup tournament was the first to be televised?
5. **Who was the first player to score in every game of a World Cup tournament ?**
6. Which country was eliminated from the 1974 World Cup on goal difference without losing a game?
7. **Who is the youngest player ever to have played in a World Cup?**
8. Who was awarded the Silver Ball trophy for goals and assists in the 1994 World Cup?
9. **Who won the Lev Yashin Goalkeeper Award in the 1994 World Cup?**
10. What is the French mascot for the 1998 World Cup?
11. **Who will host the World Cup in 2002?**
12. Who was the first player banned for drug taking by FIFA in a World Cup?
13. **Who were first team to win the World Cup outside their own continent?**
14. The first penalty to be awarded in a World Cup Final was in which tournament?
15. **What was unusual about the two goalkeepers in the 1978 World Cup Final?**

ANSWERS 1. Pele and Paul Breitner 2. Dino Zoff aged 40 of Italy **3. Which ball to use** 4. Swiss 1954 **5. Jairzinho** 6. Scotland **7. Norman Whiteside** 8. Roberto Baggio (Italy) **9. Michel Preud'homme (Belgium)** 10. A cockerel **11. Japan and South Korea** 12. Haitian Ernest Jean-Joseph, 1974 **13. Brazil in 1958** 14. 1974 **15. Jan Jongbloed wore number eight shirt and Ubaldo Fillol wore the number seven**

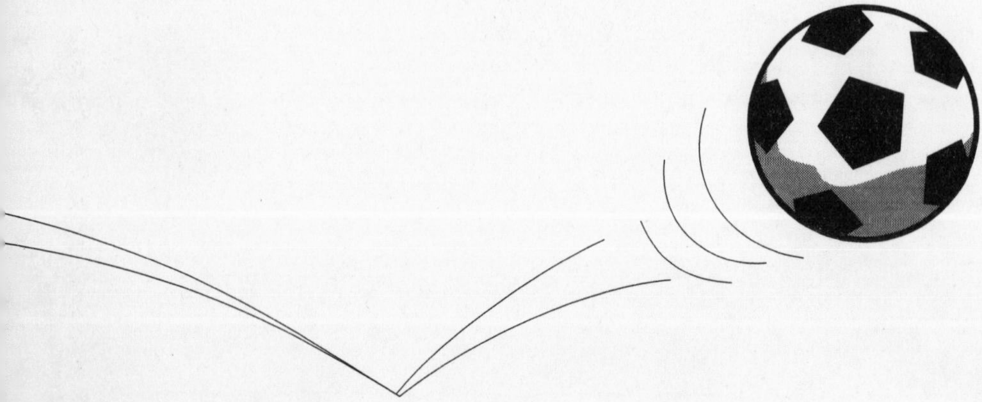

World Cup Fact Book

FACTS CONTENTS

1st World Cup Uruguay 1930

1st World Cup Uruguay 1930 Facts

Seven football-mad gentlemen, representing seven European countries, met in Paris way back in 1904 to form FIFA (Federation Internationale de Football Associations) and promptly came up with the idea of a world soccer tournament. Not a bad idea!

Those seven nations were Belgium, Denmark, France, Holland, Spain, Sweden and Switzerland. Two years elapsed before England decided it was not a bad idea and joined them.

Incredibly, 16 years after the Paris meeting, the World Cup concept finally took off at FIFA's Antwerp Congress, thanks to two Frenchmen, president Jules Rimet and secretary Henri Delaunay.

Another 10 years passed before the first World Cup tournament featuring 13 nations in Uruguay. Surprise, surprise, Uruguay won it in their centenary year!

None of the Home Countries - England, Scotland, Wales and Northern Ireland - competed because a tiff over payments to 'amateurs' had prompted all four to withdraw from FIFA in 1928.

Holland, Italy, Spain and Sweden all failed in their bids to host the inaugural tourney and declined to go to Uruguay.

Only two of the FIFA founder members, France and Belgium, made the arduous three-week sea voyage to Uruguay.

The competitors, in one pool of four and three pools of three, were: Argentina, Belgium, Bolivia, Brazil, Chile, France, Mexico, Paraguay, Peru, Romania, USA, Uruguay and Yugoslavia.

Uruguay were chosen as hosts largely because they were Olympic soccer champions in 1924 and 1928.

Another factor was the building of Montevideo's wonderful Centenario Stadium in eight hectic months.

The Uruguayans knew how to make friends and influence people. They paid the hotel and travelling expenses to all 12 visiting nations.

Uruguay's star Olympic goalkeeper Mazzali was sacked from the squad for breaking the tough curfew. His place went to Enrique Ballesteros.

A solid gold trophy, designed by French sculptor Lafleur, was ready for the grand opening match on July 13, 1930.

Spare a thought for the noble Jules Rimet. He presented the trophy to the winners, but it didn't bear his name until 1950 in Brazil.

Facts

1st World Cup
Uruguay 1930

When Brazil won the Jules Rimet Trophy outright with their third victory in 1970, the new trophy became 'The FIFA World Cup' and remains so.

Ironically, Uruguay won it again in 1950, after twenty years without competing.

Uruguay refused to defend their title in Italy in 1934, the only time the holders have so decided. They were annoyed because of the poor European representation in 1930.

Only four European countries went to Uruguay and, on July 13, 1930, France won the very first World Cup match, beating Mexico 4-1.

Romania were ordered to play by no less a person than King Carol. And he even selected the Romanian squad!

An English oil company employed several Romanian players and threatened to sack them if they took the long sea trip to Uruguay. His Majesty also 'fixed' that little problem.

Tough luck for the king was being drawn in the same group as Uruguay, who whacked them 4-0 after they had beaten Peru 3-1 in their first match.

Romania v Peru was a fair old battle. Romanian full-back Steiner was carried off with a broken leg and Peruvian skipper De Las Casas was sent off.

Surprise first entrants were the United States, who recruited a formidable squad of imported players and qualified for the semi-finals by convincingly beating Paraguay and Belgium without conceding a goal.

The Yanks' players were mostly massive and muscular, earning the title of 'The Shot-Putters' from a number of their rivals.

Their six British 'imports' included the mercurial Alec Jackson, who helped Huddersfield to win the League Championship in 1926.

Jackson was in the legendary 'Wembley Wizards' forward line when his native Scotland crushed England 5-1 in 1928.

Remember that line of wee Scots? They were Alec Jackson, Tim Dunn, Hughie Gallacher, Alex James and Alan Morton.

The first-ever World Cup goal was scored by a Frenchman, Louis Laurent, early in the first half.

France also recorded another 'first' in the opening match. Maschinot notched two goals to become the first player to score more than one goal in a World Cup tie.

1st World Cup Uruguay 1930 Facts

France's first World Cup defeat came in their next match, the only goal being scored by Argentina's Luisito Monti.

Monti 'became' an Italian, along with two other Argentine players, for the 1934 series, which the hosts duly won in Rome.

Distinguished columnist Robert Philip once listed his 'Top Fifty Most Influential Sports Figures' and placed Jules Rimet third behind Muhammad Ali and Baron Pierre de Coubertin.

Other legendary World Cup names in Philip's provocative list were: Pele 8, Sir Bobby Charlton 24, Johan Cruyff 33, Diego Maradona 44, Franz Beckenbauer 47. (What, no John Charles? No Eusebio? No Didi?).

The first World Cup semi-finalists were Argentina, Uruguay, the United States and Yugoslavia.

Yugoslavia were the surprise packet of the group matches, beating seeded Brazil 2-1. The three other seeds all topped their groups and all four semi-finalists had 100 per cent records.

Belgium and Bolivia were the whipping boys. They failed to score in any game.

The six-hitters of South America were runaway semi-final winners. USA and Yugoslavia were both slaughtered 6-1 by Argentina and Uruguay respectively.

Uruguay were conquerors of Switzerland and Argentina in the Olympic soccer finals of 1924 and 1928, the latter tie going to a replay.

The first World Cup Final, Uruguay v Argentina, was watched by 93,000 at the Centenario Stadium, including thousands of Argentines who were searched for weapons as they entered the stadium.

Uruguay were 1-2 down at half-time but triumphed 4-2, and captain Jose Nasazzi became the first to receive the new World Cup.

Hero of the Uruguay side Hector Castro, scorer of a goal against Peru and the fourth goal in the Final, had no left hand. He lost it in a childhood accident.

Facts

1st World Cup
Uruguay 1930

Uruguay declared a national holiday on August 1, 1930, the day after their victory.

There was no holiday for the Uruguayan consul in Buenos Aires, who took refuge as an incensed Argentine mob stormed the consulate.

Uruguay's Final line-up was: Ballesteros; Nasazzi (capt), Mascheroni; Andrade, Fernandez, Gestido; Dorado, Scarone, Castro, Cea, Iriarte.

Argentina: Botasso; Della Torre, Paternoster; Evaristo (J), Monti, Suarez; Peucelle, Varallo, Stabile, Ferreira (capt), Evaristo (M).

Uruguay's home-grown coach was Alberto Supicci. Indeed, no subsequent World Cup-winning team has had a foreign manager/coach.

The first World Cup Final referee was a Belgian, Jean Langenus. He had his problems.

The finalists could not agree on the match ball. So Monsieur Langenus produced one from each side, each to be used for 45 minutes. Indeed, a match of two halves!

Referee No 2 with a 1930 dilemma was Almeida Rego of Brazil. He blew for time six minutes too soon in the Argentina-France match and had to clear the pitch before re-starting much later

Bolivia's Ulysses Saucedo completed a hat-trick of refereeing oddities, Argentina being involved every time. No prisoners were taken as Mexico fell 6-3 in a match of five penalties.

The first footballer to score a World Cup Final goal was Pablo Dorado of Uruguay in the twelfth minute on July 30, 1930.

Mexico made World Cup history when fielding two brothers, Manuel and Filipe Rosas. Both scored in the 6-3 defeat by Argentina.

Alex Villaplane, who captained the French team, was executed in 1944 for collaboration with the invading Germans.

Argentina's Guillermo Stabile scored the first World Cup hat-trick in the match against Mexico - and he played only because his captain Ferreira had to return home to sit an exam.

Stabile ended the series as top scorer with eight goals. Pedro Cea (Uruguay) was second with five, including a semi-final hat-trick against Yugoslavia, and Guillermo Subriabre (Chile) third with four goals in the tournament.

The smallest attendance in the 1930 series was exactly 300 at Romania v Peru.

2nd World Cup Italy 1934

2nd World Cup Italy 1934 Facts

The first rumbles of a Second World War eruption were heard as dictator Benito Mussolini declared that his Fascist government would foot the bill for the second World Cup.

FIFA reluctantly agreed after eight meetings only on Mussolini's promise to underwrite the show.

Uruguay, still smarting from the near total snub of the 1930 tournament by European clubs, did not defend their title as first champions. They also had a players' strike at the time.

Uruguay are on record as the first and only World Cup holders ever to give up their title without a defence. They stayed out until 1950.

In the event, South America was represented only by Brazil and Argentina.

FIFA membership had increased by only five - from 41 to 46 - since the first World Cup in 1930.

Thirty-two members entered and a preliminary contest was required to achieve a final 16 for the knock-out stage.

Still no Home Countries, but Eire - then known as the Irish Free State - competed for the first time.

Turkey, Chile and Peru withdrew without playing in the qualifying competition, due to cost and the political implications.

There were no 'free rides' to the last 16. Even hosts Italy had to play in a 'group' - consisting of Italy and Greece!

Mussolini and the rest of the country hardly dared to breathe until March 25, 1934, when Italy beat Greece 4-0.

Thirteen nations failed to reach the last 16 of the competition. They were Haiti, Cuba, Mexico, Palestine, Lithuania, Estonia, Portugal, Greece, Bulgaria, Poland, Yugoslavia, Luxembourg ... and Eire.

The Irish fought bravely before being narrowly dismissed in one of the toughest European groups of three, despite scoring six goals.

Facts

2nd World Cup
Italy 1934

Group 11 results were: Eire 4 Belgium 4; Holland 5 Eire 2; Belgium 2 Holland 4.

GROUP 11 TABLE

Country	P	W	D	L	F	A	Pts
Holland	2	2	0	0	9	4	4
Belgium	2	0	1	1	6	8	1
Eire	2	0	1	1	6	9	1

Eire still managed to make World Cup history, Paddy Moore scoring four times in a qualifying match.

Easy riders to the Finals were the four non-European qualifiers: USA, Brazil, Argentina and Egypt.

Egypt became the first African nation to compete in the World Cup. They lost 4-2 to Hungary in Naples, Fawzi scoring both their goals.

Egypt's goalkeeper that day was Moustafa Kamel. Make what you can of that!

Earlier, in the space of four days, Egypt had scored 11 goals to dispose of their only qualification rivals, Palestine.

Group One favoured USA, who waited for Mexico to emerge from three winning games with Cuba, who first had to eliminate Haiti.

The aggrieved Mexicans then left for Rome, only to lose their group final to the United States by 4-2. Fourteen goals in the qualifying competition but no finals place!

Argentina and Brazil free-wheeled to Rome - and both were knocked out in the first round proper.

Top scorers in the qualifiers were Germany (9-1 v Luxembourg) and Spain (9-0 v Portugal).

Twenty-five qualifying games produced an avalanche of 139 goals!

The 12 European qualifiers were: Austria, Belgium, Czechoslovakia, France, Germany, Holland, Hungary, Italy, Romania, Spain, Sweden, Switzerland.

2nd World Cup Italy 1934 Facts

The eight seeds were: Italy, Argentina, Brazil, Czechoslovakia, Hungary, Austria, Germany, Holland.

Only five seeds survived to round two: Italy, Czechoslovakia, Hungary, Austria and Germany. All except Hungary went through to the semi-finals.

There were eight venues for the games in Italy: Bologna, Florence, Genoa, Milan, Naples, Rome, Trieste, Turin.

All eight second-round survivors were European. Out went France, Belgium, Holland and Romania.

The Czechs set an all-time record of fielding a team drawn from only two clubs, Sparta and Slavia Prague, in reaching the Final.

Argentina fielded a reserve team, rightly fearing Italian 'poachers' after losing flying winger Orsi before the 1930 World Cup, followed by their star in Montevideo, Luisito Monti, and a third player in Guaita.

Brazil disappointed in their only match, losing tamely 3-1 in Genoa to Spain, the surprise packet of the series, captained by their great goalkeeper, Ricardo Zamora.

Spain's Iraragorri converted a penalty in the first half; Valdemar De Brito failed from the spot for Brazil, the first penalty miss in World Cup history.

De Brito later earned fame in Brazil as the mentor of a young lad called Pele.

Zamora was worshipped by Spanish fans as 'The Man in Black'. He was beaten only 40 times in 46 international matches.

Zamora had nightmares at the mention of England, Dixie Dean and all. He conceded seven goals at Highbury in 1931.

Dean scored only once in this game, his last goal of 18 in 16 matches for England.

Oddly, three of the 16 qualifiers had goalkeeper-captains. The others were Planicka of Czechoslovakia and Combi of Italy, the latter sharing the job with full-back Rosetta.

Mussolini strutted as his 'world-beaters' crushed USA 7-1 in the first round on May 27. They went on to win in 1934 and 1938. His luck ran out on a bigger field in the mid-Forties.

The Americans' sole goalscorer was Donelli, a Neapolitan. He remained in Italy after the finals to continue his playing career.

Italy's inspiration of the Thirties was their manager, Vittorio Pozzo. Under him, Italy were twice World Cup winners and 1936 Olympic champions

Facts

2nd World Cup
Italy 1934

Centre-forward Angelo Schiavio scored against USA the first of three hat-tricks in the 1934 finals. The others came from Edmund Conen (Germany) against Belgium in round one and Oldrich Nejedly (Czechoslovakia) against Germany in the semi-finals.

Nejedly (5), Schiavio and Conen (4 each) were the series top scorers from 17 games yielding 70 goals - over four per game on average.

Fastest scorer of the 1934 games was Ernst Lehner, just 24 seconds from the start against Austria in Germany's 3-2 win in the third-place play-off.

Biggest disappoinment in the finals were Austria under coach Hugo Meisl. They had beaten Italy 4-2 in Turin earlier in 1934 and were known as the 'Wunderteam'.

Austria squeezed past France 3-2 in extra time, helped by an 'offside' goal by Schall, and Hungary 2-1 in 'a brawl, not a football match' (Meisl's description).

Hungary had Imre Markosa, their outside-right, sent off in the quarter-final against Austria. It was the only sending-off of the 1934 tournament.

Austria finally ran out of luck in the semi-final in Milan, played in torrential rain, to the only goal by Italy's right-winger Guaita.

England have memories of Meisl. Assisted by English coach Jimmy Hogan, he had failed to topple England in the 1932 'Battle of the Bridge' at Chelsea. Austria were beaten and bruised 4-3.

The only replay was between Italy and Spain. Their first quarter-final in Florence was a violent affair, so that for the next-day replay, Italy called on three reserves and Spain seven!

Italian forward Giuseppe Meazza, glamour boy and bicycle-kick specialist known as Peppino, was in the 1934 Cup-winning team. His was the solitary, vital quarter-final goal against Spain in that replay.

The Czechs moved smoothly to the 1934 World Cup Final in Rome on June 10, where they watched the Italians raise their right arms in the Fascist salute before the kick-off.

2nd World Cup Italy 1934 Facts

The Czechs raised both arms in the 70th minute when Puc scored to a deafening silence from 55,000 people. Play was held up as police rescued one of their players whose hair was being pulled by distraught home fans behind the wire barriers!

Italy's life-saver was Orsi with an amazing dipping shot over the bemused Planicka eight minutes from normal time. The winger could hardly believe his luck.

The day after the Final, Orsi tried to repeat the shot with an empty goal. He gave up after total failure from 20 attempts.

Italy's winning goal in the seventh minute of extra time was scored by Angelo Schiavio, and Mussolini presented the World Cup to goalkeeper Giampiero Combi.

Italy's winning team: Combi (capt); Monzeglio, Allemandi; Ferraris, Monti, Bertolini; Guaita, Meazza, Schiavio, Ferrari, Orsi.

Czechoslovakia: Planicka (capt); Zenisek, Ctyroky; Kostalek, Cambal, Krcil; Junek, Svoboda, Sobotka, Nejedly, Puc.

Both teams in the Rome final were captained by goalkeepers, Italy by Combi and the Czechs by Planicka.

The Belgian referee of the 1930 Final, Jean Lagenus, summed up the 1934 success of Italy with tongue in cheek: 'Italy wanted to win but made it far too obvious. It was a sporting fiasco.'

3rd World Cup France 1938

3rd World Cup France 1938 Facts

After home victories in the first two World Cups, defenders Italy broke the trend in 1938 by winning deservedly the Third World Cup in France.

Europe was on the verge of all-out war, Spain had its own civil war, and Austria withdrew despite qualifying, having been invaded by Hitler's Germany.

The 1934 system of sudden-death knock-out again operated. Qualifying rounds produced 16 for the finals, although this time the holders (Italy) and hosts (France) were exempt.

The 16 were: Austria, Belgium, Brazil, Cuba, Czechoslovakia, Dutch East Indies, France, Germany, Holland, Hungary, Italy, Norway, Poland, Romania, Sweden, Switzerland.

For the only time in 15 World Cups, South America had just one competing nation - Brazil.

Uruguay still had the 'sulks' and Argentina were also absent because the 1936 FIFA Congress preferred France as venue instead of the South American country.

There were originally 36 entries for 1938 but the threat of war largely caused nine withdrawals without taking part. They were: Colombia, Costa Rica, Dutch Guiana, Egypt, El Salvador, Japan, Mexico, Spain, USA.

Although the Home Countries again stayed out, Eire tried again but failed to qualify in yet another tough group.

Yugoslavia were eliminated from Group 2 along with Eire, despite two brave Irish performances against Norway (3-3 and 2-3).

Also eliminated before the finals were: Estonia, Finland, Portugal, Palestine, Greece, Bulgaria, Lithuania, Luxembourg and Latvia.

England had still not rejoined FIFA, but they were offered Austria's place by the ruling body. Some thought the Second World War might have started a year earlier had they accepted!

England did go to France in 1938 - and beat the French 4-2 in Paris.

Also in World Cup 1938 year, England beat a FIFA XI at Highbury 3-0, Germany 6-3 in Berlin, and Norway at Newcastle 4-0, but were beaten 2-1 by Switzerland in Zurich.

The Swiss winning goalscorer was Andre Abegglen, who two weeks later proved to be the country's pin-up hero in the defeat of Germany.

How would Scotland have fared? Well, in 1938 they beat Holland in Amsterdam 3-1 and Hungary in Glasgow 3-1.

Goals in the qualifiers were not as plentiful as in the 1934 series, though every match provided a score. Matches: 21. Goals: 91.

Facts

3rd World Cup
France 1938

Some sympathy is due for Greece. Having been removed in their only qualifying game 4-0 by Italy in 1934, they took an 11-1 hammering from Hungary in 1938. Hungary then went all the way to the Final against Italy.

Other big-hitters on the early road to the 1938 finals were Sweden (7-2 v Estonia) and Czechoslovakia (6-0 v Bulgaria).

Venues for the 1938 finals were Antibes, Bordeaux, Le Havre, Lille, Marseilles, Paris, Reims, Strasbourg and Toulouse.

Having occupied Austria, Germany recruited four of their players for the 1938 Final series.

Switzerland were the toast of Europe - and farther afield - when they surprisingly knocked out Germany in the first round after a replay.

Thanks to Abegglen's headed goal, the Swiss held Germany 1-1 in Paris despite extra time. Five of the seven first-round matches required extra time.

Switzerland beat the Germans 4-2 in the replay five days later, despite being 2-0 down at half-time. Abegglen was again the hero with two brilliant goals.

Hans Pesser, one of Germany's recruited Austrians at outside-left, was sent off in the first match for kicking Switzerland's Minelli.

An unhappy Herr was Germany's coach Sepp Herberger, who took over after England's 6-3 'friendly' win in Berlin.

The defeat by Switzerland was the Germans' last World Cup game before partition into East and West Germany.

West Germany waited 16 years for their next World Cup finals appearance. East Germany failed in four qualifiers from 1958 to 1970 before winning a place in the 1974 finals.

Cuba produced the real shock of round one by eliminating Romania in Toulouse, after a 3-3 first tie.

Winning scorer for Cuba in their 2-1 replay win was Maquina, who also had a first-match goal.

Sadly, Cuba's World Cup finals history ended in a 8-0 hammering by Sweden, with all five forwards scoring. The Cubans were only in the finals because Mexico withdrew.

Dutch East Indies also had their moment of glory. They qualified without playing as Asia's representatives on the withdrawal of Japan.

3rd World Cup France 1938 Facts

Their only World Cup match was in the first round against Hungary on June 5, 1938. Hungary 6 Dutch East Indies 0.

Individual World Cup scoring records were established in round one by Leonidas da Silva (Brazil) and Ernst Willimowski (Poland), who each notched four. Gustav Wetterstrom (Sweden) also scored four in the second-round slaughter of Cuba.

Leonidas's four came at muddy Strasbourg in a crazy 6-5 defeat of Poland, as also did Willimowski's quartet. Romev got Brazil's winner in extra time.

Poland sent Brazil a good-luck telegram for the rest of the tournament after their first finals appearance.

Brazil's quarter-final 1-1 draw against Czechoslovakia at Bordeaux was marred by three sendings-off, Zeze Procopio and Arthur Machado (Brazil) and Riha (Czechoslovakia).

The goalkeeper Planicka, Czech captain in the Final of 1934, had a broken arm and Nejedly, his team-mate in Rome, suffered a broken leg.

Brazil made nine team changes for the replay to win 2-1 and reach the last four.

Leonidas, known as the 'Black Diamond', was top scorer for the 1938 finals with eight, scoring in all his games, including two in the third-place play-off with Sweden.

Amazingly, Brazil manager Ademar Pimenta rested Leonidas for the semi-final against Italy, to save him for the Final. Italy won 2-1.

Hungary were worthy finalists with 13 goals from three games, seven of these from the second-top scorer of the finals, Gyula Szengeller.

Italy also reached the Final with three straight wins and kept the World Cup for 12 years with a 4-2 win at the Stade Colombes. Gino Colaussi and Silvio Piola each scored twice.

Italy's winning team on June 19, 1938: Olivieri; Foni, Rava; Serantoni, Andreolo, Locatelli; Biavati, Meazza (capt), Piola, Ferrari, Colaussi.

Hungary: Szabo; Polgar, Biro; Szalay, Szucs, Lazar; Sas, Vincze, Sarosi (capt), Szengeller, Titkos.

The forwards Giuseppe Meazza and Giovanni Ferrari were the only two Italian players to have won Final medals in 1934 and 1938.

The 18 matches produced 84 goals, with only Holland and Dutch East Indies failing to contribute to the total.

Hungary scored most with 15, and the fastest goalscorer was Arne Nyberg for Sweden in 35 seconds in a semi-final against Hungary, who then won 5-1.

The Pre-War Years

Highs and Lows of the first three World Cups

The Pre-War Years Facts

Twenty-seven nations competed in a grand total of 53 matches.

Most games were played by Italy (9), followed by Brazil and Czechoslovakia (7 each), Argentina, France, Germany and Hungary (6 each).

Least overworked were the players from Dutch East Indies, Egypt, Norway and Poland (one game each).

Only four countries played in all three pre-World War Two Finals. They were Belgium, Brazil, France and Romania.

Italy went through the 1934 and 1938 finals unbeaten. In all, they played nine times, scoring 23 goals and conceding only eight.

Vittorio Pozzo was Italy's winning manager in 1934 and 1938. No other manager since has won more than once.

The biggest pre-war win was achieved by Hungary on March 25, 1938, in Budapest where they beat Greece 11-1 in a qualifier.

The World Cup Final referees of the Thirties came from: 1930 Belgium (Langenus), 1934 Sweden (Eklind), 1938 France (Capdeville).

Argentina (6 matches): 1930, beat France, Mexico, Chile, USA, lost to Uruguay; 1934, lost to Sweden.

Austria (3 matches): 1934, beat France, Hungary, lost to Italy.

Belgium (4 matches): 1930, lost to the USA, Paraguay; 1934, lost to Germany; 1938, lost to France.

Bolivia (2 matches): 1930, lost to Yugoslavia, Brazil.

Brazil (7 matches): 1930, beat Bolivia, lost to Yugoslavia; 1934, lost to Spain; 1938, beat Poland, Czechoslovakia, drew with Czechoslovakia, lost to Italy.

Chile (3 matches): 1930, beat Mexico, France, lost to Argentina.

Cuba (3 matches): 1938, beat Romania, drew with Romania, lost to Sweden.

Czechoslovakia (7 matches): 1934, beat Romania, Switzerland, Germany, lost to Italy; 1938, beat Holland, drew with Brazil, lost to Brazil.

Dutch East Indies (1 match): 1938, lost to Hungary.

Egypt (1 match): 1934, lost to Hungary.

Facts

The Pre-War Years

France (6 matches): 1930, beat Mexico, lost to Argentina, Chile; 1934, lost to Austria; 1938, beat Belgium, lost to Italy.

Germany (6 matches): 1934, beat Belgium, Sweden, Austria, lost to Czechoslovakia; 1938, drew with Switzerland, lost to Switzerland.

Holland (2 matches): 1934, lost to Switzerland; 1938, lost to Czechoslovakia.

Hungary (6 matches): 1934, beat Egypt, lost to Austria; 1938, beat Dutch East Indies, Switzerland, Sweden, lost to Italy.

Italy (9 matches): 1934, beat the USA, Spain, Austria, Czechoslovakia, drew with Spain; 1938, beat Norway, France, Brazil, Hungary.

Mexico (3 matches): 1930, lost to France, Chile, Argentina.

Norway (1 match): 1938, lost to Italy.

Paraguay (2 matches): 1930, beat Belgium, lost to the USA.

Peru (2 matches): 1930, lost to Romania, Uruguay.

Poland (1 match): 1938, lost to Brazil.

Romania (5 matches): 1930, beat Peru, lost to Uruguay; 1934, lost to Czechoslovakia; 1938, drew with Cuba, lost to Cuba.

Spain (3 matches): 1934, beat Brazil, drew with Italy, lost to Italy.

Sweden (5 matches): 1934, beat Argentina, lost to Germany; 1938, beat Cuba, lost to Hungary, Brazil.

Switzerland (5 matches): 1934, beat Holland, lost to Czechoslovakia; 1938, beat Germany, drew with Germany, lost to Hungary.

Uruguay (4 matches): 1930, beat Peru, Romania, Yugoslavia, Argentina.

USA (4 matches): 1930, beat Belgium, Paraguay, lost to Argentina; 1934, lost to Italy.

Yugoslavia (3 matches): 1930, beat Brazil, Bolivia, lost to Uruguay.

Seventy goals were scored in 1930 (18 matches), 70 also in 1934 (17 matches) and 84 in 1938 (18 matches).

There was not a single draw in the 1930 Montevideo series.

The Pre-War Years Facts

Extra time was required in the 1934 series in three matches, including the Final, and one replay was necessary.

In 1938, six matches went to extra time and there were three replays.

With Italy disastrously involved in war, the World Cup was tucked away for 12 years in the vaults of a Roman bank.

Rumour had it that Jules Rimet hid the trophy under his bed when Germany overran France. This was later denied.

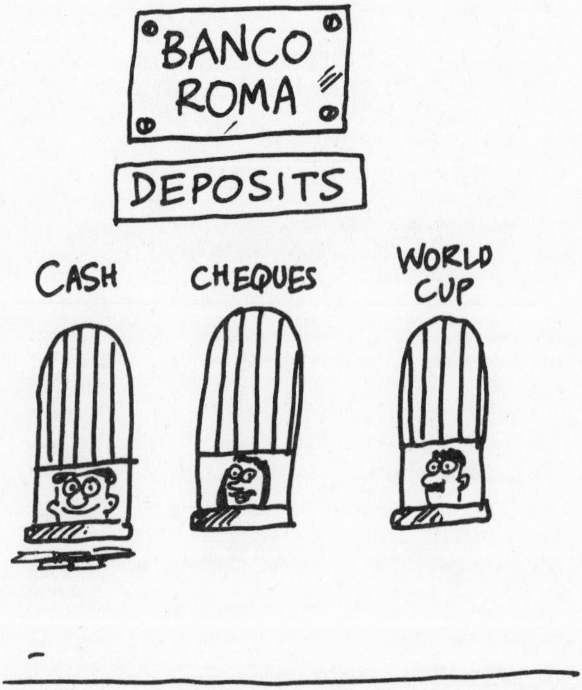

4th World Cup Brazil 1950

4th World Cup Brazil 1950 Facts

With Europe still in turmoil, FIFA not surprisingly opted at a 1948 meeting for Brazil to restore normal service.

Brazil thus created a record as the only 'ever-presents' at four World Cup finals.

Of the three previous 100 per cent participants, Belgium withdrew, Romania did not enter, while France went out in the qualifiers.

France's conquerors were Yugoslavia, their national side remarkably assembled after terrible wartime tribulations.

Yugoslavia eliminated Israel in the first World Cup match since Italy won the trophy in 1938. The date: August 18, 1949.

Yugoslavia beat Israel 11-2 on aggregate in the two-leg round one, then beat France after three games in round two.

Their two October matches each ended 1-1 and Yugoslavia won the 3-2 play-off in Italy on December 11.

FIFA's membership had increased to 68, boosted by the readmission of the four Home Countries in 1946.

Thirty-four nations entered, but nine withdrew without playing, while Scotland and Turkey pulled out after qualifying for the finals.

Germany were not invited by FIFA to participate in the 1950 series.

The nine non-players were Argentina, Austria, Belgium, Burma, Ecuador, India, Indonesia, Peru and Phillipines.

Turkey pulled out after winning their one-match group 7-0 against Syria!

Scotland qualified in Group One by finishing second in the Home International Championship, but they had already decided not to go to Brazil unless they won the title.

In the event, Scotland lost their final match 1-0 against England at Hampden Park, the goal scored by Roy Bentley.

Five of the Scottish team were from Rangers - Young, Cox, McColl, Woodburn and Waddell - with Alex Forbes of Arsenal the only 'foreigner' in the defence.

Facts

4th World Cup
Brazil 1950

Qualifying-stage eliminations were Cuba, Eire, Finland, France, Israel, Luxembourg, Northern Ireland, Portugal, Wales.

Portugal, beaten by Spain in the qualifiers, were offered Scotland's place in the finals but refused.

Patience was Portugal's virtue. Eliminated twice by Spain and also by Switzerland in qualifiers, they continued to enter every four years until finally qualifying for the 1966 finals.

The Group One results, played from October 1949 to April 1950, finished with England on maximum points.

Results: Northern Ireland 2 Scotland 8; Wales 1 England 4; Scotland 2 Wales 0; England 9 Northern Ireland 2; Wales 0 Northern Ireland 0; Scotland 0 England 1.

Jackie Milburn scored a hat-trick against Wales, the first in a World Cup match by England, and Jack Rowley hit four in the next match against the Irish.

GROUP 1 TABLE

Country	P	W	D	L	F	A	Pts
England	3	3	0	0	14	3	6
Scotland	3	2	0	1	10	3	4
Wales	3	0	1	2	1	6	1
Northern Ireland	3	0	1	2	4	17	1

Brazil as hosts and Italy the holders were exempt from qualification for the finals.

The 11 others to qualify were: Bolivia, Chile, England, Mexico, Paraguay, Spain, Sweden, Switzerland, Uruguay, USA, Yugoslavia.

Eire failed to qualify for the third successive time, although they again fought bravely in a strong Group 5 dominated by Sweden.

4th World Cup
Brazil 1950

Facts

Group 5 results were: Sweden 3 Eire 1; Eire 3 Finland 0; Finland 1 Eire 1; Eire 1 Sweden 3.

GROUP 5 TABLE

Country	P	W	D	L	F	A	Pts
Sweden	2	2	0	0	6	2	4
Eire	4	1	1	2	6	7	3
Finland	2	0	1	1	1	4	1

Teams representing Eire competed in every World Cup qualifying competition except Uruguay 1930, the Republic of Ireland team finally qualifying for the finals in 1990.

The Irish felt strongly about the injustice of the qualification group system. In 1950, Switzerland succeeded by beating Luxembourg 5-2 and 3-2, USA beat Cuba 5-2 to enter, and Yugoslavia beat Israel 6-0 and 5-2.

Because of group withdrawals, Bolivia, Chile, Uruguay and Paraguay didn't have to play in order to qualify.

Mexico were the hot-shots of the 1950 qualifiers with 17 goals from four matches, with England second on 14 from three games.

Austria were among the non-entrants, although many felt they would have been serious challengers.

Austria confirmed this opinion by beating Italy in Vienna in the holders' warm-up programme.

In fairness to Italy, it should be noted that they were badly hit by the loss of several players in the 1949 'Superga' air crash which wiped out the mighty Torino team.

The 'sudden-death' system was scrapped for the 1950 finals and a four-group system substituted.

Two pools were dominated by former champions Uruguay and Italy, but Brazil 'organised' five of their six ultimate games to be played in Rio de Janeiro.

The war and its aftermath reduced Europe's final contingent to six: England, Italy, Spain, Sweden, Switzerland and Yugoslavia.

Sweden, who came into the tournament as 1948 Olympic Games champions, were managed by a Yorkshireman, George Raynor.

Facts

4th World Cup
Brazil 1950

Two players, Alfred Bickel (Switzerland) and Erik Nilsson (Sweden), appeared in the World Cup finals of 1938 and 1950.

South America paraded five teams: Bolivia, Brazil, Chile, Paraguay and Uruguay.

The uneven nature of the groups - four in two, three in the third and only two in the fourth - clearly favoured South America.

Pool One: Brazil, Mexico, Switzerland, Yugoslavia. Pool Two: Chile, England, Spain, USA.

Pool Three: Italy, Paraguay, Sweden. Pool Four: Bolivia, Uruguay.

Brazil played the opening match at the unfinished Maracana Stadium against Mexico, after a 21-gun salute and the release of 5,000 pigeons, and won 4-0. Attendance: 81,649.

Brazil's deciding game to win the pool was against Yugoslavia, whom they beat 2-0 watched by 142,409 fans.

Yugoslavia started with 10 men against Brazil. Rajko Mitic, warming up in the dressing-room, 'headed' a wooden beam and knocked himself out.

Brazil's five 1950 World Cup games at the Maracana were watched by an astonishing total of 715,570 spectators.

The official attendance of 199,854 for the Final against Uruguay is still a world record.

England started well in Group 2 by beating Chile 2-1 in Rio.

Stan Mortensen scored England's first-ever World Cup finals goal, Wilf Mannion getting the second.

England's second match brought their first defeat. They lost 1-0 to USA at Belo Horizonte in probably the biggest shock in World Cup history.

The England team was captained by Billy Wright and at right-back was Alf Ramsey, who was due to have a better day some years later.

4th World Cup Brazil 1950 Facts

The shattered eleven: Williams; Ramsey, Aston; W Wright, L Hughes, Dickinson; Finney, Mannion, Bentley, Mortensen, Mullen.

The USA side were so convinced that they were in for a hiding that they were up most of the night before, having a party!

When the result came through in Britain, one news agency thought it was a printer's error and put it out as 10-1.

The goal came from a header in the 37th minute by a Haitian forward, Larry Gaetjens.

'Inquest' quote from Wilf Mannion: 'Bloody ridiculous. Can't we play them again tomorrow?'

England missed centre-half Neil Franklin, who had joined Bogota in Colombia, a nation not recognised by FIFA.

The American captain was a Scotsman, Eddie McIlvenny, who had been given a free transfer in 1948 by Wrexham, a Third Division club. The coach Bill Jeffrey was also a Scot!

Needing a win in their final pool match to survive, England lost to a solo headed goal by Spain's Zarra before 74,462 Rio spectators.

USA were well beaten 5-2 by Chile, for whom George Robledo, the former Newcastle forward, scored.

Robledo tells the story of being sworn at in English throughout the match by the USA centre-half. At the end of the game, George finally replied... in English.

POOL 2 TABLE

Country	P	W	D	L	F	A	Pts
Spain	3	3	0	0	6	1	6
England	3	1	0	2	2	2	2
Chile	3	1	0	2	5	6	2
USA	3	1	0	2	4	8	2

Italy lost their title in a vital 3-2 defeat by Sweden, who qualified for the Final Pool with Brazil, Spain and Uruguay.

Facts

4th World Cup
Brazil 1950

Uruguay actually qualified by beating Bolivia 8-0 in the only match of Pool 4. Juan Schiaffino scored four.

For the first and only time in World Cup history, there was no official Final as such, but Brazil v Uruguay was the final deciding match.

Brazil needed only a draw to win the Trophy but were beaten 2-1 by Uruguay, who finished with five points from three games.

The winning coach, Uruguayan as in 1930, was Juan Lopez.

The 'Final' was refereed by an Englishman, George Reader.

Uruguay's record in their first two World Cup campaigns was:

	P	W	D	L	F	A	Pts
1930:	4	4	0	0	15	3	8
1950:	5	4	1	0	17	6	9

Spain were the only team to deny Uruguay (2-2 in the Final Pool).

Third place went to Sweden, despite a 7-1 hammering from Brazil.

Four goals in this match came from Ademir Marques de Menezes, the Brazilian finishing top scorer of the 1950 series with seven.

Second-placed goalscorers were Basora (Spain) and Schiaffino (Uruguay) with five each, but star of the 'Final' was Alcides Edgardo Ghiggia.

Ghiggia scored Uruguay's winner 10 minutes from time. The classy right-winger totalled four in the series.

Uruguay's winning team: Maspoli; Gonzales, Tejera; Gambetta, Varela (capt), Andrade; Ghiggia, Perez, Miguez, Schiaffino, Moran.

Brazil: Barbosa; Augusto (capt), Juvenal; Bauer, Danilo, Bigode; Friaca, Zizinho, Ademir, Jair, Chico.

One final happy statistic: no-one was sent off for the first time in four series.

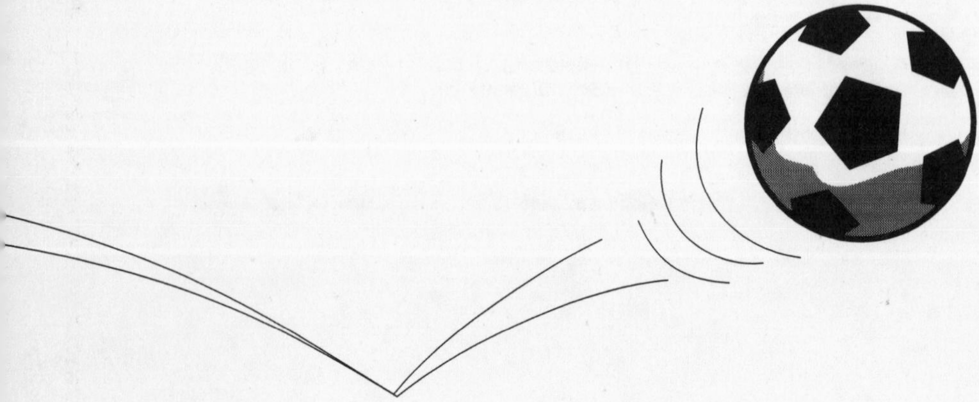

5th World Cup Switzerland 1954

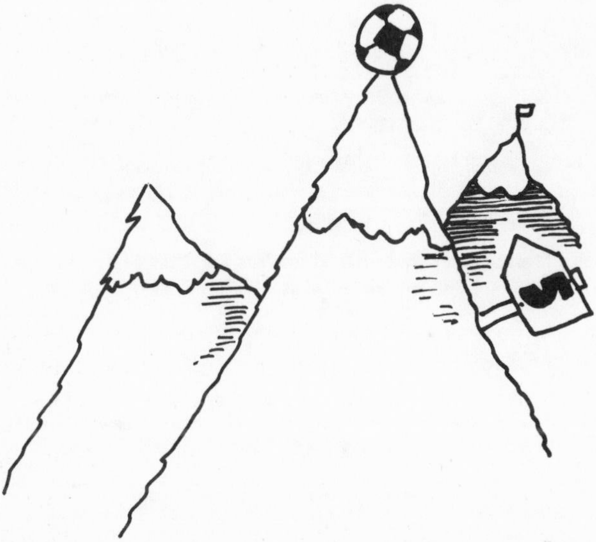

5th World Cup Switzerland 1954 Facts

FIFA decided on Switzerland as the venue for the 50th anniversary of its formation.

The choice was made at the 1946 Congress, at the same time as Brazil was favoured for the 1950 finals.

Thirty-eight nations from the 80 FIFA membership entered for the 1954 tournament.

China and Poland withdrew without playing in the qualifying competition.

Switzerland as hosts and champions Uruguay were exempt from the 13 qualifying groups.

Venues for the finals were Basle, Berne, Geneva, Lausanne, Lugano, Zurich.

The 16 qualifiers for the finals were in four pools, but two seeds in each section meant each team played only twice, the seeds not meeting.

The top two in each pool then took part in a knockout tournament from quarter-finals onwards.

The pools were (seeds named first and second each time): Pool One: Brazil, France, Mexico, Yugoslavia. Pool Two: Hungary, Turkey, South Korea, West Germany. Pool Three: Austria, Uruguay, Czechoslovakia, Scotland. Pool Four: England, Italy, Belgium, Switzerland.

Twenty were eliminated from the qualifiers: Bulgaria, Chile, Egypt, Eire, Finland, Greece, Haiti, Israel, Japan, Luxembourg, Northern Ireland, Norway, Paraguay, Portugal, Romania, Saar, Spain, Sweden, USA, Wales

There was a limited entry from behind the Iron Curtain and Germany partly reappeared as West Germany, after last competing in 1938.

They easily qualified against Norway and Saar and went on to win the World Cup in swashbuckling manner.

Their eventual opponents, Olympic 1952 champions Hungary, had a free run to the last 16 when Poland withdrew, and captivated the world with their new-style fluency on the way to the Final with West Germany.

Due largely to Hungary who amazingly netted 27 times, goals reached a record for World Cup finals.

Twenty games produced 140 goals, an average of 5.38 per match, with 26 in the quarter-finals.

The fastest goal came in two minutes from Mamat Suat of Turkey against West Germany.

Facts

5th World Cup
Switzerland 1954

Oddly, the Germans then hit the Turks for 11 in two group games.

Seven hat-tricks were scored in the 1954 finals, the sum total for the two previous finals.

Five matches in Group 2 yielded an incredible total of 41 goals.

England had a 'preview' of Hungary's potential in 1953 at Wembley, losing 6-3, and the following year in Budapest, crushed 7-1.

Their genius and inspirational captain, Ferenc Puskas, was an Army officer and was nicknamed 'The Galloping Major'.

Hungary revelled in the name of the Magnificent Magyars.

The four Home Countries again competed to produce two qualifiers, England and Scotland.

Results: Northern Ireland 1 Scotland 3; Wales 1 England 4; Scotland 3 Wales 3; England 3 Northern Ireland 1; Wales 1 Northern Ireland 2; Scotland 2 England 4.

GROUP 3 TABLE

Country	P	W	D	L	F	A	Pts
England	3	3	0	0	11	4	6
Scotland	3	1	1	1	8	8	3
Northern Ireland	3	1	0	2	4	7	2
Wales	3	0	1	2	5	9	1

Walter Winterbottom was England manager for his second World Cup and retained the job in the 1958 and 1962 series.

England's captain was Billy Wright of Wolves, and on the right wing was Stanley Matthews in his 39th year.

Scotland were managed by Andy Beattie in their first World Cup finals match, but he resigned after a dispute with team officials following a 1-0 defeat by seeded Austria.

5th World Cup Switzerland 1954 Facts

Austria had qualified by beating Portugal 9-0 and eventually finished third to West Germany and Hungary.

The Scots, dispirited by Beattie's departure, were slaughtered 7-0 by Uruguay.

Scotland's team strength was below par from the tournament's outset when Rangers withheld their players in preference to a club tour.

France in Pool One were the only seeds to be eliminated before the quarter-final knockout stage.

The only non-seeds to reach the last eight were Yugoslavia, who finished equal on points with Brazil in Group 1.

Yugoslavia's young outside-right Milutinovic scored the only goal to beat France.

Yugoslavia's other group match, with Brazil, ended 1-1 after extra time.

Of the 17 group games, only one other tie, between England and Belgium, required extra time.

Group 2 was dominated by Hungary. They beat South Korea 7-0 and West Germany 8-3, with Sandor Kocsis scoring seven in two games.

Kocsis eventually finished top scorer of the 1954 finals with 11 goals.

Kocsis was called 'Golden Head' and made the point with two headed goals in extra time in the semi-final with Uruguay.

Uruguay's defeat by Hungary in the semi-finals ended an unbeaten record of 11 games since the World Cup started.

West Germany coach Sepp Herberger craftily fielded a near all-reserve team against Hungary, aiming to lose to ensure an easier quarter-final tie.

The scheme worked, they beat Turkey 7-2 in a group play-off, then moved smoothly to the Final by beating Yugoslavia 2-0 and Austria 6-1.

England had an extra-time group thriller with Belgium, ending 4-4, with England scoring five!

Ivor Broadis and Nat Lofthouse each scored twice - and Portsmouth's Jimmy Dickinson's own-goal was Belgium's fourth.

Goals by Wolves' pair Dennis Wilshaw and Jimmy Mullen beat Switzerland 2-0 to qualify England for the last eight.

Facts

5th World Cup Switzerland 1954

England departed in the quarter-finals 4-2 to Uruguay, with goals by Lofthouse and Finney as consolation.

Austria set up a record goals aggregate with Switzerland in their quarter-final, winning 7-5.

In the first half, the Austrians scored five in a seven-minute spell.

The Swiss, having earlier beaten Italy 2-1 in a group match, watched open-mouthed as the controversial Brazilian referee Mario Viani ran for his life, pursued by angry Italian players.

Referee Arthur Ellis, a Yorkshireman, was in charge of the infamous quarter-final 'Battle of Berne' between Hungary and Brazil.

Jozsef Bozsik (Hungary) and Nilton Santos (Brazil) were sent off for fighting, and Humberto Tozzi (Brazil) was later dismissed for foul play.

Tozzi begged to the referee on his knees to be allowed to stay, but in vain and he left in tears.

Two penalties were converted, one each side, and 42 free kicks were awarded before Hungary won 4-2.

After the match, the Brazilian team invaded the Hungary dressing-room and many players on both sides were injured in an almighty punch-up.

The Final in Berne on July 4, 1954, before 55,000 spectators was won 3-2 by West Germany, after each side scored twice in the first 16 minutes.

West Germany scored seven minutes from time through Helmut Rahn, to the delight of nearly 30,000 travelling fans.

5th World Cup Switzerland 1954 Facts

The teams were: West Germany: Turek; Posipal, Kohlmeyer, Eckel, Liebrich, Mai, Rahn, Morlock, O. Walter, F. Walter (capt), Schaefer.

Hungary: Grosics; Buzansky, Lantos, Bozsik, Lorant, Zakarias, Czibor, Kocsis, Hidegkuti, Puskas (capt), J. Toth.

The Germans' all-round fire power was reflected in the goalscorers' list, in which they had four in the top nine: Max Morlock (6), Hans Schaefer, Ottmar Walter and Helmut Rahn (4 each).

For the second successive Final, an Englishman, Bill Ling from Cambridgeshire, was referee.

Hungary's manager Gustav Sebes and his team were jeered in Budapest on their return and Sebes had his house windows smashed.

Austria deservedly won the third-place play-off, Ernst Ocwirk scoring the final goal in the 3-1 defeat of Uruguay.

The Austria-Uruguay play-off was the 100th World Cup match.

A sign of the world ahead was the appearance of TV cameras for the first time.

There was limited TV coverage and Scottish viewers had mixed feelings about their first live match from Basle on June 19, 1954. Result: Uruguay 7, Scotland 0.

Final note for commentators: The longest surname of any footballer in World Cup finals came from Turkey in 1954... Lefter Kucukandonyadis.

6th World Cup Sweden 1958

6th World Cup Sweden 1958 Facts

Sweden's year was unique in that countless millions watched the series for the first time through worldwide television.

The finals venue was a popular choice by FIFA, as Sweden now accepted professionalism after losing the heart of their purely amateur Olympic-winning side of 1948.

Their manager was still George Raynor, the Yorkshireman who led them to third place in Brazil eight years earlier.

Sweden in 1950 had put paid to the holders Italy 3-2 in a vital group match.

Italy's startling decline dated from there. In 1954, they were denied a quarter-final place by Switzerland.

The twice-champions' demise was complete on January 5, 1958, when they failed to qualify for the finals for the first time - beaten 2-1 by Northern Ireland.

Two more lean years, 1962 and 1966, were to follow before the Italians' dramatic recovery took them to the Mexico Final with Brazil in 1970.

Coincidentally, twice-champions Uruguay went into similar decline, ultimately to sweep back to the 1970 finals.

Also like Italy, Uruguay were surprisingly eliminated in a qualifying group.

In the vital match on July 14, 1957, they were thrashed by Paraguay 5-0.

Yet another major qualifying scalp was the powerful Spanish side in European Group 9, won by Scotland.

Spain were beaten 4-2 at Hampden Park on May 8, 1957, but their crucial lapse was being held to a draw by Switzerland.

This was Switzerland's only point in four games, four years after hosting the finals and reaching the quarter-final stage.

Little Blackpool forward Jackie Mudie recorded Scotland's first World Cup hat-trick in the Hampden defeat of Spain.

The war clouds had finally dispersed by 1958, so 53 nations entered from far and wide.

The only problems were in the Afro-Asian Group, comprising four sub-groups with obvious political and religious undertones, and with a final farcical outcome.

Facts

6th World Cup
Sweden 1958

Sub-Group 1: Formosa China withdrew; Indonesia won a three-match series with Nationalist China on goal average ... then withdrew.

Sub-Group 2: Turkey withdrew, so their only opponents, Israel, qualified for the Group Final.

Sub-Group 3: Cyprus withdrew, so only opponents Egypt qualified for the Group Final ... and withdrew.

Sub-Group 4: Two games: Sudan 1 Syria 0; Syria 1 Sudan 1. So Sudan qualified for the Group Final... and withdrew.

Now the pickle! There was one other finalist, Israel, hence the withdrawal of Muslim countries Indonesia, Turkey, Egypt and Sudan.

The solution? FIFA sent for Wales, a mostly religious nation, but free-thinking.

Wales who had already been eliminated in a hard group, were nominated to meet Israel and duly won twice, 2-0.

Wales thereby became proud representatives of Africa and Asia in the 1958 finals - their one and only appearance.

There were three other groups: Central & North America, South America and Europe, the last-named accounting for nine qualifiers.

Central & North America qualifiers were Mexico, who beat Costa Rica in the Group Final.

Failing to qualify were Curacao, Guatemala, Canada and USA, with the States conceding 13 goals to Mexico in two Games. Their 1950 glory days were long since gone!

Three finalists came from South America - Brazil, Argentina and Paraguay.

South American failures were Peru, Chile, Bolivia, Uruguay and Colombia.

Uruguay had the chance to get back in by an offer to play Israel for the final qualifying place. They declined, much to Wales' delight.

Brazil first tried out on April 14, 1957, what was a completely revolutionary formation of 4-2-4 against Peru in the qualifying round.

They drew 1-1 and scraped through eight days later by a single goal.

6th World Cup Sweden 1958 Facts

Brazil were on their way to making World Cup history, with the 17-year-old genius Pele in the squad.

Pele was years later to coin the immortal phrase in describing football as 'the beautiful game'.

Nine European Group qualifiers were England, France, Hungary, Czechoslovakia, Austria, Soviet Union, Yugoslavia, Northern Ireland, Scotland.

The hosts Sweden and holders West Germany were exempt from the qualifying rounds.

For the first and only time, all four Home Countries qualified for the finals in Sweden.

Most of the countries involved in the 1954 tournament had complained about allowing two qualifiers from the Home Internationals.

The rules were revised, FIFA putting England, Northern Ireland, Scotland and Wales in different qualifying groups.

Wales came through by the lucky-break Israel match but the three others were worthy group leaders.

England, in Group 1, convincingly eliminated Eire and Denmark, winning three and drawing 1-1 in the Republic, for a goal average of 15-5.

Scotland headed Group 9 with three wins out of four against Switzerland and Spain.

Northern Ireland, captained by Danny Blanchflower and managed by Peter Doherty, put out Italy and Portugal in Group 8.

The Irish, who thus qualified for the finals for the first time, were to repeat the achievement in 1982 and 1986.

Their goalkeeper, Harry Gregg, had survived the Manchester United air crash at Munich on February 6, 1958.

The finals were in four pools of four, as in Switzerland, but there were no seeds, each country playing three games before the eight-team knockout stage.

Teams level on points for second place in the pools had to have a play-off, rather than goal average being decisive.

In the event, three of the pools required play-offs and all were to involve Home Countries.

Facts

6th World Cup
Sweden 1958

Ironically, two of these resulted in a 'reversal' of goal-average figures and favoured lucky Wales and Northern Ireland.

The third match was England v Soviet Union, each with three points and identical 4-4 goals columns. England went out 1-0.

The World Cup 1958 brought an unexpected windfall for Swedish tour operators when FIFA approved 11 venues.

This remained the highest number of grounds for finals until Spain's record total of 14 in 1982.

The 1958 venues: Boras, Eskilstuna, Gothenburg, Halmstad, Helsingborg, Malmo, Norrkoping, Orebro, Sandviken, Stockholm, Vasteras.

The pools were: Pool One: Argentina, Czechoslovakia, Northern Ireland, West Germany. Pool Two: France, Paraguay, Scotland, Yugoslavia. Pool Three: Hungary, Mexico, Sweden, Wales. Pool Four: Austria, Brazil, England, the USSR.

Northern Ireland had probably the toughest pool, with 1954 winners West Germany and 1962 finalists-to-be Czechoslovakia. This after removing twice-champions Italy in the qualifiers.

Wee Wilbur Cush scored Northern Ireland's first goal in a finals series on June 8, 1958, to beat the Czechs 1-0 at Halmstad.

Cush earned 26 Irish caps over a period of 12 years while playing with Glenavon, Leeds and Portadown.

Three days later, the Irish lost 3-1 to Argentina, who were reappearing in the World Cup for the first time since 1934.

Four days later, Northern Ireland qualified for a play-off by holding champions West Germany to a 2-2 draw at Malmo, Peter McParland scoring both their goals.

Two days later, McParland was again the Irish hero in the play-off, scoring twice - the second in extra time - to shock the Czechs 2-1.

McParland, whose nine-year international career produced 34 caps, ended as top scorer of Pool One with five goals, one ahead of Germany's Helmut Rahn.

McParland had thrilled Wembley fans the previous spring by scoring both goals from the left-wing in Aston Villa's 2-1 FA Cup Final defeat of Manchester United.

6th World Cup Sweden 1958 Facts

Injuries and fatigue finally took toll of the brave Irish. They had a 200-mile coach journey to meet France in the quarter-finals at Norrkoping and lost 4-0.

Northern Ireland had thus played five World Cup matches in only 12 days. Their next appearance was Spain in 1982.

A distinguished member of the Irish team was Billy Bingham, who won 56 caps and twice became manager of Northern Ireland, in 1968 and 1980.

He was in charge when they qualified for the finals in 1982 and 1986.

Group Two signalled the goalscoring talent of Just Fontaine, Moroccan-born inside-forward with France. He scored six in three games, including a hat-trick in the 7-3 slaughter of Paraguay.

Fontaine, who played for Nice and Reims, went on to set an all-time World Cup scoring record of thirteen in the series.

His forward colleague, Raymond Kopa, who returned from Real Madrid to partner Fontaine at Reims, was European Footballer of the Year in 1959.

Scotland drew their first match 1-1 with Yugoslavia to win their first-ever World Cup point.

The honour of scoring the first goal for Scotland in the World Cup finals went to Murray of Hearts.

The Scots failed by one-goal margins to Paraguay and France and finished bottom of the group.

Facts

6th World Cup
Sweden 1958

Scotland had thus finished last of their group in their only two finals, at that stage 1954 and 1958, and stayed out for a further 16 years.

Wales worked wonders in Group Three in a period of 10 days to qualify for a quarter-final place.

They drew all three group games - against Hungary (1-1), Mexico (1-1) and Sweden (0-0) - and beat Hungary 2-1 in a second-place play-off.

The Wales-Hungary play-off was bitterly contested, Ferenc Sipos of Hungary being sent off.

Two other sendings-off in the 1958 finals were Titus Bubernik of Czechoslovakia (v Northern Ireland) and Erich Juskoviak of West Germany in the semi-final with Sweden.

Hungary were without many of their 1954 stars, including Puskas and Kocsis, who left the country after the 1956 uprising.

Kocsis scored 75 goals in 68 matches for Hungary, having made his debut aged 19. He joined Barcelona after the Revolution.

Puskas scored 83 goals in 84 games for Hungary, then joined Real Madrid for eight years, winning five Spanish League titles.

Wales' group goalscorers were Ivor Allchurch, Terry Medwin and the great John Charles, equally brilliant at centre-half and centre-forward.

John Charles was playing with Juventus, who signed him from Leeds for £65,000 in June, 1957.

Charles was the first British player to be transferred to a foreign club.

Known as the 'Gentle Giant', he was never sent off or even cautioned in a first-class career lasting 17 years.

John Charles missed the quarter-final tie with Brazil, but his brother Mel performed nobly at centre-half.

Brazil got the only goal in the 65th minute from a Pele shot which was cruelly deflected past goalkeeper Jack Kelsey.

England failed to reach the quarter-finals despite being the only team that Brazil did not beat. Result: 0-0.

This was the only time since the World Cup began that Brazil had failed to score in a finals series match.

6th World Cup Sweden 1958 Facts

Brazil's 4-2-4 formation was counteracted by a defensive scheme devised by Bill Nicholson, Tottenham coach at the time and assistant to England manager Walter Winterbottom.

The England team included Fulham team-mates Johnny Haynes and Bobby Robson.

Haynes was to become the first £100 per week footballer in Britain and Robson later managed England in the World Cup.

England were greatly fancied for the World Cup in the international run-up, beating Brazil 4-2 at Wembley and West Germany 3-1 in Berlin in 1956.

They also trounced France 4-0 at Wembley in 1957, Bobby Robson scoring twice, yet France went on to take World Cup 1958 third place by beating West Germany 6-3.

Those pre-1958 triumphs by England were greatly helped by Manchester United players who were to lose their lives in the Munich air crash.

Four of those who perished had been honoured by England: Roger Byrne (33 caps), Tommy Taylor (19), Duncan Edwards (18) and David Pegg (1).

Duncan Edwards made his first England appearance in 1955 to become the youngest player this century to win a full England cap, aged 18 years 183 days.

Bobby Charlton, Munich survivor, once said he would choose above all Duncan Edwards to be with him if he had to play for his own life.

Northern Ireland were also affected by the Munich disaster, losing the services of Jackie Blanchflower, brother of Danny. He survived the crash but never played first-class football again.

Jackie went on to become one of the most sought and talented after-dinner speakers on the sporting circuit.

Facts

6th World Cup
Sweden 1958

England drew all three group matches but lost to the USSR 1-0 in a play-off.

Their first match with the Russians, a 2-2 draw, was marred by the loss through injury for the rest of the finals of Tom Finney, although his penalty goal forced the play-off.

England were desperately unlucky in their play-off, Peter Brabrook twice hitting the Russian goalposts.

Later in the year, England again played the Soviet Union at Wembley, winning 5-0, three of the goals being scored by Johnny Haynes.

The Home Countries' Final Table

Country	P	W	D	L	F	A	PTS
Wales	5	1	3	1	4	4	5
Northern Ireland	5	2	1	2	6	10	5
England	4	0	3	1	4	5	3
Scotland	3	0	1	2	4	6	1

Sweden surprised their own fans by beating Soviet Union 2-0 to join Brazil, France and West Germany in the semi-finals.

Now professional, Sweden welcomed back from Italy nearly half a side, including stars Liedholm, Gren and Hamrin.

Winger Kurt Hamrin, two-goal hero of the 2-1 group defeat of Hungary, scored again to beat the Russians.

He was again on the mark to beat West Germany 3-1 in the semi-final in Gothenburg.

The Germans were lucky to reach the semi-finals with a single goal against Yugoslavia, scored by their two-goal marksman of the 1954 Final, Helmut Rahn.

Brazil were relentless in Stockholm, where they beat France 5-2 in the other semi-final and Sweden in the Final, 5-2 again.

Pele stole the limelight with a hat-trick against France and two goals in the Final.

Also on the mark for Brazil in the Final were Vava (2) and Zagalo.

Outside-left Mario Zagalo played in the 1958 and 1962 Finals and also managed Brazil in 1970. All three were winners.

6th World Cup Sweden 1958 Facts

Consolation for Fontaine came in the third-place match between France and West Germany, in which he scored four, thus netting in every match and putting the seal on his record scoring tally in the finals.

France won the third spot in a devastating 6-3 win, all nine goals coming in the second half.

Rahn scored again for the Germans to finish equal second with six goals in the tournament.

Sharing second place with six goals was a 17-year-old boy from Brazil, Edson Arantes do Nascimento. Pele for short ... but for a very long time!

Argentina, later to appear in three Finals, had a stony reception back home. They were bombarded with stones by fans in recognition of their bottom group placing.

Although Argentina beat Northern Ireland, they lost 6-1 to the Czechs. Whereupon the Irish beat the Czechs 2-1 in a play-off!

The French referee, M.Guigue, was in charge of the following Final teams:

Brazil: Gilmar; D. Santos, N. Santos, Zito, Bellini (capt), Orlando, Garrincha, Didi, Vava, Pele, Zagalo.

Sweden: Svensson; Bergmark, Axbom, Boerjesson, Gustavsson, Parling, Hamrin, Gren, Simonsson, Liedholm (capt), Skoglund.

From the Fifties

Into the Sunlight… 4–2–4 and The Beautiful Game

From the Fifties Facts

Twenty-six nations competed in the World Cup 1950, 1954 and 1958 finals, for a total of 165 matches.

More than three times as many matches were played in the Fifties than in the Thirties.

Most games were played by Brazil (15), followed by West Germany (12), Sweden (11), England and Yugoslavia (10 each), Hungary and Uruguay (9 each).

Bottom of the list came Belgium and South Korea (2 each) and beleaguered Bolivia, slaughtered 8-0 by Uruguay in their only Fifties finals.

Mexico failed to win in eight finals, their only point coming from the 1958 draw with Wales.

England's tally of wins from 10 matches in three finals was only two, against Chile and Switzerland.

Brazil topped the Fifties 'wins table' with 10, losing twice only, to Uruguay and Hungary.

West Germany came second with seven victories in only two Fifties finals.

Facts From the Fifties

Argentina (3 matches): 1958, beat Northern Ireland, lost to West Germany, Czechoslovakia.

Austria (7 matches): 1954, beat Scotland, Czechoslovakia, Switzerland, lost to West Germany; 1958, drew with England, lost to Brazil, USSR.

Belgium (2 matches): 1954, drew with England, lost to Italy.

Bolivia (1 match): 1950, lost to Uruguay.

Brazil (15 matches): 1950, beat Mexico, Yugoslavia, Sweden, Spain, drew with Switzerland, lost to Uruguay; 1954, beat Mexico, drew with Yugoslavia, lost to Hungary; 1958, beat Austria, USSR, Wales, France, Sweden, drew with England.

Chile (3 matches): 1950, beat USA, lost to England, Spain.

Czechoslovakia (6 matches): 1954, lost to Uruguay, Austria; 1958, beat Argentina, drew with West Germany, lost to Northern Ireland twice.

England (10 matches): 1950, beat Chile, lost to USA, Spain; 1954, beat Switzerland, drew with Belgium, lost to Uruguay; 1958, drew with USSR, Brazil, Austria, lost to USSR.

France (8 matches): 1954, beat Mexico, lost to Yugoslavia; 1958, beat Paraguay, Scotland, Northern Ireland, West Germany, lost to Yugoslavia, Brazil.

Hungary (9 matches): 1954, beat South Korea, West Germany, Brazil, Uruguay, lost to West Germany; 1958, beat Mexico, drew with Wales, lost to Sweden, Wales.

Italy (5 matches): 1950, beat Paraguay, lost to Sweden; 1954, beat Belgium, lost to Switzerland twice.

Mexico (8 matches): 1950, lost to Brazil, Yugoslavia, Switzerland; 1954, lost to Brazil, France; 1958, drew with Wales, lost to Sweden, Hungary.

Northern Ireland (5 matches): 1958, beat Czechoslovakia twice, drew with West Germany, lost to Argentina, France.

Paraguay (5 matches): 1950, drew with Sweden, lost to Italy; 1958, beat Scotland, drew with Yugoslavia, lost to France.

Scotland (5 matches): 1954, lost to Austria, Uruguay; 1958, drew with Yugoslavia, lost to Paraguay, France.

South Korea (2 matches): 1954, lost to Hungary, Turkey.

Soviet Union (5 matches): 1958, beat Austria, England, drew with England, lost to Brazil, Sweden.

From the Fifties Facts

Spain (6 matches): 1950, beat USA, Chile, England, drew with Uruguay, lost to Brazil, Sweden.

Sweden (11 matches): 1950, beat Italy, Spain, drew with Paraguay, lost to Brazil, Uruguay; 1958, beat Mexico, Hungary, USSR, West Germany, drew with Wales, lost to Brazil.

Switzerland (7 matches): 1950, beat Mexico, drew with Brazil, lost to Yugoslavia; 1954, beat Italy twice, lost to England, Austria.

Turkey (3 matches): 1954, beat South Korea, lost to West Germany twice.

Uruguay (9 matches): 1950, beat Bolivia, Sweden, Brazil, drew with Spain; 1954, beat Czechoslovakia, Scotland, England, lost to Hungary, Austria.

USA (3 matches): 1950, beat England, lost to Spain, Chile.

Wales (5 matches): 1958, beat Hungary, drew with Hungary, Mexico, Sweden, lost to Brazil.

West Germany (12 matches): 1954, beat Turkey twice, Yugoslavia, Austria, Hungary, lost to Hungary; 1958, beat Argentina, Yugoslavia, drew with Czechoslovakia, Northern Ireland, lost to Sweden, France.

Yugoslavia (10 matches): 1950, beat Switzerland, Mexico, lost to Brazil; 1954, beat France, drew with Brazil, lost to West Germany; 1958, beat France, drew with Scotland, Paraguay, lost to West Germany.

Biggest win of the Fifties was recorded by Soviet Union in Helsinki on August 15, 1958, when they beat Finland 10-0 in a qualifier.

Biggest finals win of the Fifties was Hungary's 9-0 defeat of South Korea in Zurich.

This finals win, on June 17, 1954, remained unsurpassed for 28 years.

Fifties World Cup Final referees came from: 1950 England (Reader), 1954 (Ling), 1958 France (Guigue).

7th World Cup
Chile 1962

7th World Cup Chile 1962 Facts

Chile, who played in the first World Cup of 1930, were surprise hosts for 1962, even though FIFA made the decision six years earlier.

Serious thought was given to a change of host when Chile was devastated by an earthquake which claimed 5,000 victims in May 1960.

Argentina, unsuccessful original bidders, thought they would take over but Chile amazingly went ahead *because* of the 'quake!

Chilean FA president Carlos Dittborn pleaded successfully: 'Without the World Cup now, we have nothing.'

Carlos never lived to enjoy his coup. He died weeks before Chile opened the series in Santiago on May 30 against Switzerland.

Sixty-five thousand fans observed one minute's silence before the game, a tribute made even more poignant as Dittborn's two young sons held aloft the two teams' flags.

His memory lives on in Arica, his hometown, whose stadium now bears his name.

Fifty-six nations originally entered and all but Brazil (holders) and hosts Chile were drawn in the qualifying groups.

Six withdrew without participating: Austria, Canada, Egypt, Indonesia, Romania, Sudan.

All four Home Countries and Eire competed but only England qualified for the finals.

England had an easy time in Group 6 against Portugal and Luxembourg, dropping one point from four games for a goals return of 16-2.

Luxembourg were demolished 9-0 in the opening match on October 19, 1960, and 4-1 at Highbury 11 months later.

Jimmy Greaves and Bobby Charlton each scored three in the first match, Charlton also netting two in the Highbury game in Greaves' absence.

The first Luxembourg match came during a prolific scoring sequence by Greaves, in which he scored 11 in five consecutive winning games for England.

He scored two against Northern Ireland (5-2), three v Luxembourg (9-0), one v Spain (4-2), two v Wales (5-1) and three v Scotland (9-3).

Greaves missed the next England match at home to Mexico, so Bobby Charlton scored three in an 8-0 win!

Facts

7th World Cup
Chile 1962

Portugal also hammered Luxembourg 6-0 but lost the return in the Grand Duchy 4-2.

England were held 1-1 in Lisbon, only five weeks after the famous 9-3 Wembley slaughter of Scotland in the annual happy gathering. Finally, England won 2-1 in what was already a lost-cause match for Portugal.

Scotland were eliminated after three tough games with Czechoslovakia, losing 4-2 after extra time in a play-off on a neutral Belgian pitch, the Heysel Stadium in Brussels, on November 29, 1961.

Play-offs instead of goal difference applied in the eliminators, but the reverse applied in the finals to decide ties.

Scotland had lost 4-0 to the Czechs in Bratislava in May 1961, but came back at Hampden in September with a 3-2 victory.

Ian St John (Liverpool) got the first goal, followed by a couple from Denis Law, who was then with Torino.

Scotland deserved a better fate, as Czechoslovakia went on to the 1962 Final.

Third team in Scotland's group were Eire, who finished pointless with 17 goals conceded in four games. The Scots beat them 4-1 and 3-0.

Back from the dizzy heights of 1958 and Swedish quarter-final glory, Northern Ireland and Wales went out fighting in the qualifying competition.

Wales emerged from a group involving six nations with home-and-away clashes with Spain in April and May 1961, resulting 1-2 and 1-1.

Wales then watched enviously as Spain clinched a finals place by twice beating Morocco in the group decider.

Wales were never again to qualify for the finals, in fact for the rest of the Twentieth Century.

Northern Ireland, who were to hit the big time with two more World Cup finals appearances this century, were considered to be virtual non-starters in 1962.

They were drawn in Qualifying Group 3 against the powerful West German team coached by Sepp Herberger, and by Greece.

West Germany finished with a 100 per cent record, but the fighting Irish suffered honourable defeats against them, 3-4 in Belfast and 1-2 in Berlin.

Northern Ireland lost surprisingly in Greece 2-1 to finish P4 W1 D0 L3 F7 A8 Pts2.

7th World Cup Chile 1962 Facts

The Irish consoled themselves by drawing at Wembley 1-1 to help in denying England the British Championship in the run-up to Chile.

Consolation for Scotland came in similar form. They beat England 2-0 at Hampden Park in 1962 and 2-1 at Wembley the following year, both goals coming from Jim Baxter, to win the British Championship twice with maximum points.

Shock of the 1962 Qualifying Competition was the elimination of the 1958 hosts and Finalists Sweden.

Sweden were unfortunate to be drawn in the toughest European group which also included Switzerland, 1954 hosts and quarter-finalists, and Belgium.

The Belgians were whipping boys, beaten in all four games, but the Swedes went down narrowly after three bitter battles with the Swiss.

After a 4-0 Swiss miss in Sweden in May 1961, Switzerland came back 3-2 at home five months later to force a decider.

The play-off two weeks later in West Germany resulted in a 2-1 finals passport for Switzerland.

Qualifying Groups 2 and 4 were also strong and hard-contested, with Bulgaria emerging together with Hungary for an impressive Eastern European representation alongside well-fancied Soviet Union, Yugoslavia and Czechoslovakia.

Qualifying Group 2 was won 1-0 by Bulgaria in a play-off with France in neutral Italy, on December 16, 1961.

The Bulgarians thus celebrated Christmas by qualifying for the World Cup finals for the first time - in which they were to clash with England.

Qualifying Group Four went to Hungary, with wins over East Germany (twice) and Holland, ending with a thrilling 3-3 home draw against the Dutch - thus also earning a clash with England in the finals.

South America also had strong representation in the finals, with Argentina, Uruguay and Colombia joining 'free riders' Chile and Brazil.

Top scorers in the qualifying matches were England, 9-0 against Luxembourg, followed by Mexico (7-0 v Netherlands Antilles) and Czechoslovakia (7-1 v Eire).

Sixes were recorded by Portugal (6-0 v Luxembourg), Israel (6-1 v Cyprus), Italy (6-0 v Israel), Costa Rica (6-0 v Netherlands Antilles) and Argentina (6-3 v Ecuador).

Remarkably, in a total of 91 qualifying matches, there was not a single goalless draw in all matches among European nations - and only four in all involving six teams.

Facts

7th World Cup
Chile 1962

Netherlands Antilles and Mexico drew 0-0 and also had blank sheets in games with Surinam and Paraguay respectively. Also goalless was Ghana v Morocco.

The 16 finalists were drawn in four fours, hitherto called pools but now, by FIFA edict, to be known as groups, not to be confused with groups (qualifying).

Groups (finals, that is) comprised: Group 1: Colombia, Soviet Union, Uruguay, Yugoslavia. Group 2: Chile, Italy, Switzerland, West Germany. Group 3: Brazil, Czechoslovakia, Mexico, Spain. Group 4: Argentina, Bulgaria, England, Hungary.

Brazil were rightly established firm favourites at 4-1 with most bookmakers, with Soviet Union generally listed next in view of their European Number One status.

The Russians established their superiority by winning the European Championship in its inaugural year, 1960, for the Henri Delaunay Cup, named after the French founder of the tournament.

That European trophy, contested between World Cup finals, was first held by the Russians after they beat Yugoslavia 2-1 in an extra-time thriller in Paris.

The Soviet Union were to meet Yugoslavia again in their first 1962 finals match on May 31, 1962.

This second encounter again went the Soviets' way, by two clear goals, but both sides eventually reached the quarter-finals.

Brazil were the choice of most world critics for World Cup 1962, having retained nine of their 1958 Final-winning team.

The missing Brazilian Cup winners were Bellini and Orlando, their places going to Mauro and Zozimo respectively. Each was destined to win a 1962 Final spot.

Also absent from the Brazilian squad of 1958 was Mazzola, who had switched allegiance to Italy for the 1962 finals under the new name of Jose Altafini.

7th World Cup Chile 1962 Facts

Altafini was one of only four players to have appeared for two countries in World Cup finals. The first was Luis Monti, who also had Italy as his second home four years after playing for Argentina in 1930.

The hat-trick of 'switcheroos' in 1962 was completed by two going over to Spain - Ferenc Puskas (Hungary 1954) and Jose Santamaria (Uruguay 1954).

Also in the Italian `League of Nations' squad was Enrique Omar Sivori, the Argentinian midfielder who moved to Juventus as a teammate of John Charles in 1957.

Sivori was capped by Argentina (18 times) and Italy (nine) and was European Footballer of the Year in 1961.

Puskas' teammate at Real Madrid, Alfredo Di Stefano, was also due to play for Spain but he claimed to be injured and said he was in Chile `as a tourist'.

Alfredo, the `White Knight', considered by many a greater player than Pele, also did not see eye to eye with the Spanish World Cup manager Helenio Herrera.

Di Stefano, twice European Footballer of the Year, won 31 caps for Spain and was a member of the Real Madrid side that won the European Cup five successive years from 1956 to 1960.

Among his greatest admirers was Sir Matt Busby, who once said that in the days when forwards and defenders did separate jobs, `Di Stefano did everything'.

Italy introduced among their stars an 18-year-old prodigy from AC Milan, midfielder Gianni Rivera, for his first of four World Cups.

The Soviet Union were without their star forward Edouard Streltsov for the second successive World Cup.

Streltsov had been sentenced to a labour camp for 12 years for alleged rape shortly before the 1958 series and hopes of an early release were dashed.

Streltsov's misery was compounded when he was freed after seven years, too late to win a place for the 1966 series.

The Soviet Union dominated Group 1 with five points from three games but were disappointing and almost met with disaster against Colombia, playing in their first finals.

Having led Uruguay, twice champions, at half-time before losing 2-1, Colombia four days later gave the Russians the shivers by pulling back from 1-4 to 4-4 in a purple eight-minute spell after the interval.

Facts

7th World Cup
Chile 1962

In goal for the Soviets was the redoubtable man in black, Lev Yashin, playing in the second of his three World Cup finals series.

Colombia were on their knees four days later when they were finally eliminated 5-0 by Yugoslavia. They stayed out for 28 years.

Valentin Ivanov scored in all three group matches for the Soviets, one of them in a violent game with Yugoslavia.

The Russian full-back Dubinski suffered a broken leg in a clash with Mujic, who was promptly sent back to Yugoslavia.

The Slavs were involved 48 hours later against Uruguay, not noted for coolness under fire. The fists were flying as Yugoslavia closed the shop with a 3-1 lead and 20 minutes to go.

The referee was unimpressed by the fighting qualities of Vladimir Popovic (Yugoslavia) and Ruben Cabrera (Uruguay) and both were sent off.

Even so, this was handbags-at-ten-paces compared with the brutal happenings in the Group 2 'Battle of Santiago' between Chile and Italy.

Sixty-six thousand fans, incensed by Italian newspaper criticism of Chile in general, screamed for blood as the Italian forward Giorgio Ferrini was ordered off by the English referee Ken Aston.

7th World Cup Chile 1962 Facts

Police were called when Ferrini refused to go, and play was held up for eight minutes.

Worse followed for the Italians as full-back Mario David was knocked out by a left hook from retaliating Chilean winger Leonel Sanchez, unobserved by the officials but picked up by the TV camera.

It wasn't David's day. The unsaintly Italian tried to kick a lump out of Sanchez minutes after regaining consciousness and was sent off.

It wasn't Italy's day either. One of their remaining nine, Umberto Maschio, had his nose broken, then conceded a free kick leading to Chile's first of two late winning goals.

The FIFA commissioners were lenient after seeing the match film. Poor Ferrini had been provoked, they thought, and got a one-match ban; David and Sanchez were admonished.

Ken Aston, a lofty, dignified schoolmaster, survived to whistle again, albeit with an injured tendon. His after-match comment: 'It was uncontrollable'.

Facts

7th World Cup
Chile 1962

West Germany went quietly about the business of heading Group 2 with five points from three games, Chile earned four points, and the Italians and Swiss packed their bags.

Group 3 predictably was Brazil's all the way from their opening match - as fate would have it, against unfortunate Mexico.

Remarkably, for the third World Cup finals in four series, poor Mexico had to kick off against mighty Brazil, having lost 4-0 in 1950 and 5-0 in 1954.

This time they improved for only a 2-0 defeat at the beautiful seaside centre of Vina del Mar, one of the four venues designated by Chile after the earthquake tremors and subsequent chaos.

The other three centres were arid Arica (the Dittborn stadium), thousands of miles away from the main new and superb stadium in Santiago, and Rancagua, England's headquarters.

Brazil's opening-match scorers were Mario Zagalo and Pele, but this was Pele's last full match of the series.

Three days later and with only a quarter of the match gone, Pele suffered a severe muscle strain and the Brazilians were happy to share the points in a goalless draw with Czechoslovakia.

Mexico and Spain, two points each after four games, were eliminated as Brazil and the Czechs joined the last eight, though few would have predicted at that stage that these two would ultimately contest the Final.

Pele's teenage deputy Amarildo scored both goals in the third group match, Brazil beating Spain 2-1 after being one down at half-time.

Amarildo kept his place all the way to the Final, this being the only change by Brazil from start to finish.

England's three matches in Group 4 were watched by a total of just 23,432 spectators, Hungary's by precisely 107 fewer.

There was probably more noise in the dressing-rooms on finding that they had both qualified - Hungary comfortably with five points but England perilously on goal average over Argentina.

Hungary beat England 2-1 and hit Bulgaria for six, with Florian Albert (four) and Lajos Tichy (three) their main scorers over the two games.

7th World Cup Chile 1962 Facts

England looked better in the second match, beating Argentina 3-1 with Ron Flowers of Wolves converting a penalty for the second successive match. Bobby Charlton and Jimmy Greaves also scored.

England's new captain for the series was Fulham's Johnny Haynes, but the major plus was the emergence of Bobby Moore.

Moore made his England debut in a 4-0 friendly win against Peru in Lima, on the way to the World Cup.

Moore came in at right-half for all four matches in the finals, displacing a West Brom man who had played in all four qualifying games. Tough luck, Bobby Robson!

Robson had played his last of 20 appearances for England, including the previous World Cup finals in Sweden.

The final Group 4 matches, Argentina v Hungary and England v Bulgaria, were ultra-defensive, boring and goalless.

Of the 32 matches played in Chile, the only other scoreless meeting was West Germany v Italy, watched by 65,440 in the super new Santiago stadium specially built for the start of the series.

All six games in England's group were watched by nearly 20,000 fewer at the Braden Copper Company ground at dingy Rancagua!

Apart from Santiago, Chile 1962 match attendances were all under 20,000, with the total attendance figures of 776,000, for an average of 24,250 per match, the lowest in World Cup post-war history.

The quarter-final qualifiers were Brazil, Chile, Czechoslovakia, England, Hungary, Soviet Union, West Germany and Yugoslavia.

Brazil and West Germany headed their groups with identical figures: P3 W2 D1 L0 F4 A1 Pts5. The quarter-finals revealed them as poles apart.

The closing stages reflected Brazilian superiority, three convincing wins in eight days, to emulate Italy's pre-war feat of successful defence of the title.

Once again the host nation reached the quarter-final stage, Chile emulating Sweden (1958 Finalists), Switzerland (1954), Brazil (1950 Finalists), France (1938), Italy (1934 winners) and Uruguay (1930 winners).

England, managed for the fourth and last time by Walter Winterbottom, were to leave for home hoping for the sequence to continue with the eighth finals in 1966. Hosts: England.

Facts

7th World Cup
Chile 1962

Winterbottom was the first England team-manager, appointed in 1946 after wartime service in the Royal Air Force.

He also worked for the Football Association as Director of Coaching before resigning after 17 years in the position.

England, facing the toughest quarter-final task, fought gamely to hold Brazil 1-1 at half-time, Garrincha and Gerry Hitchens the scorers, while Jimmy Greaves headed against the crossbar.

Garrincha and Vava scored for a 3-1 final score, Vava again scoring for Brazil in the next two vital matches to create a record.

Vava - real name Edwaldo Izidio Neto - became the first player to score in two successive Finals, 1958 and 1962.

Next to score in two Finals was a Brazilian - the irresistible Pele in 1958 and 1970.

West Germany met Yugoslavia in the quarter-final for the third consecutive time, having won 2-0 in Switzerland and 1-0 in Sweden.

The Slavs averted a 'hat-trick' dramatically with four minutes remaining, before a crowd of 63,324, when right-half Radakovic, playing with a bandaged head wound, scored the only goal.

Chile won 2-1 to move to the last four when Lev Yashin in the Russian goal was twice at fault in the first half, but Czechoslovakia were the surprise packet.

The Czechs won two 'Curtain-call' games against Hungary (1-0) and Yugoslavia (3-1), with three of the goals by Scherer.

Chile encountered the full power of Brazil in the semi-final, losing 4-2 to goals by Garrincha and Vava (two each).

This semi-final attracted easily the biggest gate of the tournament - 76,594 - nearly 8,000 more than at the Final and 10,000 more than at the play-off (Chile 1 Yugoslavia 0) for third place.

Honorino Landa (Chile) and Garrincha were sent off in the semi-final, but Brazil's 'Little Bird' was surprisingly allowed to play in the Final against Czechoslovakia.

The Czechs, beaten Finalists in 1934 in extra time, scored first through Josef Masopust in 15 minutes - as did Sweden in the previous Final - but Brazil were too good, as Pele's stand-in Amarildo, Zito and Vava took the score to 3-1.

7th World Cup Chile 1962 Facts

Brazil set a remarkable record for a winning World Cup nation by using only 12 players throughout the tournament. The Final line-ups:

Brazil: Gilmar; D Santos, Mauro (capt), Zozimo, Santos N, Zito, Didi, Garrincha, Vava, Amarildo, Zagalo.

Czechoslovakia: Schroiff; Tichy, Novak, Pluskal, Popluhar, Masopust (capt), Pospichal, Scherer, Kvasnak, Kadraba, Jelinek.

For the first time, the referee at the Final was an Eastern European, Latychev of the Soviet Union.

Another famous old ref at the Final was an Englishman, Sir Stanley Rous. He presented the Jules Rimet Trophy to Brazil's captain Mauro in his role as FIFA president.

Drazan Jerkovic of Yugoslavia was the leading marksman for the finals with five goals, and five players shared second place with four each: Albert (Hungary), Garrincha (Brazil), Sanchez (Chile), Ivanov (Soviet Union) and Vava (Brazil).

Hat-tricks were scored by Jerkovic (Yugoslavia v Colombia) and Florian Albert (Hungary v Bulgaria).

Final tribute to the courage of Chile on their recovery from the earthquake came in the form of a lap of honour by both Finalists, bearing aloft the Chilean flag.

Immediately after the tournament, bets were placed on Brazil to win the trophy outright four years hence - some at a mere 7-2.

8th World Cup England 1966

8th World Cup England 1966 Facts

This was the greatest year in England's international history, dating back to the first game in 1872, a goalless draw with Scotland in Glasgow.

England won the World Cup for the first and only time at their fifth attempt.

It was the finest achievement in the football life of Alf Ramsey, who had been appointed to succeed Walter Winterbottom as team manager in 1963.

It also helped to ease the memory of England's blackest day 16 years earlier when Ramsey was in the team that was beaten incredibly by USA in Brazil.

The parting gesture to Winterbottom was the award of the CBE in the 1963 New Year Honours list for services to sport.

Ramsey adopted a 4-3-3 formation for the last three matches of the 1966 finals and his team became known as the 'Wingless Wonders'.

Later, he admitted that he fielded this formation because he didn't think the wingers available for the World Cup were good enough.

On being appointed to the England job after demanding complete authority, Ramsey said simply: 'England will win the World Cup.'

World Cup year opened disastrously when the Jules Rimet Trophy was stolen. It became a one-man-and-his-dog story for newspapers across the world.

The trophy disappeared from a cabinet at a Stanley Gibbons stamp exhibition at the Central Hall, Westminster, on March 20, 1966, only for the 'lid' to reappear at FA headquarters with a ransom demand.

One week later, the trophy was found, wrapped in a copy of the *News of the World*, in the front garden of a house in South London, by Pickles, a black-and-white mongrel owned by David Corbett.

The thief was caught, Mr Corbett was rewarded and Pickles was given a doggie medal, a film part and a year's supply of canine goodies.

Pickles also received the final accolade from the *News of the World* for sniffing a good newspaper a mile away!

The original entry for the 1966 World Cup totalled 70, but before a ball was kicked, Syria withdrew from the group in which Spain eliminated Eire, and no fewer than 16 of the 18 nations in Group 16 also pulled out, leaving North Korea to qualify by twice beating Australia (6-1 and 3-1).

The 16 countries withdrew in protest over FIFA's allocation of only one finals place for a group comprising teams from two continents, Africa and Asia.

Facts

8th World Cup
England 1966

They were: Algeria, Cameroon, Ethiopia, Gabon, Ghana, Guinea, Liberia, Libya, Morocco, Nigeria, Senegal, South Africa, South Korea, Sudan, Tunisia and United Arab Republic.

Disappointment for Great Britain fans was that, for the first time since FIFA admitted the Home Countries, there was not a winner from the qualifying round. England qualified as hosts.

Northern Ireland, Scotland and Wales, all in groups of four, fought well against tough opposition and each finished as runners-up.

Northern Ireland came closest to qualifying and had only themselves to blame for being pipped on the post by Switzerland, despite a home win over the Swiss and winning three of the four points against Holland.

The Irish, having beaten the Albanians 4-1 at home, needed only to score a reasonable victory in Albania, in the closing match of the group, to qualify for the finals.

Albania, without a point from five matches (goals-for total one and against 11), astonishingly held out for a 1-1 draw.

Scotland also fell at the last hurdle, finishing second to Italy above Poland and Finland.

In the last two games in Group 8, Scotland beat Italy 1-0 in Glasgow to put the two teams level on seven points, but were soundly beaten 3-0 in Naples on December 8, 1965.

Wales had probably the hardest task in Group 7, but they had the satisfaction of ruining the 100 per cent record of the qualifiers, Soviet Union, with a 2-1 win in Cardiff to finish ahead of Greece and Denmark.

The interesting feature of the European qualifying groups was the dramatic emergence of Portugal as a major force, inspired greatly by the presence of the young genius from Benfica, Eusebio.

They beat Turkey twice and Czechoslovakia, who were the beaten World Cup Finalists of 1962, and failed only against Romania in the last group match.

Portugal were not worried about that 2-0 defeat by Romania, for they had already clinched a place in the finals for the first time at their seventh attempt.

Hungary won through for their fourth successive series by disposing of East Germany and Austria, as did West Germany at the expense of Sweden, the 1958 Finalists, and Cyprus.

8th World Cup England 1966 Facts

Yugoslavia failed to qualify for the first time since the Second World War, finishing third to group leaders France and Norway.

Away from Europe, Mexico won six out of eight group matches to keep up their 100 per cent qualifying record since the War, removing USA, Costa Rica, Honduras and Jamaica in the process.

South America came up with a powerful trio of qualifiers in Uruguay, Argentina and Chile, the last-named after a 2-1 defeat of Ecuador in a play-off. Completing the South American challenge were Brazil, who, as holders, did not have to qualify.

The draw for the 1966 finals took place at a televised ceremony at the Royal Garden Hotel, London, resulting as follows:

Group 1: England, France, Mexico and Uruguay (matches to be played at Wembley and White City).

Group 2: Argentina, Spain, Switzerland and West Germany (at Villa Park and Hillsborough).

Group 3: Brazil, Bulgaria, Hungary and Portugal (at Goodison Park and Trafford).

Group 4: Chile, Italy, North Korea and Soviet Union (at Ayresome Park and Roker Park).

The rules were the same as 1962, with the top two of each group qualifying for the quarter-finals.

Brazil predictably started the tournament as the bookies' favourites, the best price on offer being 7-2 in a field of 16 which included 13 of the 1962 qualifiers.

The missing nations from 1962 were Colombia, Czechoslovakia and Yugoslavia.

Three of the 16 finalists were bidding to win the trophy outright, Uruguay, Brazil and Italy.

Facts

8th World Cup
England 1966

Uruguay had won the World Cup twice from only four appearances in the finals, winning 11 matches (including 4-2 v England in 1954), drawing one and losing four.

Brazil's equivalent record from seven finals appearances covering 28 matches was won 18, drawn 5, lost 5.

Italy had competed in five previous finals involving 17 matches. They won 11, drew two and lost four.

Remarkably, the only finals matches in which the three nations had clashed resulted thus: Italy 2 Brazil 1 (France 1938), Uruguay 2 Brazil 1 (Brazil 1950). Each time, Brazil's conquerors went on to win the tournament.

A good deal of money went on England to win, which was well-founded optimism based on growing confidence in the new Ramsey regime reflected by the international match results leading up to the finals.

Following the 1962 finals, England played 41 matches in the four years before the 1966 series for these figures;

Country	P	W	D	L	F	A
Home	16	9	5	2	34	19
Away	25	17	4	4	69	32
Total	41	26	9	6	103	51

This included whirlwind victories at home to Northern Ireland (8-3) and away to Switzerland (8-1) and USA (10-0). 'Now shall we forget Belo Horizonte?' Alf Ramsey might have asked.

From the start of 1965 to the first match in the World Cup the following year, England played 21 games and lost only once, 2-3 at home to Austria.

That surely was a 'rogue result', as Austria failed miserably to qualify for the 1966 finals in losing three and drawing one against Hungary and East Germany in the group matches.

Bobby Charlton, describing these Ramsey pre-World Cup years, said: 'We had our ups and downs, good results and bad, but all the time we felt that something was happening.'

Three months before the finals began, Ramsey announced a preliminary list of 41 players, which was boiled down to 26 and finally to 22 for the close-season tour of Scandinavia from June 24 to July 6.

8th World Cup England 1966 Facts

The tour was totally successful with these winning scores: Finland 3-0, Norway 6-1, Denmark 2-0, Poland 1-0.

Eighteen clubs were represented in the list of 41 named by Ramsey on April 7, 1966. Chelsea and Liverpool topped the list with seven players each, Everton had four and Blackpool, Manchester United, Leeds and West Ham three each.

Chelsea's seven were Bonetti, Bridges, Hinton, Hollins, Osgood, Tambling and Venables.

Liverpool's seven were Byrne, Callaghan, Hunt, Lawler, Milne, Smith and Thompson. Making up the Merseyside eleven were Everton's Pickering, Temple, West and Wilson.

The threesomes were: Armfield, Ball, Waiters (Blackpool); J Charlton, Hunter, Reaney (Leeds); R Charlton, Connelly, Stiles (Manchester United); Hurst, Moore, Peters (West Ham).

The 11 solo candidates were: Baker (Nottingham Forest), Banks (Leicester), Cohen (Fulham), Eastham (Arsenal), Flowers (Wolves), Greaves (Tottenham), Harris (Burnley), Kaye (West Brom), Newton (Blackburn), Paine (Southampton), Springett (Sheffield Wednesday).

The 'heartbreak' four omitted from the tour party were Gordon Milne, Keith Newton, Peter Thompson and Bobby Tambling, who had in fact been a late addition to the original Ramsey list of 40.

Star performer on the tour was Jimmy Greaves with four goals against Norway.

Star performer off the field was World Cup Willie, the official mascot 'lion' clad in a Union Jack shirt and further 'lionised' in a popular song by Lonnie Donegan.

The final party of 22 was: Goalkeepers, Banks, Bonetti, Springett; Full-backs, Armfield, Byrne, Cohen, Wilson; Half-backs, J Charlton, Flowers, Hunter, Moore, Peters, Stiles; Forwards, Ball, Callaghan, R Charlton, Connelly, Eastham, Greaves, Hunt, Hurst, Paine.

Eight of the squad were to play in all six matches of the finals: Banks, Cohen, Wilson, Stiles, J Charlton, Moore, R Charlton, Hunt.

Although the reserve goalkeepers Ron Springett and Peter Bonetti were not called upon for the World Cup, all three played in the preceding Scandinavian tour matches.

The trio of 'keepers, Banks, Springett and Bonetti, became almost inseparable during the World Cup matches and were laughingly called 'The Marx Brothers' by their colleagues.

Facts

8th World Cup
England 1966

Peters played in five matches, Ball four, Hurst and Greaves three each, with Paine, Connelly and Callaghan one each, thus making a total of 15 players for the tournament.

The Queen declared the tournament open on a sunny evening, July 11, and the Wembley crowd of 87,148 cheered England in a goalless draw against a totally defensive Uruguay.

This was the first time that England had failed to score in an international match at Wembley.

France were virtually out of the running in Group 1 after three days, winning only one point from Mexico and Uruguay.

England went on to win the group comfortably with 2-0 wins over Mexico and France, Roger Hunt scoring three of the four goals.

In goal for Mexico against Uruguay for his last appearance in the tournament was Antonio Carbajal, setting up an individual record of five successive World Cups. He kept a clean sheet.

Uruguay were convincingly dealt with in the quarter-finals, 4-0 by West Germany, whose form inspired a rush of money with the bookies.

England were lucky to avoid West Germany at that stage, being matched instead for a last-eight meeting with Argentina.

The Germans bulldozed Switzerland 5-0 in the group, the losers having had star players Leimgruber and Kuhn suspended for 'breaking bounds'.

England were hoping that West Germany would have softened up the Argentines in a brutal, goalless conflict at Villa Park, where the South Americans' Jorge Albrecht was sent off for tackles above the belt. It wasn't to be!

In addition to Albrecht, three of the four other players sent off in the finals were playing West Germany at the time. They were Horacio Troche and Hector Silva (Uruguay) and Igor Chislenko (Soviet Union).

Troche and Silva were sent off in a five-minute spell for foul play against West Germany in the quarter-finals, and Uruguay finished the game with nine men.

The pair were each suspended for three matches, but double the punishment was doled out to Cortes for kicking referee Jim Finney after the match!

The form book was torn up in Group 3, with Brazil and Bulgaria ousted by a rampant Portuguese side and Hungary.

8th World Cup England 1966 Facts

Brazil started their campaign by beating Bulgaria 2-0, Pele scoring in the 14th minute to register the first goal of the tournament.

Their second match brought them face to face with Hungary, the victors in the infamous 'Battle of Berne' of 1954, and without the injured Pele.

Brazil had since enjoyed an unbeaten World Cup run of 13 games, and though 19-year-old Tostao scored on his World Cup debut, Hungary beat them 3-1.

Hungary were Olympic football champions in 1964 and again in 1968.

The demoralised champions Brazil made seven changes to face Portugal, but in vain. Pele was again injured and ten men were beaten 3-1, Eusebio scoring twice.

Pele blamed the team changes. He wrote: 'Our directors put their faith in the old dictum that God is a Brazilian, forgetting that God also helps those who help themselves'.

Looking back on his third World Cup finals, Pele bitterly criticised the referees of the group matches with Bulgaria and Portugal.

Pele was cruelly hacked by Jetchev (Bulgaria) at Goodison, and again repeatedly by Morais (Portugal) at the same ground, but both escaped being sent off.

The referees for those matches were both British, Jim Finney in the Bulgaria game and George McCabe in the Portugal tie.

Pele claimed unfairly in one of his books that the referees, 'under orders in my opinion, managed to overlook every infraction.'

Pele also swore that he would never play in another World Cup game.

Portugal were 100 per cent Group 3 winners, as were the Soviet Union in Group 4 with wins over North Korea, Italy and Chile.

North Korea caused a few raised eyebrows by finishing second to the Russians. They scored only twice in three games, but compiled three points from Chile (1-1) and a bemused Italy (1-0) to reach the last eight.

The Italian manager Edmondo Fabbri was sacked, the Italians flew back to be pelted with rotten tomatoes at Genoa airport, and North Korea found loyal support from the whole of Middlesbrough.

The North Koreans were caught by surprise, having booked accommodation only for the qualifying rounds in their one-and-only World Cup finals.

The Middlesbrough fans travelled in thousands to support their adopted team of little Koreans for their quarter-final match with Portugal at Goodison Park.

Facts

8th World Cup
England 1966

The other quarter-finals were England v Argentina, Soviet Union v Hungary, West Germany v Uruguay.

The powerful attacking forces of West Germany and the hard tackling of the Soviet Union took the two nations through for a semi-final clash.

North Korea were a sensation against Portugal. Roared on by a crowd of nearly 52,000, they scored three times in the first 24 minutes.

Just in case you have forgotten, the scorers were Pak Seung Zin, Yang Sung Kook and Li Dong Woon. These are not anagrams.

Then Eusebio took over, with two goals in the first half and two in the second. Augusto rounded off the scoring for a Portuguese 5-3 win.

England were in the World Cup quarter-final for the third time running and aiming to become semi-finalists for the first time.

They were happy to be at Wembley for a fourth match, facing Argentina again after beating them in Chile in 1962.

8th World Cup England 1966 Facts

Geoff Hurst and Alan Ball came in for Greaves, who was injured, and Callaghan, and Operation 4-3-3 was duly launched.

Argentina pulled every trick in the trade in their efforts to unsettle England in the first 35 minutes.

Bobby Charlton went on record: 'We were kicked, tripped, spat upon and body-checked.'

At last, the West German referee Rudolf Kreitlin, having taken three Argentine names, ordered off their provocative centre-half and captain, Antonio Rattin.

As Rattin refused to leave the field, pretending not to understand the referee, his teammates argued and jostled the referee and threatened to walk off *en masse*.

World Cup officials and interpreters entered the fray until Rattin finally left, after a ten-minute hold-up and with nine minutes to half-time.

Twenty-four hours after the match, the World Cup Committee fined Rattin £85, the maximum permitted under the rules of the tournament.

Rattin was also suspended for four international matches, with his teammates Onega and Ferreiro suspended for three international matches for their supporting roles in the chaos.

Ray Wilson, sitting on the ball throughout the shambles, pointed out to Gordon Banks the latest score from Goodison: Portugal 0 North Korea 3.

'They've got it wrong,' said the goalkeeper, and they both agreed they must have got the scores confused. Surely it couldn't be North Korea as the next opponents for England - or Argentina!

The niggling tactics continued on resumption, before a West Ham special, Peters crossing for Hurst's superb header, settled the issue 12 minutes from time.

After the match, several Argentine players invaded the England dressing-room. They were ejected, only to kick the closed door in a final act of frustration.

After the match, Alf Ramsey caused a few diplomatic tremors by expressing the hope that England would next play 'a team who came to play football and not act as animals.'

Contrastingly, the semi-final with Portugal at Wembley on July 26, before 94,493 spectators, was a classic from start to finish.

Describing the match years later, Gordon Banks said that the quality of football that evening had never been surpassed in his experience.

Facts

8th World Cup
England 1966

Portugal's scoring potential was clear, with 14 goals from their first four matches in their first World Cup finals, seven of these to Eusebio.

England had scored only five in four ties, but without conceding a goal, and decided to field an unchanged side.

England's heroes in a 2-1 win were the Manchester United men Nobby Stiles, who completely shackled Eusebio, and Bobby Charlton playing his greatest game for England - the unanimous opinion of Press and players alike.

The first goal in the 20th minute came from Charlton after the goalkeeper Jose Pereira had parried a shot by Roger Hunt.

Charlton scored the second nine minutes from time, a scorching shot from nearly 30 yards from Hurst's pass.

Panic reigned a minute later when Jack Charlton handled a Torres header with Banks off his line and stranded.

Eusebio took the penalty to score the first goal against England after nearly seven-and-a-half hours with a clean sheet.

England held out to qualify for a World Cup Final for the only time in history, but sportingly applauded Portugal off the pitch.

Eusebio set the style for World Cup semi-final tears, exactly 24 years to the month before Paul Gascoigne wept in similar circumstances.

Consolation for Eusebio was top spot as marksman for the 1966 series with nine goals, four of them from the penalty spot.

The semi-final between West Germany and the Soviet Union was tatty by comparison, the Germans winning faint praise after struggling to win 2-1 over their hard-hit opponents and their gallant goalkeeper Lev Yashin.

The Russians had midfielder Sabo limping almost from the start, then Chislenko returned after going off for treatment, only to be sent off for retaliation.

West Germany scored in each half, through Haller and Beckenbauer, but Porkujan replied for the nine-man Russians two minutes from the end.

The sour note of the semi-final was the Liverpool public's reaction to Wembley's total domination of England's matches, although no-one was to blame. That's how it worked out with the group placings.

Although German fans turned up in force at Goodison Park, there was still room for some 10,000 more on the day.

8th World Cup England 1966 Facts

Portugal deservedly won the third-place play-off at Wembley, two days after the semi-final disappointment, before a crowd of 87,696.

Eusebio, now dry-eyed, put Portugal ahead from the penalty spot but the Soviet Union equalised before half-time through Malafeev.

With two minutes to go and extra time looming, Torres scored his third goal of the finals to give Portugal a 2-1 victory.

July 30, 1966 was a beautiful summer's day in London and the most memorable day in the history of England's football.

It was a milestone in World Cup history, being the 200th match in the finals of the tournaments.

England lost the choice of colours for the Final, wearing red shirts to West Germany's white, but they won the day after 120 minutes of heart-stopping action.

Before a live Wembley crowd checked in at 93,802 and an estimated 400 million worldwide television audience, the teams lined up thus:

England: Banks; Cohen, Wilson, Stiles, J Charlton, Moore (capt), Ball, Hurst, R Charlton, Hunt, Peters.

West Germany: Tilkowski; Hottges, Schnellinger, Beckenbauer, Schulz, Weber, Haller, Held, Seeler (capt), Overath, Emmerich.

Alf Ramsey decided on an unchanged side, leaving out the fit-again Jimmy Greaves in favour of Geoff Hurst - an inspired decision.

In words of present-day football-speak, the Final was a game of three halves, the third `half' being the extra-time thriller in which England won the match.

First half: Haller scored for West Germany after 12 minutes...Hurst headed the equaliser after 18 minutes.

Second half: Martin Peters scored 12 minutes from time...Weber equalised seconds before the 90-minute whistle.

Third half: After 10 minutes of extra time, Hurst scored with a shot that rebounded off the underside of the crossbar. In the dying seconds, Hurst completed the first and only World Cup Final hat-trick.

Controversy raged over Hurst's second goal - and still does. The Russian linesman Bakhramov claimed the ball was over the goal-line and the Swiss referee Mr Dienst agreed.

Facts

8th World Cup
England 1966

When Hurst scored his third goal, commentator Kenneth Wolstenholme shouted above the din the immortal words: 'There are people on the pitch. They think it's all over. It is now!'

Wolstenholme, master match reader, writer, raconteur, was one of the pioneers of television commentating. He also had an exciting war.

He piloted a Mosquito in the RAF's elite Pathfinder wing and was awarded the Distinguished Flying Cross.

Only one person in the entire stadium appeared to remain seated after Hurst's decisive third goal: Alf Ramsey.

By a strange coincidence, the 1966 finals produced 89 goals from 32 games, precisely the same figures as for the 1962 tournament.

Most goals were scored by Portugal with 17 from six matches, West Germany totalling 15 from their six. England scored only 11 goals but conceded a mere three in six games.

One record for the North Koreans to savour was the fastest goal of the finals, scored by the pin-up hero of Middlesbrough, Pak Seung Zin, in the first minute against Portugal.

Helmut Haller (West Germany) was second top scorer to Portugal's nine-shot Eusebio. Haller scored five, followed by four fours, Franz Beckenbauer (West Germany), Ferenc Bene (Hungary), Valeri Porkujan (Soviet Union) and Geoff Hurst (England).

Attendances at the 32 matches in England totalled 1,614,677, which was higher than the seven previous finals.

8th World Cup England 1966 Facts

The average per match of 50,458 had been bettered only in the Brazil finals of 1950, when the average was 60,772.

England's six matches at Wembley were watched by a total of 559,989 spectators.

England were the first hosts to win the trophy since Italy in 1934.

The final ecstatic moment for the 90,000 hoarse fans was the sight of England's leg-weary players climbing the 39 steps to receive the World Cup from the Queen.

Thanks to Pickles.

9th World Cup Mexico 1970

9th World Cup Mexico 1970 Facts

Brazil came back from their disappointment of 1966 to conquer the world in devastating fashion and win the Jules Rimet Trophy for keeps.

The brilliant South Americans were invincible in their 12-match march, from the opening qualifier in Colombia on August 6, 1969, to the Final in Mexico City on June 21, 1970.

They steamrollered their Group 11 opponents in the qualifiers, maintaining a 100 per cent record and conceding only two goals, in the home match with Colombia. This was the table:

Country	P	W	D	L	F	A	PTS
Brazil	6	6	0	0	23	2	12
Paraguay	6	4	0	2	6	5	8
Colombia	6	1	1	4	7	12	3
Venezuela	6	0	1	5	1	18	1

Brazil's scoresheet read: Colombia 0 Brazil 2; Venezuela 0 Brazil 5; Paraguay 0 Brazil 3; Brazil 6 Colombia 2; Brazil 6 Venezuela 0; Brazil 1 Paraguay 0.

The Brazil v Paraguay match at the Maracana Stadium in Rio was watched by a crowd of 183,341, a record for a World Cup qualifier.

In the other qualifying matches in Rio de Janeiro, the official gates were recorded as Brazil v Colombia 94,977 and Brazil v Venezuela 122,841.

Mexico won the FIFA vote as hosts despite strong opposition from Europeans, who dreaded the effects of heat and altitude on players unfamiliar with such extreme playing conditions.

Argentina again tried to snatch the tournament for themselves, as they had also attempted at the expense of Chile in 1962, but Mexico was preferred despite its shortcomings as a venue.

In the event, Argentina failed to qualify for the first time since 1954 and Mexico prepared to welcome the world again, two years after hosting the Olympic Games.

Facts

9th World Cup Mexico 1970

There were 71 entries but, unlike the unrest preceding England 1966 qualifying rounds, the only withdrawal was that of North Korea.

The rules were unchanged for the finals, with four groups of four leading to quarter-finals on a knock-out basis. However, one crazy decision was that any quarter-final or semi-final matches undecided after extra time were to be settled by the toss of a coin.

One innovation was that substitutes were to be allowed for the first time in World Cup matches - two per team per game.

Brazil particularly welcomed this concession, having had the great man Pele almost literally kicked out of two of the three previous tournaments by ruthless opponents.

Pele had vowed never again to play in the World Cup after his 1966 experiences but Brazil pleaded with him to change his mind. The rest is history.

Of the 16 qualifiers, nine came from Europe (including England as holders), three from South America, leaving three from the rest of the soccer world along with the hosts Mexico.

The 'rest' was a real hotch-potch, comprising Groups 13, 15 and 16, and contained two rival nations meeting while actually at war with one another!

Even the official FIFA report on the series admitted that 'this part of the competition was necessarily more complex and provided a number of crises of different kinds.'

Group 13 took in Central and North America and the Caribbean, this being divided into four sub-groups.

Those involved were: Honduras, Costa Rica, Jamaica, Guatemala, Trinidad, Haiti, Surinam, Netherlands Antilles, El Salvador, USA, Canada and Bermuda.

El Salvador eventually emerged after 10 matches, including two third-match play-offs in neutral countries.

The flash-point came when El Salvador and Honduras found themselves paired, war being declared while the three matches were actually being contested.

The third match was played in the 'neutral' Azteca Stadium, Mexico City, before 15,000 spectators, leaving 90,000 empty places.

The score was 2-2 after 90 minutes, but El Salvador clinched the issue in the second part of extra time through winger Rodriguez.

9th World Cup Mexico 1970 Facts

As the President of El Salvador, General Hernandez, met the conquering heroes on their return home, their air force was attacking airfields in Honduras and their troops were invading.

The Hondurans counter-attacked but were overwhelmed and forced to sue for peace. The fighting ended after nearly 3,000 deaths but the hatred smouldered on for many years.

El Salvador were through to the finals for the first time, as indeed were Morocco after a similarly tortuous route in which they played 10 matches and endured minefields of a political and religious nature.

Morocco were representing the African continent as the single qualifier from 10 nations in Group 16: Algeria, Tunisia, Morocco, Senegal, Libya, Ethiopia, Zambia, Sudan, Nigeria and Cameroons.

Morocco overcame Nigeria and Sudan in the group finals and went to the 1970 finals along with Group 15 qualifiers Israel.

Israel had emerged from a jumble of nations containing also Australia, Japan, South Korea, New Zealand and Rhodesia.

Meanwhile, Peru and Uruguay were qualifying along with Brazil from South America, Argentina disappearing after losing three points from their two games with Peru.

Peru, in the finals for the first time since the 1930 opening series, were quietly fancied. Managed by the old Brazilian star Didi, they had no worries about playing in the 100 degrees Fahrenheit noon-day sun of Mexico.

Uruguay disposed of Chile in a last-match decider of Group 12 to remain undefeated in four matches and without a goal conceded.

Over in Europe, England alone were to represent the Home Countries in the finals for the third time since 1958.

The Organising Committee received complaints from Eastern and Western European nations against the apparent unfairness of the qualifying geography favouring the weaker teams of Central America and the Far East.

FIFA's reply: The World Cup is an international contest and the game of football is played in every part of the world. It is good for the game that areas where it is only developing should be represented.

Some FIFA members argued, in the 1970 official report, that 'it was not necessarily intended to present the 16 best teams, but 16 teams representative of football round the world'. So there's hope for Sark and the Scilly Isles.

Facts

9th World Cup
Mexico 1970

Eire were drawn against Hungary, Czechoslovakia and Denmark in Group 2 and mustered only a single point, from a 1-1 draw against the Czechs - after the first match, also standing at 1-1, was abandoned in a pea-souper fog.

Hungary, reigning Olympic champions and World Cup Finalists in 1938 and 1954, were top scorers in the group with 16 goals in six matches, but were well beaten 4-1 in a play-off with Czechoslovakia in Marseilles.

Group 4, consisting of three teams, was virtually a home-and-away issue between Northern Ireland and Soviet Union, since Turkey lost four times for a 13-2 goals return.

The Irish held the Russians to a goalless draw in Belfast but went down 2-0 in the deciding return match in Moscow, which George Best missed after being injured in a Manchester United game 48 hours earlier.

Scotland, captained by Billy Bremner in all six qualifying games in Group 7, finished second to West Germany, four points away, but they went down fighting.

They forced the Germans to concede their only point with a 1-1 draw at Hampden, and lost 3-2 in Hamburg.

Cyprus and Austria were also involved, the Scots finishing one point above Austria, with the Cypriots holding a massive wooden spoon after six defeats and a goals return of 2-35.

Scotland whipped Cyprus 5-0 in Nicosia (Alan Gilzean of Spurs two) and 8-0 in Glasgow (Colin Stein of Rangers four).

West Germany won only by a single goal in Cyprus, but they set a World Cup scoring record up to that stage with a 12-0 trouncing in the return fixture at Essen.

Wales faced the cruellest task in Group 3, meeting East Germany and twice-champions Italy, and predictably lost all four for a final scoreline of 3-10.

The East Germans served notice as an emerging world force in holding Italy to a 2-2 draw in East Berlin, but Italian power and experience prevailed in Naples for a 3-0 win.

Oddity of Group 1 was that the first and second teams as named by the Organising Committee - Portugal and Switzerland - ended up bottom and third respectively and were out.

Group 1 winners were Romania who, needing one point in the final match, held Greece to a 1-1 draw.

9th World Cup
Mexico 1970

Facts

Two other heads of groups were kicked out in the European eliminators - France and Spain - both having been in the last 16 of the previous tournament.

Sweden won Group 5, despite losing 3-0 to France in Paris, and Spain finished third in Group 6 to Belgium, the surprise qualifiers, and Yugoslavia.

Belgium were in the finals for the first time since 1954, losing only to Yugoslavia 4-0 in the last group match having already made sure of qualifying.

Group 8 winners as expected were Bulgaria, qualifying for the third successive time by beating Poland 3-0 away in the vital deciding game between the two East Europeans.

The five venues for the 1970 finals were Mexico City, Toluca, Puebla, Guadalajara and Leon.

The draw for the finals – Group One: Belgium, El Salvador, Mexico, Soviet Union. Group Two: Israel, Italy, Sweden, Uruguay. Group Three: Brazil, Czechoslovakia, England, Romania. Group Four: Bulgaria, Morocco, Peru, West Germany.

All previous World Cup winners were there: Uruguay (1930 and 1950), Italy (1934 and 1938), West Germany (1954), Brazil (1958 and 1962), England (1966).

Heights above sea level at the five match centres were: Mexico City 7,400 ft, Toluca 8,792 ft, Puebla 7,000 ft, Guadalajara (England's group venue) 4,767 ft, Leon 5,565 ft.

The two determined venues before the draw were Mexico as hosts in Mexico City and England as champions at Guadalajara.

Facts

9th World Cup
Mexico 1970

England were unlucky to be in the toughest group, although their chain of misfortunes started even before they arrived in Mexico.

Two successful matches were played as warm-up and acclimatisation, in Colombia (won 4-0) and Ecuador (won 2-0), over a period of five days - seven days before their opening match in Group 3 against Romania.

The manager, now Sir Alf Ramsey, fielded the same side for the two preparation games and for the first two World Cup matches.

The four-match line-up read: Banks, Newton, Cooper, Mullery, Labone, Moore (capt), Lee, Ball, R Charlton, Hurst, Peters.

Troubles started in Bogota after these games, Bobby Moore being imprisoned for four days, falsely accused of stealing a bracelet in a jeweller's shop.

Jeff Astle, a bad air traveller, then arrived in Mexico looking the worse for wear and was wrongly described as drunk.

The persecution of England's party continued with Mexican and Brazilian mobs chanting and sounding their car horns outside the squad's hotel windows into the early hours.

More jeering and catcalling greeted the England flag and the children representing England were also barracked at the opening ceremony at the Azteca Stadium.

Mexico and the Soviet Union contested the opening match on Sunday, May 31. It ended in a goalless draw, as in the 1966 series.

The Russians were not happy with the East German referee, the host nation suffering only one of five match cautions.

Mexico's opponents in their next match were also `unfortunate' in that the Egyptian referee booked four El Salvador players.

One of the goals in Mexico's 4-0 win over El Salvador resulted from a free kick awarded to the opposition but taken by Mexico!

Also in Group 1 were Belgium, who surprisingly were knocked out in their third and vital match by Mexico by the only goal from a dubious penalty award.

There was a split in the Belgian camp over the footwear being supplied by rival firms, and Czechoslovakia's side was similarly divided so that the whole team was suspended after completion of its Group 3 games.

The Mexicans qualified from Group 1 without conceding a goal, while El Salvador dropped out without scoring in three matches.

9th World Cup Mexico 1970 Facts

Group 2 games were grimly defensive, only six goals being scored from six matches. The debilitating effect of the high altitudes of Toluca and Puebla was largely to blame.

Italy headed the group with four points but only one goal from three matches.

The only 100 per cent teams in the group matches were Brazil and West Germany, and both were heavily backed to contest the Final.

The opening match in Group 4 between Bulgaria and Peru was preceded by one minute's silence in tribute to the victims of the Peruvian earthquake, which had happened after the national team had left for Mexico. Despite their concern, Peru scored three in the second half to win 3-2.

West Germany scored 10 goals in three matches, beating Peru 3-1 in the group leadership decider.

Gerd Muller was in deadly form, scoring seven, including two hat-tricks. He was the only hat-trick man of the 1970 finals.

The Germans had one nasty shock facing the Moroccans, who stole a 1-0 half-time lead through Mohamed Houmane Jarir. Seeler (56 min) and Muller (78 min) scored face-saving goals after the break.

Morocco earned further credit as Africa's first representative in the finals since Egypt in 1934. In their parting match, they fought back to draw 1-1 against Bulgaria and shared the group wooden spoon with the Bulgars on one point each.

The Moroccans left one hilarious memory for their new Mexican supporters and millions on TV. The Dutch referee started the second half of their game with West Germany while they were still drifting on to the pitch and goalkeeper Allal Benkassou raced across frantically in the nick of time to save a shot bound for the net!

In Group 3, England beat Czechoslovakia and Romania by 1-0 each and gave Brazil their closest contest in the whole series, Brazil winning by a single goal from Jairzinho.

This game will be for ever remembered for a miraculous diving save by Gordon Banks from a header by Pele. It was so good that even Pele applauded him on the spot, and he said afterwards: 'It was the greatest save I had ever seen'.

Banks said: 'I'm prepared to admit it was the save of my career'.

For their final group match, against Czechoslovakia, England made five changes and won with a dubious penalty award converted by Allan Clarke, making his international debut.

Facts

9th World Cup
Mexico 1970

England thus qualified for the quarter-finals for the third consecutive World Cup.

Finishing second in the group meant another tough task for England in the last eight, the top of Group 4 having been occupied by the old enemy West Germany, thirsting for revenge after Wembley '66!

Any other opposition would have been preferable from the other quarter-finalists, the pairings being: Soviet Union v Uruguay (in Mexico City), Italy v Mexico (Toluca), Brazil v Peru (Guadalajara), West Germany v England (Leon).

England were struck a severe blow before the start: Gordon Banks was taken ill, and Peter Bonetti came in for his first match for a month. Otherwise, the original line-up for the first two games in Mexico was restored.

One disappointed squad member was Peter Osgood, twice a substitute for Francis Lee and Allan Clarke but never in the starting line.

The two teams each fielded five players who had faced one another at Wembley four years earlier. They were Moore, Ball, R Charlton, Peters and Hurst (England), Hottges, Schnellinger, Beckenbauer, Seeler and Overath (West Germany).

Alan Mullery scored to give England a 1-0 interval lead. It was the Spurs man's only goal for England in 35 international games.

Martin Peters made it 2-0 five minutes after the break but the Germans equalised through Beckenbauer and Seeler, then Muller got the winner with 10 minutes remaining of extra time.

This was only the second defeat suffered by England in a run of 13 matches, which had started after an earlier defeat by Brazil 2-1 in Rio in June 1969.

Uwe Seeler's quarter-final goal against England was his last in World Cup finals. He set a record of 21 games in four tournaments (1958-1970), but was never on the winning side in a Final.

Three other players were later to share Seeler's record. They were Wladyslaw Zmuda (Poland 1974-86), Diego Maradona (Argentina 1982-94) and Lothar Matthaus (West Germany 1982-90, unified Germany 1994).

Extra time was required in three of the six quarter and semi-finals but all were decided before the toss of a coin could bring a farcical conclusion.

Peru went out predictably to Brazil 4-2, but they had the satisfaction of scoring in all four of their matches and totalling nine goals. That was more than all three other beaten quarter-finalists, Soviet Union (6), Mexico (6) and England (4).

9th World Cup Mexico 1970 Facts

Teofila Cubillas, the Alianza Lima striker, finished with five goals for the finals, having scored in all of Peru's four matches.

Mexico briefly raised home hopes with a 12th-minute goal against Italy, the first time the Italian defence had been pierced in four games, before Luigi Riva asserted himself with two goals for a 4-2 win.

Uruguay v Soviet Union had to go to extra time before Victor Esparrago scored the only goal, from a pass which the Russians bitterly claimed had been made from an out-of-play ball.

The semi-finals were contested by three nations bidding for a hat-trick of World Cup Final wins in Uruguay, Italy and Brazil. West Germany had one win to their credit, in 1954, and were runners-up in 1966.

West Germany took on Italy having scored 13 goals at that stage to their opponents' meagre five. The score was 1-1 after 90 minutes, Schnellinger scoring in the last minute, then came a flood of five in extra time.

Franz Beckenbauer played throughout extra time with his right arm in a sling because of a shoulder injury, but he refused to go off as the Germans had already used two substitutes.

In extra time, Muller scored, Italy equalised, Italy led, Muller equalised, then Italy got the winner with 10 minutes left.

West Germany had earned third place, which they clinched with a single first-half goal by Overath against Uruguay.

West Germany's total of 17 goals in six games was passed in the Final by Brazil, their 4-1 defeat of Italy taking their tally to 19.

Pele's farewell World Cup goal was applauded by 107,000 spectators in the Azteca Stadium, but the roof was raised when the Brazilian captain Carlos Alberto scored in the last minute.

Rivelino collapsed in a dead faint as soon as the referee, Rudi Glockner of East Germany, sounded the final whistle.

Brazil's team: Felix; Carlos Alberto (capt), Brito, Piazza, Everaldo, Clodoaldo, Gerson, Jairzinho, Tostao, Pele, Rivelino.

Italy: Albertosi; Burgnich, Facchetti (capt), Cera, Rosato, Bertini (sub Juliano 72 min), Domenghini, De Sisti, Mazzola, Boninsegna (sub Rivera 84 min), Riva.

Facts

9th World Cup
Mexico 1970

Leading scorers for the finals were: Gerd Muller (West Germany) 10, Jairzinho (Brazil) 7, Anatoli Bishovets (Soviet Union), Pele (Brazil), Teofilo Cubillas (Peru) 4 each.

Jairzinho created a World Cup record by scoring in every round of the 1970 finals. Just Fontaine scored in every round in which he played in 1958, but his country France were not in the Final that year.

Gerd Muller also wrote himself into the World Cup record books by scoring a total of 19 goals, including nine in West Germany's six qualifying games.

Pele's goal in the 1970 Final was Brazil's 100th in World Cup finals.

Pele became the second player to score in two World Cup Finals, 1958 and 1970. Vava scored for Brazil in the Finals of 1958 and 1962.

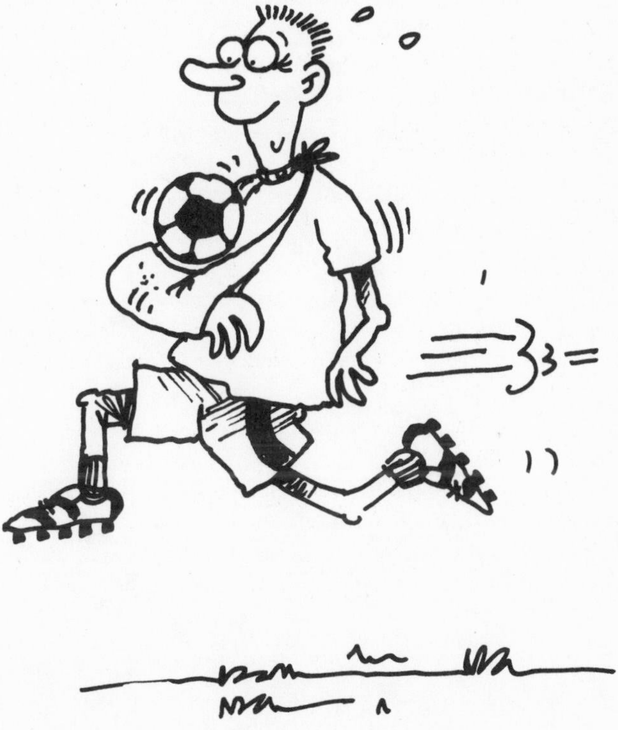

9th World Cup Mexico 1970 Facts

Although he didn't play in the 1962 Final through injury, Pele is the only player to have been a member of three World Cup winning squads, in 1958, 1962 and 1970. He played 14 matches in the World Cup finals.

The fastest goal of the finals came from Ladislav Petras for Czechoslovakia, in the third minute of their group match with Romania, who went on to win 2-1.

The first substitute to be used in the World Cup was Anatoly Puzach, of Soviet Union, in the opening match of the 1970 series against Mexico.

Total attendances in Mexico were the highest in the first nine finals. The 32 matches attracted 1,673,975 spectators for an average of 52,312 per match.

Goals scored totalled 95, an increase of six on each of the two previous finals.

FIFA introduced yellow and red cards for the first time for referees in 1970, but there were no sendings-off, only the second time since 1950.

The yellow card was flourished in 19 matches for 45 cautions, three of these being recorded as `severe cautions'.

Only two yellow cards were shown against England, both for dangerous play by Francis Lee against Brazil and West Germany.

The second time it happened, against the Germans, he received a 'severe caution',

The Swinging Sixties

Bra-zil, Bra-zil . . . and England

The Swinging Sixties Facts

A total of 186 matches – 21 more than in the Fifties trio – was played by 25 countries in the finals of 1962, 1966 and 1970.

Surprisingly, although Brazil triumphed in two of the series, the greatest number of matches over the period was played by West Germany – a positive sign that they were looking for world soccer domination in the next decade.

The leading nations in this category were: West Germany 16, Brazil 15, England and Soviet Union 14, Uruguay 13, Italy 12.

The message was that only the Soviets of the Eastern bloc were likely to threaten Western Europe and South America before the Millennium.

The nearest the Russians had been to the title was in 1966, when Portugal won the third-place play-off against them.

Brazil lost only two games in the period, against West Germany's three defeats.

Bottom of the pile were El Salvador (played 3, lost 3), holding up Morocco, Colombia and, surprisingly, France (all played three for just one point).

Another recognised soccer nation on the slide was Bulgaria, with a return over three finals of: P9 W0 D2 L7 F7 A24 Pts2.

Argentina (7 matches): 1962, beat Bulgaria, drew with Hungary, lost to England; 1966, beat Spain, Switzerland, drew with West Germany, lost to England.

Belgium (3 matches): 1970, beat El Salvador, lost to Soviet Union, Mexico.

Brazil (15 matches): 1962, beat Mexico, Spain, England, Chile, Czechoslovakia, drew with Czechoslovakia; 1966, beat Bulgaria, lost to Hungary, Portugal; 1970, beat Czechoslovakia, England, Romania, Peru, Uruguay, Italy.

Bulgaria (9 matches): 1962, drew with England, lost to Argentina, Hungary; 1966, lost to Brazil, Portugal, Hungary; 1970, drew with Morocco, lost to Peru, West Germany.

Chile (9 matches): 1962, beat Switzerland, Italy, Soviet Union, Yugoslavia, lost to West Germany, Brazil; 1966, drew with North Korea, lost to Italy, Soviet Union.

Colombia (3 matches): 1962, drew with Soviet Union, lost to Uruguay, Yugoslavia.

Czechoslovakia (9 matches): 1962, beat Spain, Hungary, Yugoslavia, drew with Brazil, lost to Mexico, Brazil; 1970, lost to Brazil, Romania, England.

El Salvador (3 matches): 1970, lost to Belgium, Mexico, Soviet Union.

Facts

The Swinging Sixties

England (14 matches): 1962, beat Argentina, drew with Bulgaria, lost to Hungary, Brazil; 1966, beat Mexico, France, Argentina, Portugal, West Germany, drew with Uruguay; 1970, beat Romania, Czechoslovakia, lost to Brazil, West Germany.

France (3 matches): 1966, drew with Mexico, lost to Uruguay, England.

Hungary (8 matches): 1962, beat England, Bulgaria, drew with Argentina, lost to Soviet Union; 1966, beat Brazil, Bulgaria, lost to Portugal, Soviet Union.

Israel (3 matches): 1970, drew with Sweden, Italy, lost to Uruguay.

Italy (12 matches): 1962, beat Switzerland, drew with West Germany, lost to Chile; 1966, beat Chile, lost to Soviet Union, North Korea; 1970, beat Sweden, Mexico, West Germany, drew with Uruguay, Israel, lost to Brazil.

Mexico (10 matches): 1962, beat Czechoslovakia, lost to Brazil, Spain; 1966, drew with France, Uruguay, lost to England; 1970, beat El Salvador, Belgium, drew with Soviet Union, lost to Italy.

Morocco (3 matches): 1970, drew with Bulgaria, lost to West Germany, Peru.

North Korea (4 matches): 1966, beat Italy, drew with Chile, lost to Soviet Union, Portugal.

Peru (4 matches): 1970, beat Bulgaria, Morocco, lost to West Germany, Brazil.

Portugal (6 matches): 1966, beat Hungary, Bulgaria, Brazil, North Korea, Soviet Union, lost to England.

Romania (3 matches): 1970, beat Czechoslovakia, lost to England, Brazil.

Soviet Union (14 matches): 1962, beat Yugoslavia, Uruguay, drew with Colombia, lost to Chile; 1966, beat North Korea, Italy, Chile, Hungary, lost to West Germany, Portugal; 1970, beat Belgium, El Salvador, drew with Mexico, lost to Uruguay.

Spain (6 matches): 1962, beat Mexico, lost to Czechoslovakia, Brazil; 1966, beat Switzerland, lost to Argentina, West Germany.

Sweden (3 matches): 1970, beat Uruguay, drew with Israel, lost to Italy.

Uruguay (13 matches): 1962, beat Colombia, lost to Yugoslavia, Soviet Union; 1966, beat France, drew with England, Mexico, lost to West Germany; 1970, beat Israel, Soviet Union, drew with Italy, lost to Sweden, Brazil, West Germany.

The Swinging Sixties Facts

West Germany (16 matches): 1962, beat Switzerland, Chile, drew with Italy, lost to Yugoslavia; 1966, beat Switzerland, Spain, Uruguay, Soviet Union, drew with Argentina, lost to England; 1970, beat Morocco, Bulgaria, Peru, England, Uruguay, lost to Italy.

Yugoslavia (6 matches): 1962, beat Uruguay, Colombia, West Germany, lost to Soviet Union, Czechoslovakia, Chile.

World Cup Final referees from this period came from: 1962 Soviet Union (Latychev), 1966 Switzerland (Dienst), 1970 East Germany (Glockner).

10th World Cup West Germany 1974

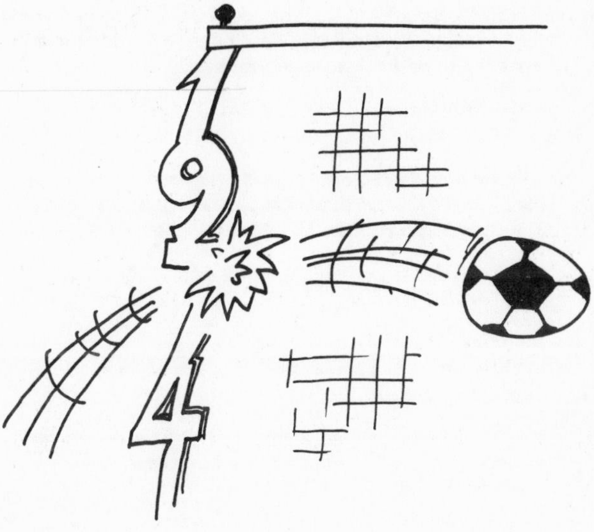

10th World Cup West Germany 1974 Facts

The World Cup came back to Europe in 1974 and with it the domination of the host country and ultimate winners West Germany.

Brazil fought to remain in the main echelon, but European supremacy was such that six of the last eight in the finals were from the Continent.

Argentina joined Brazil as representatives of South America - and indeed the rest of the world - in the last eight.

Brazil, having won the Jules Rimet Trophy outright in 1970, offered to supply a replacement in a goodwill gesture.

The offer was rejected and a new trophy was produced and paid for by FIFA, to be called 'The FIFA World Cup Trophy'.

The new trophy is cast in gold, weighs 11 pounds and is 20 inches high.

FIFA, ever keen to spread the soccer gospel, were delighted with an initial entry of 97 nations, an increase of more than 30 per cent over 1970, from a total membership of 140.

Three teams withdrew without playing a match - Jamaica (Central and North American Group), Madagascar and Gabon, both in the African zone.

A further dramatic withdrawal involved the Soviet Union, who had to win their European Group 9 to meet the winners of South American Group 3 in the qualifying competition to decide who went into the finals.

The Russians duly eliminated Eire and France, while Chile won two of three tussles with Peru.

The Soviet Union and Chile then played a goalless draw in the first leg in Moscow, but the Russians refused to play in Santiago in the same stadium in which they claimed political prisoners had been imprisoned and tortured.

FIFA would not accede to the Soviets' request for the match to be switched to a neutral country, so they withdrew and thus ended a run of four consecutive World Cup finals appearances.

Chile lined up to face a deserted half of the field, 'scored' in an empty net and then the match was abandoned.

There were the usual surprises in the more remote areas of the football world, but England's failure to qualify for the 1974 finals on familiar territory was the biggest shock of the nine European groups.

Facts

10th World Cup
West Germany 1974

This was the first time since the war that England had failed to reach the finals.

Scotland alone were left to fly the flag for the Home Countries, having qualified for the first time in 16 years.

In two previous finals (1954 and 1958), the Scots had gathered only one point from five matches. Their record: Drawn one, lost four, goals 14-4.

England's record after eight successive finals was:

P	W	D	L	F	A	Pts
24	10	6	8	34	28	26

England were drawn in Group 5 along with Poland and Wales, each of whom had figured in only one World Cup finals.

Indeed, Poland had played only a single finals match, against Brazil in France in 1938, when they lost 6-5 in extra time.

The shining hour for Wales had been Sweden 1958, when they went out in the quarter-final by the only goal against Brazil, the ultimate winners of the trophy.

The warning signs for England in the Tenth World Cup came some 18 months before the finals, when their first two matches against Wales ended 1-0 and 1-1.

Only Bobby Moore and Alan Ball of the 1966 Final team survived for the matches with Wales, but Martin Peters reappeared for the two clashes with Poland.

Norman Hunter and Colin Bell scored in the two matches with Wales, and Allan Clarke (penalty) supplied the only goal from the matches with Poland, which Poland won 2-0 in Katowice and drew 1-1 at Wembley.

Poland's performance in the finals underlined their rapid progress on the international stage. They finished third after coming close to winning the tournament.

10th World Cup West Germany 1974 Facts

Poland were the Olympic soccer champions of 1972 and silver medallists in 1976. Here's how they qualified for the World Cup finals:

Country	P	W	D	L	F	A	Pts
Poland	4	2	1	1	6	3	5
England	4	1	2	1	3	4	4
Wales	4	1	1	2	3	5	3

The Welsh helped England's cause by beating the Poles 2-0 at Cardiff, only to lose 3-0 and have Trevor Hockey sent off in a violent match in Katowice.

England's failure to beat Poland finally led to the departure of manager Sir Alf Ramsey on May 1, 1974.

Joe Mercer moved in as caretaker-manager until the autumn of 1974, when the highly successful Leeds United manager Don Revie took up the reins.

Needing to beat Poland on October 17, 1973, England were defied by goalkeeper Jan Tomaszewski's amazing saves - hardly the work of 'a clown' as he had been described by the outspoken Brian Clough.

The great Irish 'keeper Pat Jennings, commenting after the match on the Polish goalkeeper's performance, said that he had 'never seen a bloke play so badly and so great inside one match'.

For the record, Tomaszewski's prowess reached further heights in the finals in Germany when he saved penalties against Sweden and West Germany.

Facts

10th World Cup
West Germany 1974

The Poles also included two outstanding strikers in Lato and Szarmach, who were to become the leading goalscorers in the finals.

Bobby Moore was dropped for the match with Poland at Wembley, the honour of captaincy for the first time in a World Cup match going to Martin Peters.

Ramsey brought back Moore in place of Hunter for the first match after being eliminated from the World Cup.

Moore resumed at Wembley as captain for his 108th and final international match on November 14, 1973. Italy won 1-0 to complete a double defeat for England.

Five months earlier, Italy had beaten England 2-0 in Turin.

Italy went on to the World Cup finals of 1974, only to be knocked out by Poland - yet again cold comfort for England!

Ramsey could feel well satisfied with his record as England manager of only 17 defeats in 113 matches.

Scotland had their managerial problems as they came up for the qualifying rounds, Bobby Brown having paid the price for failure in the preliminaries to Mexico 1970.

Tommy Docherty took over and was immediately successful. He managed the side for the first two matches in the new World Cup campaign, then left to take over as manager of Manchester United.

However, showing a sense of occasion, Scotland in 1973 emerged at the head of Group 8 to celebrate the centenary of the Scottish FA, which had been formed on April 6, 1873.

The first two group matches under Docherty in 1972, both against Denmark, resulted in a 4-1 win in Copenhagen, followed by a 2-0 win in Glasgow four weeks later.

Willie Ormond had a shattering baptism as manager, Scotland losing 5-0 to England at Hampden Park, but his luck changed with a 2-1 World Cup home win over Czechoslovakia before a 100,000 crowd on September 26, 1973.

That was enough to send the Scots through to the finals, thanks to goals by Jim Holton (40 min) and Joe Jordan (75 min) and the inspiration of their fiery captain Billy Bremner.

10th World Cup West Germany 1974 Facts

A 1-0 defeat by the Czechs in Bratislava three weeks later was of no consequence, the final Group 8 table reading thus:

Country	P	W	D	L	F	A	Pts
Scotland	4	3	0	1	8	3	6
Czechoslovakia	4	2	1	1	9	3	5
Denmark	4	0	1	3	2	13	1

Northern Ireland's hopes of qualifying from Group 6 were extinguished in the first two of their six scheduled matches, although they fought back to avoid defeat in their remaining games.

All Northern Ireland's scheduled home matches had to be played in England because of the political unrest in the province.

Their home-match venues were Sheffield Wednesday (v Bulgaria), Coventry (v Portugal) and Fulham (v Cyprus).

They were beaten 3-0 in Bulgaria, but hardly dared to return home after losing by a single goal in Cyprus.

Cyprus lost their five other games without scoring, conceding 14 goals, three of these to the Irish in the return match.

Northern Ireland's other scores: Bulgaria away, lost 3-0; Portugal 'home', drew 1-1; Bulgaria 'home', drew 0-0; Portugal away, drew 1-1.

The most striking qualifiers from the European sector were Holland, playing a kind of football perfected by the great Ajax team of the early Seventies, under the inspiring captaincy of Johan Cruyff.

Total Football, as the Dutch style was termed, ignored set patterns such as 4-2-4 and 4-3-3 but encouraged exciting, interweaving passing movements among all members of the side, regardless of defending or attacking roles.

Even so, Holland found stern opposition in their neighbours Belgium in Group 3, each having beaten Iceland and Norway twice.

Facts

10th World Cup
West Germany 1974

Both their matches ended 0-0, so that the top of Group 3 read:

Country	P	W	D	L	F	A	Pts
Holland	6	4	2	0	24	2	10
Belgium	6	4	2	0	12	0	10

Under the new ruling for the 1974 series, Holland went through to the finals on goal difference.

Incredibly, Belgium were eliminated without being beaten and without conceding a goal!

By a remarkable coincidence, Italy won Group 2 with an identical record to that of poor old Belgium: 6-4-2-0-12-0-10.

Dino Zoff kept three clean sheets and went to the finals unbeaten in 12 internationals with Italy.

Italy, still looking for their third World Cup triumph, won easing up against Turkey, Switzerland (6 pts each) and Luxembourg, who surprised Turkey 2-0.

Luxembourg's only other World Cup win was over Portugal 4-2 in the 1962 qualifiers. Their record for seven tournaments reads:

P	W	D	L	F	A	Pts
32	2	0	30	26	125	4

The closest of contests involved three nations all finishing on eight points in Group 1. Hungary went out on goal difference, but Sweden and Austria returned identical goals figures and had to meet again in a play-off in West Germany.

Sweden just managed to beat the Austrians 2-1 at Gelsenkirchen to qualify for their sixth finals.

10th World Cup West Germany 1974 Facts

Malta, competing for the first time, suffered at the grounds of the Group 1 trio, but caused a little discomfort on their own pitch for Hungary (0-2), Austria (0-2) and Sweden (1-2).

That one goal by Malta was the catalyst for the third meeting and a lot of travelling expense for Sweden.

In Group 4, East Germany won a close encounter with Romania to qualify for the finals for the first time.

Romania finished one point adrift and lived to rue the 1-1 draw in their first match in Finland. The two met again one year later, Romania making sure this time ...by 9-0.

Yet another group went to a third meeting of the top two, with Yugoslavia and Spain equal on goal difference in Group 7.

They met again in February 1974 in neutral West Germany, Yugoslavia sneaking through to the last 16 by the only goal.

The European challengers for the 1974 finals consisted of nine countries including West Germany, who as hosts were exempt from the qualifying rounds.

The nine were: Bulgaria, East Germany, Holland, Italy, Poland, Scotland, Sweden, West Germany, Yugoslavia.

The South American challenge was headed by Brazil, exempt from the qualifiers as holders, Uruguay, Argentina and Chile - a formidable force on paper with a World Cup record of five winners, two runners-up and two third places in nine finals.

The three remaining places were contested in three groups, Central and North America, Asia and Africa, by a total of 49 nations.

Apart from Chile, who had a virtual free pass to the finals, Uruguay appeared to have the easiest task against Colombia and Ecuador.

In the event, Colombia beat them and were unbeaten themselves in four games, but goal difference decided in favour of Uruguay, who were no longer a formidable force having had many of their star players lured by the money of foreign clubs.

Argentina won the contest with Paraguay, the deciding group match ending 3-1 in their favour. Bolivia disappeared pointless and with only one goal from four matches.

The Central and North American Group provided shock winners in Haiti in a field of 13, involving 33 matches, although runners-up Trinidad were not impressed after having four goals disallowed when the two met in a vital match. Haiti won 2-1.

Facts

10th World Cup
West Germany 1974

Trinidad had the satisfaction of the biggest win of the 1974 series, beating Antigua 11-1 at Port of Spain in November 1972. This equalled Hungary's 11-1 defeat of Greece in 1938 but fell short of West Germany 12 Cyprus 0 in 1970.

Mexico, quarter-finalists in their own country in the 1970 finals, failed to qualify for the first time since the Second World War.

Mexico were veterans of seven World Cup finals, involving them in 21 matches, with Belgium and Czechoslovakia their biggest conquests.

Mexico seemed to be in line for qualification, having beaten Netherlands Antilles 8-0 to register the biggest win of the group, but unbelievably were beaten 4-0 in Trinidad.

Mexico then beat Haiti 1-0 four days later in the closing match of the group. It was Haiti's only defeat but they were already home and dry and celebrating.

Fifteen teams contested the Asian Group, involving 41 matches, which was won by Australia's collection of allsorts from around the world.

Australia were in the finals for the first time after playing 11 qualifying games, with three previous finalists, North Korea, South Korea and Israel, eliminated.

Australia topped their sub-group, squeezed through on goal difference against Iran (3-0 and 0-2) in the next round, and played three matches against South Korea to win through.

Jim Mackay was their goalscoring hero in the 1-0 victory in a play-off in Hong Kong, following draws in the first two matches.

Twenty-one teams competed for the African Group qualifying prize, Zaire emerging for their first finals appearance after playing 10 games.

Morocco, who performed creditably in the 1970 finals in Mexico, were beaten along with Zambia in the Africa Group Final.

Their second meeting with Zaire was not played, Morocco refusing to welcome them because of a disputed penalty in their first match, but Zaire had already clinched their finals place in West Germany by then.

The success of Zaire was a triumph for Blagoje Vidinic, their manager, who was in charge of Morocco when they qualified in 1970.

Only one other man had led different countries in successive World Cup finals up to that point. Rudolf Vytlacil was in charge of Czechoslovakia in 1962 and Bulgaria in 1966.

The 1974 finals were decided on a new basis of four groups of four, followed by a further two pools of four, with the leaders of these meeting in the Final and the two runners-up contesting third place.

10th World Cup West Germany 1974 Facts

Nine venues were allocated for the increased number of 38 matches. They were: Berlin, Dortmund, Dusseldorf, Frankfurt, Gelsenkirchen, Hamburg, Hanover, Munich, Stuttgart.

The three 'minnows' appearing for the first time in the finals stage, Australia, Haiti and Zaire, were allocated to different groups for the finals draw, which resulted thus:

Group One, Australia, Chile, East Germany, West Germany. Group Two, Brazil, Scotland, Yugoslavia, Zaire. Group Three, Bulgaria, Holland, Sweden, Uruguay. Group Four, Argentina, Haiti, Italy, Poland.

The West Germans were clear favourites to win the new trophy, having the mighty Franz Beckenbauer, Muller and Overath of their 1966 Wembley squad still in peak form.

West Germany had demonstrated their strength by winning the 1972 European Championship, beating the Soviet Union 3-0 in the final.

Oddity of the opening match, between Brazil and Yugoslavia, was that the result was a goalless draw, the third time it had happened in consecutive finals.

The opening match in Group 1, West Germany v Chile, produced the first goal of the finals, by Breitner, and the first sending-off.

Chile lost 1-0 and also Carlos Caszely, for retaliation.

There were four other sendings-off in the series, all from different countries. They were: Raymond Richards (Australia v Chile), Julio Montero-Castillo (Uruguay v Holland), Luis Edmundo Pereira (Brazil v Holland) and Mulamba N'daye (Zaire v Yugoslavia).

One disturbing feature of the 1974 finals was that 84 cautions were issued, almost double the number of yellow cards four years earlier, in addition to the five dismissals.

Facts

10th World Cup
West Germany 1974

The meeting of the two German teams for the first time ended in a single goal win for the East, scored six minutes from time by Sparwasser. This was the West's only defeat in seven games.

Both qualified for the next stage, with East Germany undefeated on top but flattering to deceive. They failed to win any of their three next-stage matches.

Australia were not disgraced. They conceded only five goals to the two Germanys and won their first World Cup finals point with a 0-0 result against Chile despite Richards' sending-off.

Group 2 was a story of desperately bad luck for Scotland, who failed to eliminate Brazil simply because they didn't 'murder' Zaire. The table explains all:

Country	P	W	D	L	F	A	Pts
Yugoslavia	3	1	2	0	10	1	4
Brazil	3	1	2	0	3	0	4
Scotland	3	1	2	0	3	1	4
Zaire	3	0	0	3	0	14	0

In their first match, the Scots beat Zaire only 2-0, the goals coming in the first 33 minutes from Lorimer and Jordan, and therefore set Yugoslavia and Brazil the minimum target to aim for in their meetings with Zaire.

Having held Brazil to a goalless draw, Scotland still nursed hopes of joining the last eight. They needed to beat Yugoslavia in their last group match to advance instead of Brazil.

Yugoslavia had slaughtered Zaire a few days earlier by 9-0, which equalled the record score for a finals match set up by Hungary against South Korea in 1954.

It was not to be. Yugoslavia presented a nine-man defence at Frankfurt until, nine minutes from time, their substitute Karasi scored.

Two minutes from time, Tommy Hutchison equalised and Scotland thought they had levelled up their points and goals difference figures with Brazil, whose match with Zaire at Gelsenkirchen was going on simultaneously.

Then came news on the electronic scoreboard that Brazil had scored a late third goal - and the Scots were left to curse their luck.

10th World Cup West Germany 1974 Facts

A consoling statistic for Scotland... they were the only unbeaten side in the whole tournament!

Billy Bremner was an inspiring captain in six of the seven qualifiers and finals games for Scotland. Davie Hay deputised unfortunately against Czechoslovakia in the last qualifying match, which the Scots lost.

Bremner captained Scotland in the World Cup more times than anyone. During the 1970 and 1974 series, he led 12 times, winning seven, drawing three and losing only two.

Later, Graeme Souness was captain 11 times in 1982 and 1986, winning four, and Roy Aitken 10 times in 1990, also winning four.

Bremner played 15 times in World Cups, spanning three finals.

Denis Law made his last World Cup appearance against Zaire at the age of 34. He took part in four World Cup series, from 1962 to 1974, played 11 times and scored five goals.

Law's cap against Zaire was his 55th for Scotland in a career spanning 16 years and producing 30 goals.

Group 3 was dominated by Holland as expected, with five out of six points and only one goal conceded, but Sweden were to cause an upset.

The Swedes held the Dutch 0-0, then shook Uruguay in their final group match with three second-half goals for the second qualifying spot.

Group 4 brought another big shock, with Italy failing to qualify for the last eight. They could not beat Haiti by more than 3-1, drew with Argentina and lost their last hope by losing 2-0 to Poland, the group winners with maximum points.

Back to earth was Dino Zoff, the Italian goalkeeper, being beaten for the first time in 13 international matches.

Zoff's run ended in the 63rd minute, after an unbroken spell of 1,143 minutes, by Emmanuel Sanon scoring Haiti's first-ever goal in a World Cup finals tie.

The last eight, in two groups, were: Group A, Argentina, Brazil, East Germany, Holland. Group B, Poland, Sweden, West Germany, Yugoslavia.

Holland were the sensation of their group, sweeping aside all three formidable opponents and scoring eight goals while keeping their goal intact.

Facts

10th World Cup
West Germany 1974

South America's finest, Brazil and Argentina, were dazzled by Holland's Total Football, Johan Cruyff leading from the front.

Cruyff scored two of the four against Argentina and one of the two against Brazil, who had Luis Pereira sent off for foul play.

West Germany emulated the Dutch with a 100 per cent return from their three matches, although the outcome was not decided until the last match in Group B, Poland having won their first two games.

West Germany v Poland, billed as the semi-final, was alive almost to the last kick. Tomaszewski saved a German penalty kick taken by Hoeness before Gerd Muller scored the only goal.

Munich's crowd of 77,833 witnessed a Final of pure drama. No World Cup Final before or since has opened so sensationally with a goal in the first minute.

Holland kept possession in a bewildering succession of passes before Cruyff was felled in the penalty area by Hoeness.

Jack Taylor, the English referee, pointed to the penalty spot, Neeskens took the kick and Holland were one up after 80 seconds. Not a single German had touched the ball by that stage!

After 25 minutes, West Germany were awarded a debatable penalty when Jansen brought down Holzenbein. Breitner scored from it, then Muller added a second to put Holland 2-1 down at half-time.

The Germans held out under pressure from the Dutch, and the trophy went to the host nation for a fourth time.

The West Germany manager was Helmut Schoen, who got his final reward after being runners-up in 1966 and third in 1970. The teams were:

West Germany: Maier; Vogts, Schwarzenbeck, Beckenbauer (capt), Breitner, Bonhof, Hoeness, Overath, Grabowski, Muller, Holzenbein.

Holland: Jongbloed; Suurbier, Rijsbergen (sub De Jong), Haan, Krol, Jansen, Van Hanagem, Neeskens, Rep, Cruyff (capt), Rensenbrink (sub Van der Kerkhof).

The leading scorers of the tournament were: Grzegorz Lato (Poland) 7, Andrzej Szarmach (Poland), Johannes Neeskens (Holland) 5 each, Gerd Muller (West Germany), Ralf Edstroem (Sweden), Johnny Rep (Holland) 4 each.

Lato, 24, was the hot-shot hero of Polish football fans. He played 13 years for Poland.

10th World Cup West Germany 1974 Facts

He was first chosen in 1971 and scored 45 goals in 104 international appearances.

The only hat-trick scorer was Dusan Bejevic for Yugoslavia in their 9-0 win over Zaire.

Zaire were so shattered by this defeat that they wanted to return home without playing their final group match with Brazil. FIFA officials persuaded them to see it through.

Total attendance at the finals was 1,774,022, an increase of 101,047 over Mexico 1970 figures, but there were six more matches.

The total number of goals, 97, was down in average at 2.55 per match - the lowest since the World Cup began.

11th World Cup Argentina 1978

11th World Cup Argentina 1978 Facts

Entries for the eleventh series numbered 103, the first time the total had reached three figures.

This was after the usual withdrawals from the African qualifying section - this time the Central African Republic, Sudan, Tanzania and Zaire, the last-named after a disastrous surprise presence in the 1974 finals.

Despite strong demands for an increased number of qualifiers for the finals, FIFA stuck to the previous tournament format of four groups of four, reducing to two groups of four, with the leaders contesting the Final and runners-up playing for third place.

There was great uneasiness over FIFA's decision to go ahead with the finals in Argentina, following the military coup of 1976.

Many nations had reservations about the choice, mindful of the torture and slaughter of an estimated 5,000 people and the disappearance of countless thousands more.

The qualifying rounds went on regardless, with 10 of the 16 to be supplied by the powerful European groups, including West Germany who were exempt as holders.

The Home Countries failed again to supply more than one for the finals - and again Scotland emerged as sole representatives.

England, having failed to qualify for the 1974 finals, had hopes that the new regime under manager Don Revie would bear fruit.

Revie's astonishing reign of success with Leeds United had won for the club a mound of trophies but few friends outside Yorkshire because of their aggressive brand of football.

Revie thought he could engender the same spirit and tactics at national level but indulged in much switching and swapping of team personnel.

The only regular members of the side were Ray Clemence, preferred in goal to Peter Shilton, Mick Channon and Kevin Keegan, who took over as captain after a short spell with Gerry Francis in charge.

The sign of things to come was Scotland's domination of the British Championship for two successive years, 1976 and 1977.

The draw for Group 2 had England in with Italy, Finland and Luxembourg - in essence, a straight home-and-away dogfight in Rome and London.

The spring of 1976 brought early doubts for Revie, with successive defeats 2-1 by Scotland at Hampden Park and 1-0 by Brazil in Los Angeles in the US Bicentennial Tournament.

Facts

11th World Cup
Argentina 1978

He made eight positional changes for the second match in the USA against Italy, albeit keeping his cards close to his chest, and won 3-2.

Mick Channon celebrated his debut as England captain with two goals in this New York match.

Finland home and away were safely negotiated only in terms of maximum points gained, 4-1 in Helsinki and 2-1 at Wembley, while the Italians sharpened their claws in beating Luxembourg 4-1.

A Wembley crowd of 98,000 at the second Finland meeting gave vent to their feelings about England's performance with shouts of 'Rubbish'.

Four weeks later, Italy drew World Cup first blood over England with victory by 2-0.

The state of uncertainty over England's team selection for the two matches in the qualifiers is illustrated by these line-ups:

Finland (home, October 13, 1976): Clemence, Todd, Beattie, P Thompson, Greenhoff, Wilkins, Keegan, Channon, Royle, Brooking, Tueart. Subs: Mills and Hill for Brooking and Tueart.

Italy (away, November 17, 1976): Clemence, Clement, Mills, Greenhoff, McFarland, Hughes, Keegan, Channon, Bowles, Cherry, Brooking. Sub: Beattie for Clement.

Came the dramatic happenings of 1977! Having lost 2-0 to Holland at Wembley in February, with seven positional changes, Revie made a further eight alterations for the World Cup qualifier with Luxembourg only one month later.

Now the line-up was: Clemence, Gidman, Cherry, Kennedy, Watson, Hughes, Keegan, Channon, Royle, T Francis, Hill. Sub: Mariner for Royle.

It was a formation brimful of goals - on paper - but England notched only five clear goals where, in the event, a cricket score was required.

Revie must have suspected then that England were not going to qualify for the World Cup finals for the second time running.

Defeats followed at Wembley in the Home Internationals by Wales (1-0) and Scotland (2-1) - the first time England had been beaten in two consecutive games at Wembley.

The victory for Wales, with a penalty goal by Leighton James, was their first in England for 42 years and their first ever at Wembley.

England then left for an 'acclimatisation tour' of South America... without their manager.

It transpired later that Don Revie had flown secretly to Dubai to negotiate a deal that was to put him in charge of the United Arab Emirates team, five years after their affiliation to FIFA.

11th World Cup Argentina 1978 Facts

England managed to draw all three matches over an eight-day period in June 1977, against Brazil (0-0), Argentina (1-1) and Uruguay (0-0), and had a taste of what to expect were they to qualify for the finals the following year.

Trevor Cherry had two teeth knocked out by a punch from Daniel Bertoni of Argentina - and both players were sent off!

Scotland, also in South America at that time, had a similar bitter experience of Argentine cynicism when Willie Johnston was felled by a savage kidney punch by the opposing full-back Pernia - and again both were sent off!

Revie was back in South America for the matches with Argentina and Uruguay, the latter his final game in charge before resigning.

The FA imposed a ten-year ban on him from English football but Revie won a court order to overturn the ruling a year later.

Ron Greenwood, West Ham's general manager, took over as caretaker manager for the remaining three games of 1977, two of them in the qualifying group, before getting the job full-time for the next four years.

Luxembourg were beaten at home by only two goals when England needed to treble that score to enhance their prospects of progress to the finals.

This was England's first win for seven matches, to be followed by a stirring 2-0 defeat of Italy at a packed Wembley.

It was too late. Italy needed to score only one goal in the last match of the group, at home to Luxembourg. They won 3-0.

England had failed to advance to the finals for the second World Cup series in succession. Group 2 ended thus:

Country	P	W	D	L	F	A	Pts
Italy	6	5	0	1	18	4	10
England	6	5	0	1	15	4	10
Finland	6	2	0	4	11	16	4
Luxembourg	6	0	0	6	2	22	0

Facts

11th World Cup
Argentina 1978

Group 7 was a triangular tournament involving Scotland, Czechoslovakia and Wales, with the Scots the seeded nation for draw purposes.

Scotland and Czechoslovakia were grouped together for the third time in World Cup qualifying stages, having met five times altogether in 1961 and 1973.

The 'score' was 3-2 to the Czechs, with Scotland's record reading: P5 W2 L3 F7 A12 Pts4.

Wales had met Czechoslovakia twice previously in World Cup action in 1957, winning 1-0 in Cardiff and losing 2-0 in Bratislava.

Scotland's manager Willie Ormond, having received the OBE for his sterling efforts after taking over from Tommy Docherty, was shaken by a 5-1 thrashing by England at Wembley on May 24, 1975.

The recovery was instant - nine matches without defeat - but there was no room for complacency as the Czechs struck first with a 2-0 win in Prague.

That win extended the Czechs' unbeaten run to 24 matches since October 1974, when they took a 3-0 beating from England at Wembley in a European Championship match.

The Czechs did not travel well, however, and conceded three goals each to Scotland and Wales on British soil.

They deserved some sympathy in that because of an air strike, they had to sit in a train throughout their night journey to Glasgow because there was no sleeping accommodation available.

The defeat of the Czechs was greeted with an 85,000-strong Hampden Roar and praise for Ally MacLeod who had taken over management of Scotland when Ormond decided to go back to club life and control of Hearts.

MacLeod, who was cruelly nicknamed 'Concorde' because of his large nose, came in on a winning tide of leading Aberdeen to a Scottish League victory in 1976.

So Czechoslovakia, veterans of six World Cup finals, were out along with the Welsh, whose only finals appearance in 1958 was now a distant memory.

Wales, whose last away win over Scotland had been in 1951 by a single goal, tried hard to upset the Scottish applecart in their match at Hampden, before a crowd of 63,000.

The Scots could not afford to drop a point after their opening-match defeat in Prague and their luck was in after 15 minutes' play.

A shot by Dalglish was turned into an own-goal by defender Ian Evans of Crystal Palace, then Rioch and Gemmill hit the woodwork. Scotland 1 Wales 0.

11th World Cup
Argentina 1978

Facts

The return match, which Scotland needed to win to clinch their passport to Argentina, was switched to Liverpool by the Welsh FA because of crowd restrictions at Wrexham and Cardiff.

It was virtually another home match for Scotland as thousands crossed the border to swell the Anfield crowd past the 50,000 mark.

Wales were desperately unlucky when, having held out for 79 minutes, they were penalised for a hand-ball which TV proved clearly had been committed by Joe Jordan.

Don Masson converted the penalty and Dalglish made it 2-0 for Scotland with three minutes left. So Wales were unhappy wooden-spoonists in the Group 7 table:

Country	P	W	D	L	F	A	Pts
Scotland	4	3	0	1	6	3	6
Czechoslovakia	4	2	0	2	4	6	4
Wales	4	1	0	3	3	4	2

The Scots earned the highest praise in eliminating the Czechs, who had surprisingly won the European Championship in 1976 by beating England, Soviet Union, Holland and finally West Germany 5-3 on penalties after extra time.

Northern Ireland in Group 4 were virtually doomed from the day of the draw, which put them in with the Low Countries.

Holland, strongly fancied to win the trophy by the punters, carried all before them to reap 11 points from six games.

Their only blemish was at home to the Irish, who upset the odds by holding the Dutchmen to a 2-2 draw.

The Irish were totally unpredictable. They lost 1-0 in Iceland then wound up the group matches with a resounding 3-0 win over Belgium. Group 5 table:

Country	P	W	D	L	F	A	Pts
Holland	6	5	1	0	11	3	11
Belgium	6	3	0	3	7	6	6
Northern Ireland	6	2	1	3	7	6	5
Iceland	6	1	0	5	2	12	2

Facts

11th World Cup
Argentina 1978

Holland's big worry was that they would be going to Argentina without their inspiring leader Johan Cruyff, who decided to retire from the international scene despite all efforts to persuade him to change his mind. Several other Dutch stars also refused to travel.

Cruyff, three times European Footballer of the Year, scored 33 times for Holland in 48 games.

Eire's eternal hopes of reaching a World Cup finals stage were diminished by the luck of the Group 5 draw which put them in with France, veterans of six finals, and Bulgaria, who had qualified for the previous four.

Eire won three points from their home matches (1-0 v France, 0-0 v Bulgaria) and conceded only three goals in four games.

France went through after missing the two previous finals, thanks partly to their new young star Michel Platini.

Group 3 produced surprise qualifiers in Austria, for the first time in 20 years, at the expense of East Germany, quarter-finalists of 1974.

East Germany were the current Olympic soccer champions, having beaten Poland for the gold medal in 1976.

Poor Malta finished bottom of this group, without a point or indeed a single goal, while letting in 27.

The Maltese were twice savaged 9-0, by East Germany and Austria, although both had been happy to escape earlier on by a single goal from their experience of football on the island soil.

Cyprus suffered similarly in Group 1, pointless and with 24 goals conceded, as Poland went through to the finals and aiming to reach the semi-finals as they did in 1974. They dropped only one point, a 1-1 draw with Portugal.

Sweden went through to their seventh finals appearance, overcoming Norway and Switzerland in Group 6.

Group 8 was won by Spain, who gave away only one goal in four matches - the best defensive record of all nine European groups.

Group 9 featured the Soviet Union against Hungary and Greece and, like England, the Russians failed to qualify for the second successive series - and this after a run of four finals starting with Sweden in 1958.

Hungary's last appearance in the finals had been in England in the Sixties when they reached the quarter-finals, only to be beaten 2-1 by the Soviet Union.

The Russians were surprisingly beaten 1-0 in Greece, allowing Hungary to meet Bolivia from the South American section in a two-match play-off.

11th World Cup Argentina 1978 Facts

The Hungarians won both matches, 6-0 at home and 3-2 in Bolivia, thus completing the European challenge for Argentina 1978.

Europe's ten for the finals were Austria, France, Holland, Hungary, Italy, Poland, Scotland, Spain, Sweden and West Germany.

Brazil came through as usual in Group 1 of the South American qualifiers at the expense of Paraguay and Colombia.

Brazil won their first three matches with their net intact and drew 1-1 with Paraguay in the closing match with the issue beyond doubt.

Uruguay took a shock early exit at the hands of Bolivia in Group 2, having appeared in seven finals for a total of 29 matches.

Bolivia's last appearance in a finals stage, at Brazil 1950, lasted 90 minutes and a defeat of 8-0... by Uruguay!

Peru removed Chile and Ecuador in Group 3 to enter the play-off group of Brazil, Peru and Bolivia. Brazil and Peru qualified, while Bolivia went off to meet Hungary.

The dream ended for Bolivia with the defeat by Hungary, so that in the end they had nothing to show for eight matches.

Their return from those matches read: P8 W3 D1 L4 F10 A25 Pts7. They were left to soldier on for another 16 years before qualifying for the 1994 finals in USA.

The trio of Argentina (as hosts), Brazil and Peru left three vacant spots to be contested by the rest of the world.

These produced, as usual, 100-1 outsiders for the finals. This time there were two, Iran and Tunisia, never before or since at the dizzy heights of a finals spectacular.

The third spot representing Central and North America was taken by Mexico for their eighth finals appearance, the only blip on the record since World War Two being Haiti in the previous series.

Mexico survived in a tight sub-group with USA and Canada, advancing only by superior goals difference. All hinged on the last game, with Mexico holding Canada 0-0. The table tells its own story:

Country	P	W	D	L	F	A	Pts
Mexico	4	1	2	1	3	1	4
USA	4	1	2	1	3	4	4
Canada	4	1	2	1	2	3	4

Facts

11th World Cup
Argentina 1978

Having come through the hard part, Mexico romped home in the six-nations group finals with a return of: P5 W5 D0 L0 F20 A5 Pts10.

Haiti came second with seven points, followed by Canada (5pts), El Salvador (5), Guatemala (3) and Surinam (0).

Top scorers in the section were Mexico, 8-1 winners over Surinam, who at least managed to play 10 matches. In fact, Guatemala and El Salvador each played 11 times.

Tunisia battled through eight matches to become Africa's representatives, beating off the challenge of Egypt and Nigeria at the last stage.

A grand total of 55 matches was played in 13 months, starting in November 1976, to find a victor in the Asia/Oceania section.

Iran were worthy winners for the first time, coming through 12 fixtures with these figures: P12 W10 D2 L0 F20 A3 Pts22.

Iran came ahead of South Korea and Australia - both previous qualifiers - Kuwait and Hong Kong in the group finals.

The draw for the finals: Group 1, Argentina, France, Hungary, Italy. Group 2, Mexico, Poland, Tunisia, West Germany. Group 3, Austria, Brazil, Spain, Sweden. Group 4, Holland, Iran, Peru, Scotland.

In view of their political and military distractions, the Argentines only just beat the clock to have all five venues ready in time. The grounds were at Buenos Aires (River Plate Stadium), Cordoba, Mar del Plata, Mendoza and Rosario.

The River Plate Stadium's pitch was problematic. It looked nice and green but the surface was erratic because of its newness.

On re-laying of the pitch, watering was done using sea water with such disastrous results that it had to be hastily re-turfed.

In its official report, FIFA criticised some of the Argentine pitches: 'Late laying of the turf, combined with wet weather during the competition, resulted in playing surfaces which, with the exception of Cordoba, were not up to the quality one expects for the Final Competition.'

11th World Cup Argentina 1978 Facts

The report particularly pinpointed the surface at Mar del Plata, which 'suffered most and the yielding turf gave poor foothold and kicked up badly.'

With days to go to the grand opening, a bomb exploded near the press centre in Buenos Aires, killing a policeman.

Amnesty International added to the tension with a protest about the Argentine junta, signed by many leading players from the nations due to play in the finals.

An explosion during the actual opening ceremony would have had catastrophic results. Seventy-six thousand people packed the stadium, with a further 1,500 working from the targeted press centre.

The opening match went off like a damp squib. For the fourth time running, it was a boring, goalless draw - this time between the champions West Germany and Poland, who were third-placed in 1974.

British high hopes in the standard-bearers from Scotland quickly changed to shame and dismay, as Peru inflicted a 3-1 defeat in the opening game of Group 4 at Cordoba.

Although the game gave early promise, with Joe Jordan scoring in the 15th minute, Peru took command to win 3-1, with two goals from their hero of the 1970 finals, Teofilo Cubillas, in the last 20 minutes.

Disgrace immediately followed the final whistle, with Scotland's left-wing wizard Willie Johnston, one of the two chosen at random for the mandatory dope check, testing positive.

The Scottish FA pre-empted FIFA action by immediately sending Johnston home and imposing an international life ban on him.

FIFA's official report described the matter as 'a major sensation' but seemed satisfied with the prompt action by the Scottish FA's 'stunned officials'.

FIFA added: 'Football authorities must take positive action to rid the game of such practices before they spread and begin to affect the young players.'

Four days later, having overcome fears that the whole contingent would be expelled, Scotland's morale sank almost without trace when they failed to beat Iran. Result: 1-1.

Scotland's only goal was 'scored' by Iran's centre-half Eskandarian with an intended back-pass from 15 yards.

Holland, rightly seeded No 1 in the group, had already beaten Iran 3-0, Robbie Rensenbrink getting all three goals, including two from penalties awarded against the Iranian 'hackers'.

Facts

11th World Cup Argentina 1978

The only other hat-trick exponent in the series was Cubillas, the Peruvian, also against the Iranians and also including two scored from penalty awards.

With Peru already having established a place in the next round, Scotland were left facing Holland for the other qualifying place.

The Scots put on a face-saving performance in beating the Dutch 3-2 but, for the second successive World Cup finals, they went out on goal difference. The placings:

Country	P	W	D	L	F	A	Pts
Peru	3	2	1	0	7	2	5
Holland	3	1	1	1	5	3	3
Scotland	3	1	1	1	5	6	3
Iran	3	0	1	2	2	8	1

Rensenbrink's first goal for Holland against the Scots, from the penalty spot, was the 1,000th goal in World Cup finals.

Little consolation for Scotland was that Holland went on to contest the Final.

Further cold comfort came from the fact that Scotland had lost only once in six World Cup finals matches in 1974 and 1978.

The short managerial reign of Ally MacLeod was over and Jock Stein was eventually persuaded to pick up many pieces.

The opening match in Group 1 was the trailer to a series of violent play and dodgy refereeing, with the bias seemingly heavy in Argentina's favour throughout.

Hungary's opening match with Argentina was bitterly contested, with the visitors giving like for like after enduring massive intimidation from Argentina's players and crowd alike.

The Hungarians held out until the 75th minute when Argentina made it 2-1, whereupon Hungary's centre-forward Andras Torocsik and the midfielder Tibor Nyilasi were sent off.

Dispirited Hungary were then beaten in this very strong group by Italy and France, 3-1 each time, to return home pointless.

By the time they met Hungary, France were already also out of the hunt, having lost 2-1 to Argentina and Italy.

11th World Cup Argentina 1978 Facts

Once again, Argentina were on the lucky end of two penalty awards, so that they met Italy in the final group match with both teams already assured of entering the next stage.

Italy's Bettega scored the only goal midway in the second half, much to the displeasure of the 77,000 River Plate Stadium crowd and the Argentine team.

As runners-up to Italy, Argentina were 'relegated' to playing their next three matches at Rosario. In retrospect, the Italians, having won all three games, said they would have preferred it the other way round.

In Group 2, the demise of Mexico and Tunisia was almost a foregone conclusion, with Poland (five points) and West Germany (four) the qualifiers. The Germans had the odd group record of P3 W1 D2 L0 F6 A0 Pts4, all their goals coming in the 6-0 demolition of Mexico.

Tunisia were the surprise team of the finals, for having beaten the Mexicans 3-1, they almost upset West Germany in the last critical group match. The Germans' luck prevailed for a 0-0 draw.

Group 3 results reflected a series of grim, defensive football, only eight goals coming from six matches.

Austria and Brazil went through to the next round at the expense of Spain and Sweden, although Brazil's form was lacking and they were lucky to survive.

Their final match was against Austria, who were already assured of progressing, whereas Brazil had to win - which they did with the only goal by Roberto.

That goal was also fortunate for the much-criticised manager Claudio Coutinho, whose effigy had been burned in the streets of Mar del Plata by angry Brazilian supporters.

The two final groups were virtually a battle between the might of Europe in 'A' and the best of South America plus an odd 'guest' from Europe in 'B':

Group A: Austria, Holland, Italy, West Germany. Group B: Argentina, Brazil, Peru, Poland.

Group A matches were allocated to Buenos Aires and Cordoba, with Group B competing at Rosario and Mendoza.

Holland brightened up the hitherto grey series with a scintillating start in their group, beating Austria 5-1.

Johnny Rep scored twice and Rensenbrink converted another penalty as the Dutch enjoyed the smooth Cordoba surface with their flowing Total Football.

Facts

11th World Cup
Argentina 1978

Holland went on for a 2-2 draw with West Germany in their second match, thus avenging to some extent their defeat by the Germans in the 1974 Final. Their equaliser by Rene Van Der Kerkhof came seven minutes from time.

West Germany having been held in a dreary 0-0 draw by Italy in their opening match, now desperately needed not only to beat Austria in their third tie but also to score heavily to boost their goal difference figures.

The Austrians, having lost two games and with only pride to fight for, thwarted their plans and came back from 0-1 at half-time to record a 3-2 victory and eliminate the trophy holders.

The decisive final match in the group, Holland v Italy, thrilled the 70,000 crowd in Buenos Aires as the Dutch fought back to win 2-1.

Italy, who needed to win in view of Holland's superior goal difference, were ahead after 19 minutes when Erny Brandts put through his own goal, but five minutes after the interval, Brandts made amends by equalising for Holland - a bizarre individual World Cup record!

The winning goal was supplied by Aarie Haan with a tremendous long-range shot, beating 'keeper Dino Zoff 14 minutes from time to put Holland into their second successive Final.

Group B started well for Argentina, with two goals by Mario Kempes too much for Poland, and Brazil beat Peru 3-0 with goals from Dirceu (2) and a penalty by substitute Zico.

The inevitable 0-0 draw between Brazil and Argentina took the outcome of the group to the wire.

Brazil were content with a 3-1 win over Poland for a 6-1 goals total, but Argentina responded later in the day with a devastating 6-0 defeat of Peru to a background of alleged bribery.

The eccentric Peruvian goalkeeper Quiroga - he of the crazy dashes into the enemy half and of Argentine birth - rushed into print later to emphasise the integrity of himself and his team-mates.

So to the World Cup Final, a near travesty of a football match, full of fouls and foul tempers, to be won 3-1 after extra time by Argentina.

Kempes again scored twice for the winners, the third time he had done so in Argentina's last four matches.

He finished the series as top scorer with six goals, followed by Cubillas (Peru) and Rensenbrink (Holland) on five each and Leopoldo Luque (Argentina) and Hans Krankl (Austria) on four.

11th World Cup Argentina 1978 Facts

Brazil had to be content with third place over Italy, coming back from one down at the interval to win 2-1.

Argentina's Final team: Fillol, Passarella (capt), Olguin, Galvan, Tarantini, Ardiles, Gallego, Ortiz, Bertoni, Luque, Kempes. Subs: Larrosa, Houseman.

Holland: Jongbloed, Krol (capt), Poortvliet, Brandts, Jansen, Haan, Neeskens, W Van Der Kerkhof, Rep, R Van Der Kerkhof, Rensenbrink. Subs: Suurbier, Nanninga.

The referee was Sergio Gonella (Italy), after Argentina had objected to FIFA over their choice of Abraham Klein (Israel).

The total attendance for the 38 matches in the finals was 1,610,215 - a fall of over 160,000 on the 1974 tournament.

The total number of goals was five up at 102, an average of 2.68 per match.

12th World Cup
Spain 1982

12th World Cup Spain 1982 Facts

The 12th tournament brought a welcome increase in the number of qualifiers for the finals - from 16 to 24 - as the result of persistent pressure on FIFA from the African sector.

Fourteen places went to Europe, including Spain who were exempt as hosts from qualifying.

Africa now had two places, Central and North America two, Asia/Oceania two and South America four, which included Argentina as holders.

There were 109 entries, the highest in 12 tournaments, involving 305 matches for the 22 places at stake.

The increase in qualifiers was incentive for the smaller soccer nations of the world, although still meagre alongside those allocated for Europe and South American zones.

Proportionally, Europe had the edge with 33 competing for 13 places, compared with South America's nine nations battling for three places.

Apart from Europe, the Asia/Oceania sector involved most matches, 61 being played to find the two qualifiers.

The increase in qualifying places stimulated interest among the European countries, each of six groups being expanded to five nations, with two going through from each.

Group 7 took in three competitors, from which the powerful Poland team emerged 100 per cent from meetings with East Germany and Malta.

British interest in the finals, and subsequent advance bookings for 1982 holidays in sunny Spain, was highest since 1958 and Sweden.

England, Scotland and Northern Ireland all qualified, while Wales missed out only on a matter of goal difference.

Wales had tough opponents in Soviet Union and Czechoslovakia in Group 3, but aimed for full points from Iceland and Turkey.

The Soviets, as forecast, headed the group but Welsh hopes were high when the Czechs unexpectedly dropped a point in Iceland.

Three weeks later, Wales were shocked by Iceland holding them to a 2-2 draw at Swansea and went out to a Czech goals return of 15-6 against their 12-7.

England managed to qualify in Group 4, though more by luck than judgment, along with Hungary. They did so at the very last of the 20 group fixtures, after failing to reach the previous two finals.

Facts

12th World Cup
Spain 1982

England flattered to deceive in beating Norway 4-0 in the first match of the group - remarkably the biggest win of all 20 in that section.

Captained again by Phil Thompson, they went down 2-1 in Romania, and fared as badly with Kevin Keegan in charge - oddly enough, until they played Hungary.

Having won 3-1 in Hungary, thanks to two goals by Trevor Brooking, England had to beat them again to win second place and qualify.

At Wembley on November 18, 1981, Paul Mariner scored the most important of his 13 international goals. England 1 Hungary 0. They were the Magyars' only two group defeats.

Manager Ron Greenwood was not impressed by England's defensive record - eight goals conceded in eight matches - and Don Howe, Arsenal coach, was called upon.

Howe had played for England at left-back in the 1958 finals and was capped 23 times. His arrival for the finals of 1982 was to bring about a dramatic tightening-up of the defence.

Another British star from the 1958 finals to reappear in 1982 was Northern Ireland's Billy Bingham, who had won 56 caps.

Bingham was manager of the Irish team competing in Group 6 and led them to the finals for the first time since his playing days of 1958, when they actually reached the quarter-final stage.

Northern Ireland competed in the same 1982 qualifying group as Scotland, against formidable opposition in Sweden and Portugal.

The two British teams drew in both their meetings, but Scotland's unpredictable double over Sweden gave them top spot with the Irish in second place.

Scotland, now managed by Jock Stein for a second spell, were thus in the World Cup finals for the third consecutive tournament.

Gordon Strachan, who scored the vital only goal in the opening match in Sweden - it was the first of his international career - went on to excel in the finals. He was voted by the Spanish newspapers the best player of his group and was also included in their world team.

Scotland could not agree on a settled captain, despite their success in qualifying. Three different players skippered in the eight qualifying games - Gemmill, McGrain and Hartford - and McGrain (once) and Souness (twice) in the three finals matches.

12th World Cup Spain 1982 Facts

Eire, like Wales, failed by a whisker to make up a quartet of British Isles representatives in the finals, after a tense three-cornered tussle in Group 2.

The great surprise of the qualifying competition came in Group 2 with the elimination of Holland, masters of Total Football in reaching the World Cup Finals of 1974 and 1978.

Holland were among the top four in the early betting lists to win the trophy, yet failed to qualify in the modest company of Belgium, Eire, France and Cyprus.

Holland yielded three points to Eire and also lost in Belgium and France, the ultimate group qualifiers. Eire had ten points, equal with France, but with an inferior goal difference of six against the French 12.

Eire claimed one doubtful distinction. Their opening match, which they won 3-2 in Cyprus, was played on March 26, 1980 - nearly 27 months before the first game in the finals in Spain!

Groups 1 and 5 each produced clearcut qualifiers in West Germany, Austria, Yugoslavia and Italy, and were destined to supply the Final contestants.

West Germany in Group 1 were irresistible, scoring 33 goals in eight victorious matches and conceding only three. Finland went for 11 and Albania ten.

Italy, managed by Enzo Bearzot and reinforced by Paolo Rossi, star performer in the 1978 finals, finished a comfortable second behind Yugoslavia in Group 5 but moved up in the betting stakes after taking three out of four points from Yugoslavia, the eventual group winners.

Rossi had been banned for three years after alleged involvement in a betting scandal but the sentence was reduced to two years and he was back with Italy for their 1982 World Cup campaign.

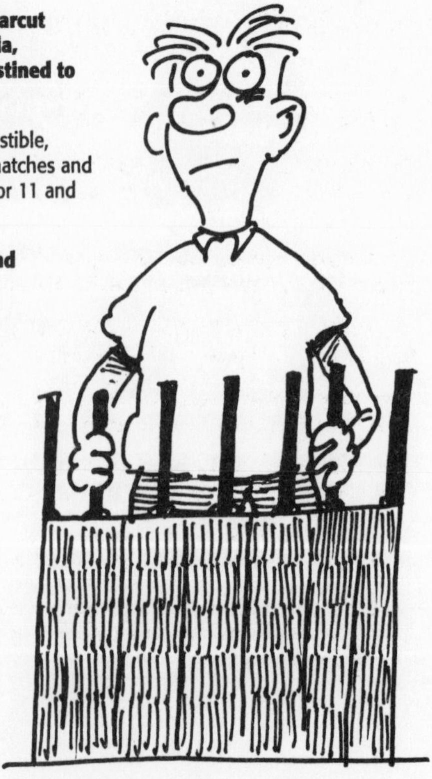

Facts

12th World Cup
Spain 1982

The European qualifiers had seen the taking of many big scalps in Holland, Bulgaria, Romania, Denmark, Sweden, Switzerland, Portugal and East Germany, but the 14-strong representation for the finals looked ominous for the rest of the world. They were:

Austria, Belgium, Czechoslovakia, England, France, Hungary, Italy, Northern Ireland, Poland, Scotland, Soviet Union, Spain, West Germany and Yugoslavia.

Argentina as holders led the South American challenge, but their supporters wondered about the psychological effect the Falklands war, which had just ended, might have on their performance.

The Argentines were confident enough, still with their 1978 manager Cesar Luis Menotti and boosted by young Diego Maradona at the start of his four spectacular and controversial World Cup series.

Along with Argentina came Brazil, Chile and Peru.

Out of Africa came Cameroon and Algeria, both first-time qualifiers, to add spice to the enlarged finals party.

They came the hard way, travelling vast distances, and each survived eight matches. Algeria lost once to Niger, Cameroon twice to Zaire and Zimbabwe.

Fifty-four matches in the Central and North American section yielded newcomers to World Cup finals in Honduras. They were accompanied to Spain by El Salvador, who played in Mexico in 1970.

All 15 group finals matches were played in Honduras, the table ending in this order: Honduras, El Salvador, Mexico, Canada, Cuba, Haiti.

The qualifiers from the Asia/Oceania sector, Kuwait and New Zealand, were footsore and weary before they even arrived in Spain.

Kuwait played nine matches, losing only to China, and headed the three other group finalists to qualify for their one and only time.

New Zealand also achieved a one-off World Cup finals appearance after playing an incredible 15 matches involving 60,000 miles of travel!

They had eight games in a sub-group, knocking out Australia, then six group finals matches and a vital play-off with China.

New Zealand won 5-0 away to Saudi Arabia in the last group finals match, exactly the margin required to draw level with the Chinese on goal difference.

12th World Cup Spain 1982 Facts

The last long haul was to Singapore for the play-off, a 2-1 victory over China - and then more air miles to Spain.

There were goals galore in this group, Fiji being thrashed in turn by Australia (10-0) and New Zealand (13-0), the latter a World Cup record score until 16 years later.

The unhappy Fijians had travelled to Melbourne and Auckland to concede those 23 goals, all in the space of 48 hours!

The scene was set for Spain and 52 finals games, an increase of 14 over the 1978 series and necessitating a new groupings system.

The first stage was six groups of four countries each, the top two of each group then forming four groups of three each. The four winners then played semi-final knock-out matches, followed by the third-place decider and the Final in Madrid.

Fourteen venues were chosen for the tournament: Alicante, Barcelona, Bilbao, Elche, Gijon, La Coruna, Madrid, Malaga, Oviedo, Seville, Valencia, Valladolid, Vigo, Zaragoza.

Five nations entered the draw for a World Cup finals for the first time: Algeria, Cameroon, Honduras, Kuwait, New Zealand. All were kept apart in the six first-round groups, which were as follows:

Group 1: Cameroon, Italy, Peru, Poland.

Group 2: Algeria, Austria, Chile, West Germany.

Group 3: Argentina, Belgium, El Salvador, Hungary.

Group 4: Czechoslovakia, England, France, Kuwait.

Group 5: Honduras, Northern Ireland, Spain, Yugoslavia.

Group 6: Brazil, New Zealand, Scotland, Soviet Union.

The opening match, traditionally involving the holders, was watched by 95,000 spectators in Barcelona and produced a goal for the first time in 20 years.

The long succession of goalless draws was broken by the highly-improved Belgium side, who had reached the European Championship Final of 1980, losing 2-1 to West Germany.

Belgium's Vandenbergh scored the only goal on the hour to beat champions Argentina, for whom Maradona struck the crossbar with a free kick but was otherwise well contained.

It was the first time that the champions had been beaten in the opening match of a series since 1950, when Italy lost 3-2 to Sweden.

Facts

12th World Cup
Spain 1982

Belgium and Argentina each won twice to qualify from Group 3, Argentina scoring a fine 4-1 win over Hungary with Maradona (2) and the former Tottenham player Ossie Ardiles among the goals.

Hungary were eliminated from Group 3 but not before registering a World Cup finals record score of 10-1 against El Salvador at Elche.

Three of the goals were scored by Laszlo Kiss - the first substitute to do the hat-trick in a World Cup finals match.

El Salvador were left to ruminate on two World Cup finals appearances, 1970 and 1982, with a point-less record of six games - 22 goals against and the only goal converted in the humiliating defeat against Hungary by Zapata somewhere in an eight-goal second half.

Group 2 featured one of the biggest upsets in the history of the World Cup, Algeria deservedly beating the well-backed West Germany team 2-1.

The Africans excelled in the intense heat, particularly their star Lakhder Belloumi, who scored the winning goal. He had earlier been voted African Footballer of the Year.

Chile, who had had an easy passage to the finals against Ecuador and Paraguay, were the group's weaklings, losing all three matches.

They had failed to win over their last three finals and had to go back 20 years to their first success, when they took third place in their own country.

West Germany's margin of victory over Chile of 4-1 was due to a hat-trick by Karl-Heinz Rummenigge, the European Footballer of the Year in 1980 and 1981, and was a major factor in the group's final reckoning.

There was grave suspicion of an unlikely 'love affair' between the Germans and Austria in their last decisive match. A score of 1-0 to West Germany suited both contestants but the Algerians rightly felt aggrieved. The final group table explains why:

Country	P	W	D	L	F	A	Pts
West Germany	3	2	0	1	6	3	4
Austria	3	2	0	1	3	1	4
Algeria	3	2	0	1	5	5	4
Chile	3	0	0	3	3	8	0

12th World Cup Spain 1982 Facts

Algeria protested to FIFA but without success. The watching manager of the French squad, Michel Hidalgo, was said to have recommended the European 'collaborators' for the Nobel Peace Prize.

Group 1 was a dreary affair of five draws out of six, with Poland's 5-1 demolition of Peru the only positive result. They finished top.

Italy looked anything but potential champions as their 1-1 draw in the last match against Cameroon sent them through to the next round. They had scored twice to the Africans' once in three matches. Close as that.

England in Group 4 opened spectacularly, Bryan Robson making World Cup history with the fastest goal, after only 27 seconds, against France.

England conceded their only goal in the group games in beating the French 3-1 and finished 100 per cent to qualify for the next stage.

England were very tight in defence under the captaincy of full-back Mick Mills, but the goals dried up as the tournament progressed and they were to return home unbeaten after five games with a 6-1 goals aggregate.

Controversy, with a touch of pure farce, surrounded the meeting between Kuwait, who were coached at great expense by Brazilian Carlos Alberto, and France.

With less than 15 minutes to go and France leading 3-1, the Kuwaitis walked off after a long protest about a further French goal which they claimed should not have counted as they had stopped playing on hearing a whistle. It was not the referee's.

Prince Fahid, resplendent in flowing robes, went to the touchline with Carlos Alberto to persuade them to return to the pitch. They did so - and the referee then disallowed the 'goal' that brought it all on.

Safety first seemed the order of the day in Group 5 matches, with Northern Ireland and Spain qualifying for round two. Three of the six matches were drawn, with a total of only nine goals - the lowest of the six groups.

Spain emulated Italy in that they went through on the slender thread of a better goals aggregate. Had the Irish beaten Spain by more than a single goal in the closing group game, Yugoslavia would have stayed in to Spain's embarrassment in their big year.

Facts

12th World Cup
Spain 1982

Northern Ireland gave their finest display of the tournament in beating Spain against the odds, mainly the stifling heat of Valencia and an eccentric Portuguese referee.

Gerry Armstrong got the goal two minutes into the second half and the Irish held out with ten men for the last half-hour after Mal Donaghy was sent off for 'pushing'. Pat Jennings in goal was unbeatable.

The Irish set up a World Cup record by giving a first cap to Manchester United's youngster Norman Whiteside against Yugoslavia, at the age of 17 years 41 days, making him the youngest player ever to appear in a finals.

Scotland were unfortunate to have Brazil in their Group 6, which boiled down to a tussle with Soviet Union for second place.

The Scots had Kenny Dalglish and skipper Danny McGrain, playing in their third World Cup finals, in their opening match against New Zealand, who were a mix of a team that included three Scottish-born players.

John Wark scored twice in Scotland's five-goal haul but they were to regret giving away two second-half goals, which weighed in the Soviet Union's favour at the death.

Graeme Souness took over the captaincy after the first game, and was to retain it for Scotland's next six World Cup matches.

There was a brief moment of Scottish glory when David Narey put them ahead against Brazil but the dream faded as their opponents moved up a gear after 1-1 at the interval to finish on 4-1.

The Scots had been eliminated after three matches for the third time in successive World Cup finals - purely on goal difference.

The second-round qualifiers therefore added up to ten Europeans against two South Americans... and on European soil.

The four groups comprising 12 matches, all for some strange reason to be played in only two cities, were thus:

Group A, Belgium, Poland, Soviet Union. Group B, England, Spain, West Germany. Group C, Argentina, Brazil, Italy. Group D, Austria, France, Northern Ireland.

Groups A and C were in Barcelona at Nou Camp and Sarria Stadiums respectively, with Group B at the Bernabeu and Group D at the Calderon, both in Madrid.

The sudden resurgence at this point of the 'old soldiers' of World Cup campaigning, West Germany and Italy, seemed to justify the move to grander stages.

The big names of world soccer, like Zico, Falcao, Boniek, Rossi, Rummenigge and Platini, emerged to the bright lights of greater theatre.

12th World Cup
Spain 1982

Facts

England failed to rise to the occasion, watched as they were by two gates of 75,000 each for their quarter-finals at Bernabeu.

Both matches ended goalless, against West Germany then Spain, although a shot from the injured Rummenigge which hit the bar in the closing minutes would have sealed England's fate at the outset had it been a couple of inches lower.

Glenn Hoddle's non-selection for the quarter-finals brought wide criticism of Greenwood, particularly as the injured Kevin Keegan and Brooking were to appear only as substitutes in the very last of five matches.

Hoddle had played only one full match - against Kuwait - and as a substitute for injured Robson in the previous game against the Czechs.

West Germany settled the issue by beating Spain 2-1 to the disappointment of most of the 90,000 at the Bernabeu Stadium.

Group C produced the fireworks of the round, and most goals, with Italy now looking irresistible under the inspiration of Paolo Rossi.

Argentina were dismissed, first by Italy 2-1 and then by Brazil 3-1, and had a player sent off in each game - Americo Gallego and Diego Maradona.

The scene was set for one of the greatest World Cup clashes, Italy v Brazil, watched unfortunately by a capacity crowd of only 44,000 at Barcelona's smaller Sarria Stadium.

This was Rossi's finest hour, his rehabilitation after the alleged bribes scandal finally accomplished with a brilliant hat-trick for an Italian 3-2 win and qualification for the semi-finals.

It was a match that Italy had to win - a draw would have given Brazil top group spot on goal difference - and they attacked from the start.

The goals came in the this order: Rossi 1-0, Socrates 1-1, Rossi 2-1 (half-time), Falcao 2-2, Rossi 3-2. With 15 minutes left, Dino Zoff then stopped everything the desperate Brazilians threw at him.

Poland virtually clinched the qualification from Group A in their first match against Belgium with a 3-0 win, all three scored by Zbigniew Boniek, with solid backing-up from Grzegorz Lato, top scorer in the 1974 finals.

The Soviet Union could manage only a single goal against Belgium, so that Poland put up the shutters against their old Russian rivals and bored rigid 65,000 at Nou Camp and countless TV millions.

Northern Ireland fought Austria to a 2-2 draw in Group D, Billy Hamilton scoring twice, but French class told in their other tie - as indeed it had done in the last Irish appearance in the finals.

Facts

12th World Cup
Spain 1982

France beat Northern Ireland 4-0 in a 1958 quarter-final; this time it was 4-1 (Giresse 2, Rocheteau 2), with the consolation goal for Gerry Armstrong - his third in the series.

The semi-final pairings were Italy v Poland (in Barcelona) and West Germany v France (in Seville).

Italy, buzzing as never before with the help of the re-born Rossi, were clear favourites to dispose of Poland, who were without their inspirational striker Boniek.

Boniek, who was due to join Juventus for £1 million after the finals, was under suspension after receiving two yellow cards.

Lato moved up as striker but his best days were past and Poland were well beaten 2-0.

Rossi was again on target with a goal in each half.

The other semi-final was a real cliffhanger, with six goals, extra time and a penalty shoot-out.

West Germany were first to score through Littbarski, but France made it 1-1 ten minutes later with a Platini penalty.

There was no further scoring in the second half, during which the tables were turned against France in sickening fashion.

The German goalkeeper Schumacher knocked substitute Patrick Battiston unconscious with a vicious forearm blow as the Frenchman was rounding him towards an empty goal. Amazingly, Schumacher stayed on.

Battiston lost some teeth and was badly hurt, so that manager Hidalgo had to call on his remaining substitute, leaving him nothing in hand for extra time.

Tresor and Giresse put France 3-1 ahead after the first period of extra time, then the Germans made an inspired change by bringing on the injured Rummenigge.

Rummenigge made it 3-2 with eight minutes left, then Klaus Fischer equalised two minutes from time.

For the first time in World Cup history, a semi-final was to be decided on penalties. The contest was breathtaking.

Giresse scored for France, Kaltz equalised; Amoros scored, Breitner equalised; Rocheteau scored, Stielike didn't. France 3-2 up.

Didier Six failed, Littbarski scored; Platini scored, Rummenigge scored. France 4 West Germany 4.

Finally, Schumacher saved from Max Bossis, then Horst Hrubesch scored. France cruelly lost 5-4 and West Germany advanced to their fourth World Cup Final.

12th World Cup Spain 1982 Facts

France, exhausted, bruised and dispirited, still managed to raise themselves for the losers' play-off, but Poland won 3-2 to take third place for the second time in three tournaments.

The competitive edge for the Final could hardly have been keener, with West Germany and Italy on identical records of three previous Finals and two victories.

What greater incentive than to draw level with the great Brazilians as hat-trick winners?

Italy: Zoff (capt), Bergomi, Scirea, Collovati, Cabrini, Oriali, Gentile, Tardelli, Conti, Rossi, Graziani. Subs: Altobelli, Causio.

West Germany: Schumacher, Kaltz, Stielike, K-H Forster, B Forster, Dremmler, Breitner, Briegel, Rummenigge (capt), Fischer, Littbarski. Subs: Hrubesch, Muller.

The crowd of 90,000 in the Bernabeu Stadium saw a disappointing, negative first half, although Italy failed to take a half-time lead by missing from the penalty spot.

After 25 minutes, Antonio Cabrini shot wide of the German goal to become the first player to miss a penalty in a World Cup Final.

The second half was much sharper and Rossi - who else? - put Italy ahead after 57 minutes.

The Germans were now forced to open up and Italy soared to 3-0 with goals by Tardelli (69 minutes) and Altobelli (81 minutes). The Tardelli goal was hailed as one of the best-worked moves in World Cup history.

The Germans came back six minutes from time with a goal by Breitner, but Italy were worthy winners and Rossi the man of the tournament.

For the first time the Final was refereed by a South American - Arnaldo Cesar Coelho from Brazil.

Rossi's six goals in the late stages of the competition put him top of the scorers, with Rummenigge second on five and Boniek and Brazil's Zico on four each.

Dino Zoff, at the age of 40, was the oldest captain to lift the World Cup trophy.

At 17, Italy's defender Giuseppe Bergomi became the youngest player ever to appear in a World Cup Final.

Italy were unbeaten in the series, with 12 goals for and six against from seven games.

Denmark were the only team to beat them in the entire World Cup campaign, taking in eight qualifying round matches. Italy lost to the Danes 3-1 back in June 1981.

France were the top-scoring team with 16 goals, and the average per game in the finals was 2.81, an increase over the two previous finals.

The Changing Years

Total Football and the Cry from Africa

The Changing Years Facts

The three finals of 1974, 1978 and 1982 showed a total increase of 32 matches over the three series of the Swinging Sixties.

Thirty-six nations were involved in 128 matches, a figure boosted by FIFA's decision to step up the number of qualifiers to 24 in 1982.

Argentina emerged as the strong force from South America and Italy were back on song with their third win and the main challenge to West Germany as the No 1 European power.

Holland thrilled students of the game with their sweeping Total Football, taking them to two successive Final matches.

The bigger challenge from the African nations resulted in four coming through the qualifiers. Tunisia became the first African country to win a finals match in 1978, followed by Algeria's stunning defeat of West Germany in 1982.

Britain's flag was kept flying by Scotland, who qualified for three consecutive finals, but England were in the doldrums, missing out twice.

Poland improved dramatically and shared top spot with West Germany of 20 matches in the three tournaments. Brazil played 19, Argentina 18, Italy 17 and Holland 14, the last-named in only two finals series.

Algeria (3 matches): 1982, beat West Germany, Chile, lost to West Germany.

Argentina (18 matches): 1974, beat Haiti, drew with Italy, East Germany, lost to Poland, Holland, Brazil; 1978, beat Hungary, France, Poland, Peru, Holland, drew with Brazil, lost to Italy; 1982, beat Hungary, El Salvador, lost to Belgium, Italy, Brazil.

Australia (3 matches): 1974, drew with Chile, lost to East Germany, West Germany.

Austria (11 matches): 1978, beat Spain, Sweden, West Germany, lost to Brazil, Holland, Italy; 1982, beat Chile, Algeria, drew with Northern Ireland, lost to West Germany, France.

Belgium (5 matches): 1982, beat Argentina, El Salvador, drew with Hungary, lost to Poland, USSR.

Brazil (19 matches): 1974, beat Zaire, East Germany, Argentina, drew with Yugoslavia, Scotland, lost to Holland, Poland; 1978, beat Austria, Peru, Poland, Italy, drew with Sweden, Spain, Argentina; 1982, beat Soviet Union, Scotland, New Zealand, Argentina, lost to Italy.

Bulgaria (3 matches): 1974, drew with Sweden, Uruguay, lost to Holland.

Cameroon (3 matches): 1982, drew with Peru, Poland, Italy.

Facts

The Changing Years

Chile (6 matches): 1974, drew with East Germany, Australia, lost to West Germany; 1982, lost to Austria, West Germany, Algeria.

Czechoslovakia (3 matches): 1982, drew with Kuwait, France, lost to England.

East Germany (6 matches): 1974, beat Australia, West Germany, drew with Chile, Argentina, lost to Brazil, Holland.

El Salvador (3 matches): 1982, lost to Hungary, Belgium, Argentina.

England (5 matches): 1982, beat France, Czechoslovakia, Kuwait, drew with West Germany, Spain.

France (10 matches): 1978, beat Hungary, lost to Italy, Argentina; 1982, beat Kuwait, Austria, Northern Ireland, drew with Czechoslovakia, lost to England, West Germany (on penalties), Poland.

Haiti (3 matches): 1974, lost to Italy, Poland, Argentina.

Holland (14 matches): 1974, beat Uruguay, Bulgaria, Argentina, East Germany, Brazil, drew Sweden, lost to West Germany; 1978, beat Iran, Austria, Italy, drew with Peru, West Germany, lost to Scotland, Argentina.

Honduras (3 matches): 1982, drew with Spain, Northern Ireland, lost to Yugoslavia.

Hungary (6 matches): 1978, lost to Argentina, Italy, France; 1982, beat El Salvador, drew with Belgium, lost to Argentina.

Iran (3 matches): 1978, drew with Scotland, lost to Holland, Peru.

Italy (17 matches): 1974, beat Haiti, drew with Argentina, lost to Poland; 1978, beat France, Hungary, Argentina, Austria, drew with West Germany, lost to Holland, Brazil; 1982, beat Argentina, Brazil, Poland, West Germany, drew with Poland, Peru, Cameroon.

Kuwait (3 matches): 1982, drew with Czechoslovakia, lost to France, England.

Mexico (3 matches): 1978, lost to Tunisia, West Germany, Poland.

New Zealand (3 matches): 1982, lost to Scotland, USSR, Brazil.

Northern Ireland (5 matches): 1982, beat Spain, drew with Yugoslavia, Honduras, Austria, lost to France.

Peru (9 matches): 1978, beat Scotland, Iran, drew with Holland, lost to Brazil, Poland, Argentina; 1982, drew with Cameroon, Italy, lost to Poland.

The Changing Years Facts

Poland (20 matches): 1974, beat Argentina, Haiti, Italy, Sweden, Yugoslavia, Brazil, lost to West Germany; 1978, beat Tunisia, Mexico, Peru, drew with West Germany, lost to Argentina, Brazil; 1982, beat Peru, Belgium, France, drew with Italy, Cameroon, USSR, lost to Italy.

Scotland (9 matches): 1974, beat Zaire, drew with Brazil, Yugoslavia; 1978, beat Holland, drew with Iran, lost to Peru; 1982, beat New Zealand, USSR, lost to Brazil.

Soviet Union (5 matches): 1982, beat New Zealand, Belgium, drew with Scotland, Poland, lost to Brazil.

Spain (8 matches): 1978, beat Sweden, drew with Brazil, lost to Austria; 1982, beat Yugoslavia, drew with Honduras, England, lost to Northern Ireland, West Germany.

Sweden (9 matches): 1974, beat Uruguay, Yugoslavia, drew with Bulgaria, Holland, lost to Poland, West Germany; 1978, drew with Brazil, lost to Austria, Spain.

Tunisia (3 matches): 1978, beat Mexico, drew with West Germany, lost to Poland.

Uruguay (3 matches): 1974, drew with Bulgaria, lost to Holland, Sweden.

West Germany (20 matches): 1974, beat Chile, Australia, Yugoslavia, Sweden, Poland, Holland, lost to East Germany; 1978, beat Mexico, drew with Poland, Tunisia, Italy, Holland, lost to Austria; 1982, beat Chile, Austria, Spain, France (on penalties), drew with England, lost to Algeria, Italy.

Yugoslavia (9 matches): 1974, beat Zaire, drew with Brazil, Scotland, lost to West Germany, Poland, Sweden; 1982, beat Honduras, drew with Northern Ireland, lost to Spain.

Zaire (3 matches): 1974, lost to Scotland, Yugoslavia, Brazil.

Referees over the three tournaments came from: 1974 England (Taylor), 1978 Italy (Gonella), 1982 Brazil (Coelho).

13th World Cup Mexico 1986

13th World Cup Mexico 1986 Facts

Europe's international footballers heard with dismay that Mexico had been named by FIFA to stage the World Cup finals for the second time in 16 years.

They recalled matches played in intense heat to suit the all-powerful TV lords, plus the high altitude of many grounds.

There was also the fact that no European country had ever won the World Cup outside that continent.

Colombia was originally chosen as host but it had neither the money nor facilities to cope with 24 competing nations.

While the qualifying rounds were being contested worldwide by a record 118 countries throughout 1985, severe earthquakes shook Mexico City, resulting in 9,500 deaths.

Fortunately for the World Cup, none of the nine venues was seriously damaged and everything went to schedule.

England, Scotland and Northern Ireland again survived the qualifying rounds, although European hopes rested elsewhere.

West Germany were aiming for their fifth World Cup Final appearance under their new manager, Franz Beckenbauer.

First, the Germans had to negotiate a very strong European Group 2 containing Sweden, Czechoslovakia and Portugal, with Malta as target practice.

West Germany were already certain to qualify before losing at home to jubilant Portugal, whose only previous finals appearance had been in the days of Eusebio in 1966.

England, under new manager Bobby Robson since 1984, and Northern Ireland, still bubbling with Billy Bingham, qualified from Group 3.

England were unbeaten in eight games with a healthy 21-2 goals account, but the Irish squeezed through one point ahead of Romania.

Romania, suspicious of the England 0 Northern Ireland 0 scoreline, had to be reminded that the Irish had completed the double over them only four weeks before.

Scotland and Wales clashed in Group 7 at Hampden Park, where an Ian Rush goal inflicted the first home defeat on the Scots in a World Cup match in 20 years.

Facts

13th World Cup
Mexico 1986

Their return in Cardiff six months later was critical for three countries. Spain, Wales and Scotland were all on six points with one match to play.

Spain beat Iceland, leaving the others to a 1-1 draw and curtains for Wales on goal difference.

That vital Scottish goal came from the penalty spot, nine minutes from time, converted by Davie Cooper who was substitute for the injured Gordon Strachan in the second half.

Thirty minutes after the final whistle, Scotland's legendary manager Jock Stein collapsed and died. The celebrating nation was instantly grief-stricken and silent.

The Scots had to overcome another hurdle before their World Cup fate was decided - a two-leg play-off against the winners of the Oceania group.

Australia had to account for Israel, New Zealand and Taiwan before facing the Scots, who finally qualified with home-and-away scores of 2-0 and 0-0.

Alex Ferguson, manager of Aberdeen, was persuaded to take over Scotland on a part-time basis for the duration of the World Cup.

From Australia to Mexico, Ferguson was to become the most-travelled, part-time, close-season manager in World Cup history.

The other European groups resulted according to the formbook, though France and Bulgaria were closely challenged by East Germany in Group 4.

East Germany had lost their way after the solitary finals experience over the Wall in 1974. Football unification was still years away.

France had much support in the betting market. Back in the squad was Jean-Pierre Papin to boost the World Cup experience of Platini, Giresse and Tigana.

Poland and Hungary won Groups 1 and 5, with the runners-up Belgium and Holland engaging in a play-off.

Holland were to miss out for a second finals running. They won and lost their play-off games but Belgium qualified on away goals.

Eire had little hope in Group 6 and were beaten at home 4-1 in the closing match by Denmark, who qualified along with runners-up Soviet Union.

With Italy already through as champions, Europe's hopes were higher than usual for a series in hot and lofty foreign climes.

Europe's challengers, 14-strong, were: Belgium, Bulgaria, Denmark, England, France, Hungary, Italy, Northern Ireland, Poland, Portugal, Scotland, Soviet Union, Spain and West Germany.

13th World Cup Mexico 1986 Facts

In South America, Brazil, Argentina and Uruguay played four games each to qualify, with the fourth place going to Paraguay after eight matches involving a play-off group.

Paraguay were back for the first time since 1958, when France whipped them 7-3 in their opening game, and Uruguay reappeared after an absence of two series.

The remaining groups far and wide yielded five interesting qualifiers to join Mexico, who were exempt as hosts. They were Algeria, Canada, Iraq, Morocco and South Korea.

This was to be the only appearance of Canada and Iraq in World Cup finals in the 20th Century and the reward of good results and arduous journeys.

Canada, initially given a free ride by Jamaica's withdrawal, came through eight matches without defeat, disposing of Haiti and Costa Rica in the final round of the North and Central American matches.

Iraq also qualified after eight games in the Asian sector, although they lost to Qatar and United Arab Emirates on the way.

South Korea won seven matches out of eight to claim the other Asian qualifying place, losing away to Malaysia.

The South Koreans had come a long way since losing to Hungary (9-0) and Turkey (7-0) in the 1958 finals. They were to qualify four times altogether before the turn of the Century.

From Africa came Morocco, revisiting Mexico after their only previous qualification in 1970, and Algeria, sensational conquerors of West Germany and Chile in Spain four years earlier.

The new format of the finals was welcomed by the majority of the 24 qualifiers, but with the same number of matches, 52, as in Spain.

Six groups of four produced 16 countries for the second round, with the four best third-placed in each group joining the top 12 in a straight knock-out. Extra time and penalty shoot-outs would apply if required in these clashes. First-round groupings were:

Group A: Argentina, Bulgaria, Italy, South Korea.

Group B: Belgium, Iraq, Mexico, Paraguay.

Group C: Canada, France, Hungary, Soviet Union.

Group D: Algeria, Brazil, Northern Ireland, Spain.

Group E: Denmark, Scotland, Uruguay, West Germany.

Group F: England, Morocco, Poland, Portugal.

Facts

13th World Cup
Mexico 1986

The nine venues selected by the Mexicans were Guadalajara, Irapuato, Leon, Mexico City, Monterrey, Nezahualcoyotl, Puebla, Queretaro and Toluca.

England's prospects seemed good on paper, but there were problems for manager Bobby Robson in the run-up games, not least over his captain namesake, Bryan Robson.

Robson the player was having shoulder problems over a protracted period, starting well before Robson the manager's appointment, and the fourth dislocation occurred after only two finals games.

The manager had to depend more on Glenn Hoddle's skills as a result, and also recalled Shilton as captain for the remaining World Cup matches.

In the early days of the Robson shoulder, which was to become almost as great a national talking-point as Denis Compton's knee 30 years past, Peter Shilton had enjoyed a run of seven matches unbeaten as stand-in skipper.

During that spell in 1983, starting against Wales in February, Shilton let in only two goals and had five clean sheets.

Bryan Robson was substituted in both of England's opening Group F games, after which an early exit was the likely outcome of defeat by Portugal and a goalless draw with Morocco.

Ray Wilkins was sent off against Morocco for foolishly throwing the ball at the referee five minutes before half-time and did not play again in the tournament.

England, without Wilkins and Robson, desperately needed to beat Poland to avoid an early return home in disgrace. They did so superbly.

The score was 3-0, all three scored by Gary Lineker - England's first World Cup finals hat-trick since Geoff Hurst's in 1966.

Morocco's meeting with Portugal in the last match of the group meant that the winners would head the group and the losers would be out. Result: Portugal 1 Morocco 3!

13th World Cup Mexico 1986 Facts

Group A supplied the opening match on May 31, champions Italy being held by a Bulgarian goal five minutes from time at the Azteca Stadium, Mexico City, watched by 95,000 spectators.

Group A also saw signs of Maradona magic to come, as Argentina collected five points from three games. Italy led them after five minutes with a penalty for handball, but Maradona scored later for a 1-1 draw.

'Oh dear', was the only comment after Maradona laid on all three goals in the 3-1 defeat of South Korea. The unfortunate 'keeper's name... Oh.

Brazil swept through Group D with three wins and not a goal conceded. Northern Ireland and Algeria shared a 1-1 draw for a meagre consoling point each.

Scotland also went out with only a single point from a goalless draw with Uruguay, who held out with ten men when Jose Batista was sent off for a foul tackle on Strachan after 45 seconds!

Scotland missed the experience of Alan Hansen, surprisingly not picked by Alex Ferguson for the finals, and Kenny Dalglish, who stayed at home because of knee injury.

The Soviet Union and France easily qualified from Group C but Canada performed heroically in all three games and conceded only five goals altogether.

They were beaten by a single Papin goal for France with barely ten minutes remaining, then lost by only 2-0 to both Soviet Union and Hungary.

Much credit for Canada's resistance was due to their manager Tony Waiters, once of Blackpool and five times England's goalkeeper.

Mexico headed Group B, much the weakest of the six, with Paraguay pipping Belgium for second place on goal difference.

Iraq, the fourth member of the group, emulated Canada's brave efforts and, though losing all three ties, held Mexico to 1-0 for final goals figures of 1-4.

Northern Ireland and Hungary were the unlucky finishers in third place, who did not go into the next round, the 16 survivors being matched thus:

Argentina v Uruguay, Belgium v Soviet Union, Brazil v Poland, Denmark v Spain, England v Paraguay, France v Italy, Mexico v Bulgaria, West Germany v Morocco.

Morocco were the toast of the African football world, having become the first African country to progress beyond the first round of a World Cup finals.

Facts

13th World Cup
Mexico 1986

Morocco had been the first African nation to qualify for the Mexico finals stage in 1970, when they were unfortunate to lose 2-1 after scoring first against West Germany.

Now they were again to meet the Germans in Mexico - and again they were to give them the fright of their lives, this time in the eighth-final stage.

As the intense heat of Monterrey took its toll, Lothar Matthaus gave West Germany a 1-0 victory with a last-minute free kick.

England's 3-0 group win over Portugal had lifted the team's morale and they repeated the score against a brutal Paraguayan defence to head for the last eight.

The superb goalkeeping of new skipper Shilton was an inspiration after Lineker's goal for an interval lead.

The Azteca crowd of 98,728, largely South American biased, hoped for an equaliser as Lineker was taken off on a stretcher after stopping a stray elbow. Instead, Peter Beardsley made it 2-0.

Back came Lineker to score again with 18 minutes to go, and England had four days to consider the prospect of a quarter-final match with Argentina - their first meeting since the Falklands War.

Two days earlier at Puebla, Argentina had survived the second-round clash with Uruguay's bruisers with a single goal by Pasculli just before half-time.

Maradona dazzled his way through a thunderstorm, hit the crossbar and had a good `goal' disallowed. How could England stop him, wondered their supporters watching him on television.

Brazil flattened Poland 4-0 and Mexico beat Bulgaria 2-0 to complete the `Rest of the World' trio facing five from Europe in the quarter-finals.

Spain were there with a surprising 5-1 win over highly-fancied Denmark, four goals coming from Emilio Butragueno.

Italy, looking tired, rather tamely surrendered their trophy as the Frenchmen Platini and Papin's replacement Stopyra scored for a 2-0 win.

The most dramatic win of the second round came from the vastly-improved Belgians, who overcame the Soviet Union 4-3 after extra time at Leon.

The Soviets were 2-1 in front with 15 minutes of normal time remaining when Belgium scored. They then hit two more in extra time for a 4-2 lead and Igor Belanov's penalty goal three minutes from time made the final score 4-3.

13th World Cup Mexico 1986 Facts

Belanov had scored all three for the Soviets - one of four hat-tricks for the tournament alongside Lineker's against Poland, Preben Elkjaer's for Denmark against Uruguay and Butragueno's four for Spain against Denmark.

The quarter-final line-up read: Argentina v England, France v Brazil, Spain v Belgium, West Germany v Mexico.

The four-day build-up to the England match was almost unbearable, the newspapers devoting pages of speculation and, on the day, a crowd of 114,580 filled the Azteca Stadium.

Thousands of that crowd were Argentines living in Mexico City, greatly outnumbering British supporters in size and sound.

There was no resumption of the Falklands War, however, for three reasons: a) massive presence of Mexican security forces, b) the match did not require extra time and a penalty shoot-out, c) Argentina won.

England brought back Trevor Francis in place of Alvin Martin, the only change from the Paraguay match, so that the team was as selected by Bobby Robson against Poland:

Shilton (capt), Stevens, Sansom, Hoddle, Fenwick, Butcher, Hodge, Reid, Beardsley, Lineker, Steven.

The three other quarter-finals all went to extra time and penalty shoot-outs, to complete two days of unforgettable drama for a worldwide TV audience larger than anything previously experienced in World Cup history.

The first half of the England match was goalless and relatively calm, with Lineker and Beardsley closely marked and Diego Maradona playing it cool. The calm before the storm!

In the 50th minute, the game exploded. Steve Hodge sliced a back pass intended for Shilton, Maradona went up together with the 'keeper and Argentina were one up.

Shilton and his team-mates protested to referee and linesman that Maradona had punched the ball into the net, as proved by the camera, but the score stood.

Maradona later confessed that he did not head the ball. It was, he said, 'the hand of God.'

In the 55th minute, the little man was there again with one of the finest goals in football history. He gained possession on the halfway line, dribbled brilliantly past three England men and, challenged by a fourth, coolly placed the ball beyond Shilton's reach.

Facts

13th World Cup
Mexico 1986

England made changes in attack, Waddle and John Barnes for Reid and Steven, and Lineker headed a goal from a perfect Barnes centre with ten minutes remaining.

Lineker nearly scored again with barely three minutes left, but the whistle went at 2-1, England beaten hand and foot by Maradona.

On the same day, June 22, Belgium again hit top form to beat Spain, albeit by 5-4 on penalties after extra time ended on 1-1.

Belgium had qualified for the semi-finals for the first time in seven World Cup finals and would now meet Argentina at the Azteca.

Twenty-four hours earlier, on June 21, West Germany and France had won through to the other semi-final meeting after penalty shoot-outs.

West Germany and Mexico ended their match at Monterrey with ten men each. Thomas Berthold was sent off after 65 minutes, and Mexico lost Javier Aguirre ten minutes into extra time. After a goalless two hours, West Germany won 4-1 on penalties.

Brazil went out the same day at Guadalajara, 4-3 on penalties after France had held them to 1-1 in two hours of high-class football.

Careca (Brazil) and Platini (France) had made it 1-1 by half-time, but Brazil failed to settle the issue a quarter of an hour from normal time when Zico missed from the penalty spot.

Brazil had reached the quarter-finals in four successive World Cups since winning the Jules Rimet Trophy outright in 1970.

West Germany's semi-final game with France, for the second time in succession, again went in favour of the Germans but was not nearly so explosive.

Goals by Brehme and Voeller put paid to France again and West Germany were to contest the World Cup Final for the second time in succession.

Argentina qualified for their third World Cup Final by beating Belgium - and again the man of the match was mercurial Maradona.

Argentina's home from home, the Azteca Stadium, was packed with their visiting fans who now believed in their manager Carlos Bilardo, the victim of 'hate mail' at the start of the tournament.

After a goalless first half, Maradona did his quarter-final trick all over again with two fine goals in a ten-minute spell soon after the interval.

The first, a typical opportunist goal, was followed by a second which was almost a replica of his wonderful goal against England. The length of the run was shorter, but four men were beaten before his scoring shot.

13th World Cup Mexico 1986 Facts

So Maradona, an inspired appointment by Bilardo as captain before the series began, led Argentina on to the Azteca on June 29 with this team:

Argentina: Pumpido, Ruggeri, Brown, Cuciuffo, Giusti, Enrique, Batista, Burruchaga, Olarticoechea, Valdano, Maradona (capt). Sub: Trobbiani.

West Germany: Schumacher, Brehme, Jakobs, K-H Forster, Berthold, Matthaus, Magath, Eder, Briegel, Rummenigge (capt), Allofs. Subs: D Hoeness, Voeller.

A Brazilian referee, Filho, was in charge for the second successive Final.

Argentina dominated the first half of the Final and led 1-0 at the interval with a headed goal by their sweeper, Jose-Luis Brown.

Jorge Valdano made it 2-0, then the Germans fought back with two goals in eight minutes (both resulting from corner-kicks) through Rudi Voeller, half-time replacement for Allofs, and Rummenigge - and nine minutes of normal time remained.

Maradona played his final card, an ace of a defence-splitting pass to Jorge Burruchaga for the winner with six minutes to go.

England headed one list - that of leading scorer for the series. Gary Lineker scored six to win the Adidas Golden Boot, with Maradona level second on five with Spain's Butragueno and Brazil's Careca.

Goals were not plentiful, the total 132 scored giving an average per game of 2.54, the lowest in all World Cup finals up to 1986. Argentina were the highest scorers with 14.

Butragueno's first goal for Spain against Northern Ireland was timed at 63 seconds, the fastest of the tournament.

The 52 matches produced an attendance record of 2,406,511 for an average of 46,279 per game.

Across the world, an estimated two billion people watched the Final on television.

Eight players were sent off in all, two from Uruguay, resulting in a fine by FIFA of 25,000 Swiss francs and the threat of expulsion from the competition.

The eight were Sweeney (Canada), Wilkins (England), Gorgis (Iraq), Bossio and Batista (Uruguay), Arnesen (Denmark), Berthold (West Germany) and Aguirre (Mexico).

14th World Cup
Italy 1990

14th World Cup Italy 1990 Facts

Goals make games and, on that basis alone, the 14th World Cup finals were a disappointment. Fifty-two matches produced 115 goals, a miserable average of 2.21 per game.

For a similar number of matches played, the averages for the two previous finals had been: 1982 Spain 2.81 (146 goals), 1986 Mexico 2.54 (132 goals).

That apart, much of the good football was lost in a deluge of foul play, poor refereeing and a record number of sendings-off, due largely to a clampdown on the 'professional foul'.

No fewer than 16 players were shown red cards, eight of them in matches involving Argentina and five in West Germany's games.

Argentina and West Germany were destined to meet in the Final for the second successive tournament, with the Germans creating a remarkable record for consistency of three consecutive Finals.

The Argentines would prefer to draw a veil over one World Cup record in 1990, that of having a player sent off in a Final. Not one in fact, but two!

Yet another record in the 1990 finals earned faint praise. Four of the matches, one more than in 1986, had to be decided unsatisfactorily on penalty shoot-outs - two of them involving Argentina.

Notwithstanding, the qualifying competition produced more than its usual share of surprises, drama and heartache for a few minnows among the 103 participants.

Six countries withdrew without kicking a ball, the list sounding more like members of the Football Outer Space League. They were Lesotho, Rwanda, Togo (African section), Bahrain, India and Yemen (Asia section).

Seventh non-players were Mexico, whose entry was thrown out by FIFA as punishment for allegedly fiddling the ages of three players in an international youth tournament.

Coming through for the Home Countries were Scotland, for the fifth time running, and England, with an added interest in the Republic of Ireland.

The Republic of Ireland's football leaders made an inspired managerial choice in appointing Jack Charlton, World Cup winner in 1966 with England and with a wealth of experience gained in charge at Middlesbrough, Sheffield Wednesday and Newcastle United.

Big Jack compiled a squad mainly of Football League players with often remote grand-maternal Irish connection, several with accents to baffle even the most cosmopolitan among Irish folk.

Charlton quickly announced his intentions by getting the Republic through to the European Championship finals in West Germany for the first time in 1988.

Facts

14th World Cup
Italy 1990

Furthermore, they shocked England 1-0 in their Championship group match, held the Soviet Union to a 1-1 draw and lost by a single goal eight minutes from time to mighty Holland, the ultimate champions.

England had failed to earn a point in the European Championship, losing to the Republic of Ireland, the USSR and Holland, for whom Marco Van Basten scored all three goals. Grim tidings for 1990!

Manager Bobby Robson rode the heavy storms of criticism to lead England through a remarkable 17 matches unbeaten, including all six group qualifying games. Goals for 25, six against.

Even so, England were very lucky to go to the finals from Group 2, the table of which told a totally false story:

Country	P	W	D	L	F	A	Pts
Sweden	6	4	2	0	9	3	10
England	6	3	3	0	10	0	9
Poland	6	2	1	3	4	8	5
Albania	6	0	0	6	3	15	0

England had three 0-0 draws, against Sweden twice and Poland, and had to finish second to qualify on goal difference against other group runners-up.

Poland would certainly have qualified at England's expense in their return match in Katowice but for superb goalkeeping by Shilton and a last-minute shot by Tarasciewicz which struck the crossbar with Shilton beaten.

Poland would then have been left to win three points in the last two matches against Sweden, who were already home and dry, and Albania. In the event, with all hope gone, they went down 2-0 at home to Sweden.

Paul Gascoigne appeared on the England scene during their unbeaten spell, with six of his first seven caps earned as a substitute.

Jack Charlton's Irish mix strode confidently through the Group 8 qualifiers, claiming 12 points from a possible 16 and winning all four home ties against Spain (the group winners), Hungary, Northern Ireland and Malta.

Spain were the top scorers in the European groups, picking up 20 goals for only two against. Yugoslavia were second with 16.

14th World Cup Italy 1990 Facts

Scotland qualified narrowly from a testing Group 5, finishing second to Yugoslavia and ahead of France and Norway.

It was a good start for the managerial successor to Alex Ferguson, Andy Roxburgh, who had been Scottish FA director of coaching for a decade and was a former team-mate of Ferguson at Falkirk.

Clyde's Craig Brown was named as his assistant and was later to succeed Roxburgh in charge of the national side.

Yugoslavia dropped only two points - away to Scotland and France - from eight matches, and Scotland were left needing a point from their last group match against Norway in Glasgow to pip the French on the post.

The Hampden Roar greeted Ally McCoist's goal seconds before the half-time whistle, and doubled in volume as it sped south to echo in the Champs d'Elysees. Norway equalised, too late, in injury time through Erland Johnsen.

France's manager Michel Platini was shattered. He had played for France in the two previous World Cups when they had reached the semi-finals.

Wales were never in the hunt in Group 4 and finished bottom of the pile with two draws from six matches, but they were not disgraced.

Their finest performance was 0-0 against West Germany in Cardiff, followed six months later by a brave 1-2 scoreline in Cologne.

The two Group 4 qualifiers, Holland and West Germany, failed to beat one another and were highly fancied for the finals on this form:

Country	P	W	D	L	F	A	Pts
Holland	6	4	2	0	8	2	10
West Germany	6	3	3	0	13	3	9

Holland had beaten the Germans 2-1 in the European Championship semi-finals and seemed invincible with such players as Ruud Gullit, Marco Van Basten, Frank Rijkaard and Ronald Koeman.

The clash of the two giants in Italy in 1990 was to have a new twist, with West Germany the victors.

Belgium and Czechoslovakia headed Group 7, but Luxembourg's 1-1 draw away to the kindly, unbeaten Belgians had them dancing in the streets of the Grand Duchy.

Facts

14th World Cup
Italy 1990

The Soviet Union and Austria eliminated moderate opposition in Group 3 but failed to progress beyond the first round in Italy.

Group 1 resolved into a straight fight between Romania and Denmark, with the Danes a point ahead before their final meeting. Romania, with home advantage, won 3-1 to reach their first finals for 20 years.

Italy were through as hosts, completing this 14-strong European challenge: Austria, Belgium, Czechoslovakia, Republic of Ireland, England, Holland, Italy, Romania, Scotland, Spain, Sweden, the USSR, West Germany, Yugoslavia.

The two places in the Asian sector were hotly contested, with South Korea again the outstanding nation, qualifying for the second finals in succession.

They played 11 matches over two rounds without defeat, scoring a total of 30 goals and giving away only one - and that was against United Arab Emirates for the point they needed to accompany the South Koreans to the finals.

Along the way, South Korea recorded the highest victory of the 1990 World Cup, beating Nepal 9-0 in Seoul.

Italy noted South Korea's progress with some interest and respect. They recalled a desperate 3-2 group win over South Korea in Mexico, when Altobelli's hat-trick outshone their opponents' world-renowned marksmen Choi Soon-Hoo and Huh Jung-Moo.

The Emirates achieved their first trip to the finals with the dreary figures of P5 W1 D4 L0 F4 A3 Pts6.

The Arabs, however, were nothing if not ambitious. They first hired the great Brazilian, Mario Zagalo, as manager, then replaced him with another Brazilian, Carlos Alberto Parreira.

With the disqualification of Mexico, the North/Central America zone was a real dogfight for the two finals places from the first match on June 19, 1988: Antigua 0 Netherlands Antilles 1.

Just four weeks later and with a mere two years to the World Cup finals, Costa Rica set off on a dream voyage to Italy and moments of history-making football.

14th World Cup Italy 1990 Facts

Costa Rica overcame Panama in round one (1-1 and 2-0), had a walkover next round because of Mexico's suspension, then headed the table in round three to qualify for the finals.

USA won the second spot with a last-ditch 1-0 away win over their Trinidad and Tobago. The final table:

Country	P	W	D	L	F	A	Pts
Costa Rica	8	5	1	2	10	6	11
USA	8	4	3	1	6	3	10
Trinidad & Tobago	8	3	3	2	7	5	9
Guatemala	6	1	1	4	4	7	3
El Salvador	6	0	2	4	2	8	2

Guatemala's two games with El Salvador could not be played because of the `domestic situation' in the latter country.

El Salvador's non-qualification was not likely to produce sighs of relief from the world's soccer powers. In their two finals appearances - Mexico 1970 and Spain 1982 - they lost all six group games, for a goals aggregate of 22-1.

There were a few nervous glances towards the ever-improving African zone and their two qualifiers, Cameroon and Egypt.

Egypt came through by beating Algeria (0-0 and 1-0), a fine result in view of Algeria's splendid showing in the 1982 and 1986 finals.

Cameroon beat Tunisia 2-0 and 1-0 for their place. Each had proud memories of previous finals appearances, Cameroon unbeaten in three games in 1982 and Tunisia with a defeat of Mexico and a goalless draw with West Germany to their credit in 1978.

Cameroon had their problems, not least a Russian manager with an unpronouncable name who couldn't speak a word of French, but they were about to shock some of the biggest names in football.

In the South American sector, Brazil and Uruguay joined the holders Argentina on the way to Italy, the fourth spot going to Colombia in a play-off with the winners of Oceania's group, Israel.

Israel, whose only previous finals appearance was in 1970 when they drew with Sweden and Italy, died fighting 1-0 and 0-0 with Colombia, who were qualifying for only their second finals since 1962.

Facts

14th World Cup Italy 1990

Brazil's deciding match with Chile was watched by an incredible crowd of 141,072 at the Maracana Stadium - a World Cup record for a qualifying match - and ended dramatically and disgracefully.

Chile, needing to win 2-0 to deprive Brazil of a World Cup finals place for the first time, were losing 1-0 midway through the second half when a flare was thrown on to the pitch.

Chile's goalkeeper Roberto Rojas collapsed, clutching his face, and was taken off on a stretcher, whereupon his team-mates walked off and the match was abandoned.

Television evidence showed that the flare had missed Rojas, who had faked injury in the hope that Chile would be awarded the match.

FIFA imposed a life ban on Rojas and some of the Chilean FA officials, threw in a hefty fine and excluded them from the 1994 World Cup. Brazil were adjudged 2-0 winners.

Cameroon were matched with the holders Argentina for the opening match at San Siro Stadium, Milan. First-round pairings were:

Group A: Austria, Czechoslovakia, Italy, USA.

Group B: Argentina, Cameroon, Romania, Soviet Union.

Group C: Brazil, Costa Rica, Scotland, Sweden.

Group D: Colombia, United Arab Emirates, West Germany, Yugoslavia.

Group E: Belgium, South Korea, Spain, Uruguay.

Group F: Egypt, the Republic of Ireland, England, Holland.

The tournament rules were unchanged - six groups with 16 'promoted' for knock-outs there onwards - with West Germany and Argentina, 1986 finalists, vying for favouritism with the bookies alongside, as ever, Brazil.

The twelve venues for the matches were: Bari, Bologna, Cagliari, Florence, Genoa, Milan, Naples, Palermo, Rome, Turin, Udine, Verona.

The match at San Siro at the opening ceremony was almost a closing ceremony for Argentina. They were beaten by Cameroon in a shock result to rank alongside the USA-England nightmare of 1950.

Cameroon were 1-0 winners despite finishing with nine men, having had one sent off each side of the headed goal by Omam Biyik midway through the second half.

Maradona was tackled out of the game, then Cameroon proved the win was no fluke six days later by beating Romania 2-1.

14th World Cup Italy 1990 Facts

Their star with both goals was the great entertainer Roger Milla, a national hero, leading the attack at the age of 38.

Milla had been brought on as substitute only half an hour before the end with the game still goalless.

The topsy-turvy form in Group B continued to the end, with the Soviet Union beating the Africans 4-0, Cameroon already being assured of qualifying for round two.

Argentina survived by holding Romania 1-1, both teams having beaten and thereby eliminated the Soviets. The table tells the story:

Country	P	W	D	L	F	A	Pts
Cameroon	3	2	0	1	3	5	4
Romania	3	1	1	1	4	3	3
Argentina	3	1	1	1	3	2	3
Soviet Union	3	1	0	2	4	4	2

Group F attracted great interest and some excitement, despite only seven goals coming from six games.

The first four matches ended in draws, Egypt having surprised everyone by holding highly-talented Holland and Jack Charlton's Irish.

All four teams were on two points for the fateful day, June 21, with Ireland v Holland and England v Egypt kicking off simultaneously.

England's form in the first two matches had been disappointing, Gary Lineker scoring their only goal in 180 minutes. Likewise Ireland and Kevin Sheedy.

England lost their captain Bryan Robson, injured in their second match, for the rest of the series but Mark Wright came to rescue with the single goal to beat Egypt.

Wright, of Southampton, Derby County and Liverpool, played 45 times for England and chose the right time to score his only international goal.

Niall Quinn saved the Irish 20 minutes from time for a 1-1 draw, after Gullit had given the Dutch the lead after ten minutes.

England, the only team to win, topped the group, with Eire and Holland jointly second with identical returns but just sufficient to stay in. Here's how Group F ended:

Facts

14th World Cup
Italy 1990

Country	P	W	D	L	F	A	Pts
England	3	1	2	0	2	1	4
Eire	3	0	3	0	2	2	3
Holland	3	0	3	0	2	2	3
Egypt	3	0	2	1	1	2	2

Group D supplied the goals, with treble the number in England's group. West Germany looked near invincible with ten, United Arab Emirates a disaster area with 11 conceded.

West Germany hit Yugoslavia for four and UAE for five, with the deadly trio Matthaus, Klinsmann and Voeller each time on target.

In their final match they could, surprisingly, only draw with Colombia, both goals coming in the last two minutes.

The Germans were the great attraction in Milan, thousands of their travelling fans boosting the crowds total for three games to 218,442.

In fact, over the seven games they were to play up to and including the Final, they were watched by 502,579 spectators.

Italy's total over seven matches was 477,039, yet they were never to meet the Germans in World Cup 1990.

The last time Italy and West Germany had met in the World Cup was eight years earlier in the Final in Spain, when Italy won the trophy.

The Italians were comfortable winners of Group A, beating the USA, Austria and Czechoslovakia, without a goal being conceded by Walter Zenga.

Zenga, a worthy successor to Dino Zoff, created a World Cup goalkeeping record by keeping his goal intact for 517 minutes into the semi-finals stage.

The young Americans lost all three games but earned rousing and appreciative cheers in Rome by restricting the hosts to a single goal.

The situation seemed bleak for USA when Giannini scored after only 11 minutes, but the Americans defended heroically and died happy after Gianluca Vialli missed from the penalty spot.

Italy's form was back in their next match, in which goals by Schillaci and Baggio gave them their first win over Czechoslovakia for 37 years.

14th World Cup
Italy 1990

Facts

Group E saw the departure of South Korea without a point, though they were not disgraced by the three qualifiers, Spain, Belgium and Uruguay, and were to be back in the finals for a third successive series in 1994.

Spain's Michel scored a hat-trick in the 3-1 win over the Koreans. The only other hat-trick scorer in the series was Tomas Skuhravy of Czechoslovakia against Costa Rica in a second-round match.

Costa Rica were the second of the `minnows' to reach the eighth-finals, leaving egg on the faces of Scotland and Sweden in Group C.

At the seventh attempt, Scotland failed yet again to advance beyond the first round and, in so doing, suffered their most humiliating World Cup defeat at the hands of Costa Rica.

Four minutes into the second half, Cayasso scored the one vital goal to silence the Scottish fans among the 30,000 in Genoa.

Although Brazil remained 100 per cent, the Costa Ricans earned second place in the group by beating Sweden to the delight of their fifth manager since the start of the qualifying rounds.

Sweden's supremo was the experienced Bora Milutinovic, the Yugoslav who had led Mexico to the last eight of the 1986 finals.

Brazil, in their final group match, knew they had only to draw with the Scots to head the table. They won with the only goal eight minutes from time.

They also knew that by winning the group, they would next meet the third team in Group B. They didn't know that that team was to be Argentina!

Second-round groupings, to be decided on a knock-out basis, were: Brazil v Argentina, Cameroon v Colombia, Czechoslovakia v Costa Rica, Ireland v Romania, England v Belgium, Italy v Uruguay, Spain v Yugoslavia, West Germany v Holland.

Four of the eight ties went into extra time, although the matches were resolved in the supplementary 30 minutes in three of them.

The exception was in Genoa where Romania, without their suspended star Marius Lacatus, battled goalless with Eire and it came to a penalty decider.

Nobody in the Republic watching on TV dared breathe after Packie Bonner saved Romania's fifth penalty. David O'Leary, an extra-time substitute, came up for the Irish fifth penalty, said a quick prayer and fired. Spot on!

History was still being made. Jack Charlton's no-hopers were in the quarter-finals of their first World Cup finals and a new plane load of supporters took off from Shannon Airport, bound for Rome.

Facts

14th World Cup
Italy 1990

Their next giant opponents were to be Italy, who had disposed of Uruguay with two second-half goals by Schillaci and Serena.

A crowd of 50,026 saw the clash between Cameroon and Colombia in Naples. Both countries were competing in only their second World Cup finals.

The match, played in the shadow of Vesuvius, was slow to erupt. Roger Milla, as usual, came on as a substitute ten minutes into the second half to set the lava flowing.

Milla made it all happen with two dramatic goals in two minutes in the first half of extra time, the first after a dazzling solo run and the second after pure pantomime.

Colombia's eccentric Rene Higuita, launching into one of his crazy outfield excursions, neared the halfway line and was dispossessed by Milla, who placed the ball into the empty net.

Redin's reply for Colombia came too late and an African country prepared for a quarter-final debut and another night in Naples - against England!

Costa Rica's bid for glory ended with a Skuhravy hat-trick (all headers) in Czechoslovakia's 4-1 triumph in Bari, and the Czechs were to learn of their quarter-final opponents after the West Germany-Holland clash of giants 24 hours later in Milan.

This match was the classic of the tournament, played by ten men each side after the sending-off - only 20 minutes into the game - of Holland's Frank Rijkaard and the German, Rudi Voeller.

After a goalless first half, the magnificent Jurgen Klinsmann scored in the 50th minute and then hit a goalpost before Brehme made it 2-0 five minutes from time.

Ronald Koeman's penalty goal in the 88th minute made it 2-1, but those German dreams of a third World Cup were nearing reality.

England, now captained by Terry Butcher with Bryan Robson's World Cup over, were lucky to survive 90 minutes with their goal intact after Belgium had twice struck the goalposts.

David Platt, a second-half substitute for Steve McMahon, won the day barely 60 seconds from a dreaded penalty shoot-out by volleying home a Gascoigne free kick.

Dragan Stojkovic scored twice for Yugoslavia at Verona, the second from a free kick in extra time, to deprive luckless Spain of a third consecutive quarter-final place.

Brazil went out at their earliest stage since the England finals of 1966, after dominating the match with Argentina, to a single goal less than ten minutes from time, scored by Caniggia after a brilliant running dribble by a far-from-fit Maradona.

14th World Cup Italy 1990 Facts

Much more drama was to come in these quarter-finals: Italy v Ireland (Rome), West Germany v Czechoslovakia (Milan), England v Cameroon (Naples), Argentina v Yugoslavia (Florence).

Yugoslavia fought bravely for an hour with ten men against South America's sole quarter-finalist, then a further half-hour of extra time before the penalty shoot-out.

They lost Refik Sabanadzovic on two yellow cards, and also a hit-and-miss shoot-out by three penalties to two. The star marksmen of each side failed with their kicks, Maradona shooting wide and Stojkovic hitting the Argentine crossbar.In Rome, Jack Charlton's Irish legion suffered the inevitable against an Italian defence that had stayed intact for nine matches. The Irish, brave to the end, were finally beaten by a lone goal just before half-time by Toto Schillaci.

West Germany, sweltering in the Milanese heat on the first day of July, fought to hold on to a first-half lead against the Czechs, achieved with a penalty from their skipper, Lothar Matthaus, after Klinsmann had been brought down.

Czech hopes faded when Moravcik was sent off 20 minutes from time. He got a second yellow card for kicking his boot into the air to display his disagreement with the referee's decision!

British hopes were maintained by England's victory over buoyant Cameroon, but again extra time and a whole load of luck were needed.

Roger Milla was again the villain of the piece in his usual second-half substitute act. Leading 1-0 from a Platt header, England had to face a penalty when Gascoigne fouled Milla and Kunde converted the spot kick.

Cameroon made it 2-1 almost immediately through a new substitute, Ekeke, from a pass by Milla, but Lineker replied from the penalty spot after being brought down.

Mark Wright was bandaged and bloody after a collision of heads with Milla (who else?) as England went into extra time. Again Lineker was felled; again he took the kick successfully and Cameroon's fairytale ended, self-inflicted, at 3-2.

Spectators continued to get value for money as both semi-finals went to extra time and penalty kicks, Argentina v Italy in Naples and West Germany v England in Turin.

Italy were one up in 17 minutes through Schillaci and held Argentina at bay until halfway through the second half, when Zenga of all people made his first goalkeeping mistake in six matches.

Caniggia got to the ball first with a header and the scene was set for a sordid half-hour of extra time, replete with fouls and a sending-off for Argentina's Ricardo Giusti for an attack on Roberto Baggio.

The shoot-out was tragedy for Italy and triumph for the South Americans' goalkeeper Sergio Goycoechea. He saved brilliantly from Donadoni and Serena for a winning margin of 4-3.

Facts

14th World Cup
Italy 1990

England played superbly in Turin the next day and were unlucky to lose, like Italy, by 4-3 on penalties.

The England line-up was: Shilton, Parker, Pearce, Wright, Walker, Butcher capt (sub Stevens, 70 min), Platt, Waddle Gascoigne, Lineker, Beardsley.

There was no scoring for an hour, when Brehme's shot was cruelly deflected by Paul Parker and eluded Shilton. An equaliser by Lineker, ten minutes from the end of normal time, set up a nailbiting half-hour of extra time during which Chris Waddle hit a goalpost.

Everything stopped in England on Wednesday, July 4, as the penalty shoot-out approached. The British TV audience was recorded as 25 million.

On the pitch, Paul Gascoigne was in tears and inconsolable, having been booked and realising he would miss the Final should England qualify.

England went first on the shoot-out. This was it: Lineker (1-0), Brehme (1-1), Beardsley (2-1), Matthaus (2-2), Platt (3-2), Riedle (3-3), Pearce (saved), Thon (3-4), Waddle (over bar).

The third-place play-off in Bari went to Italy 2-1, with goals by Baggio and Platt before Schillaci won it from the penalty spot.

The Final between Argentina and West Germany, on Sunday, July 8, in Rome, was described by several newspapers as the worst in World Cup history. The teams were:

Argentina: Goycoechea, Ruggeri (sub Monzon), Simon, Serrizuela, Lorenzo, Basualdo, Troglio, Burruchaga (sub Calderon), Sensini, Dezotti, Maradona (capt).

West Germany: Illgner, Berthold (sub Reuter), Kohler, Augenthaler, Buchwald, Brehme, Littbarski, Matthaus (capt), Hassler, Voeller, Klinsmann.

The Argentines were booed almost continuously for their cynical tactics by the crowd, which included an estimated 40,000 from Germany.

14th World Cup Italy 1990 Facts

For the first time in a World Cup Final, a man was sent off. He was Pedro Monzon, in the 65th minute, and yet another Argentine, Gustavo Dezotti, was dismissed minutes before the end.

In between the sendings-off by referee E. Codesal of Mexico, Brehme scored five minutes from time with a penalty to give the Germans their third World Cup triumph.

England came out with one prize, the Fair Play Award, for the best disciplinary record of the tournament. England players finished with six bookings in seven matches.

Not surprisingly, Argentina had the worst record - 22 bookings and three sent off.

The disciplinary figures were the worst ever - 16 sent off and 164 yellow cards. The previous worst was in 1986 in Mexico, when eight were dismissed and 133 cautioned.

England's manager, Bobby Robson, was the first to lead the nation to a semi-final on foreign soil.

After the penalties drama against the Germans, he said: 'Nobody beat us, did they? It was probably the best performance of my time ... but it's time for a new man now.'

Leading scorers were: Schillaci (Italy) 6, Skuhravy (Czechoslovakia) 5, Lineker (England), Matthaus (West Germany), Michel (Spain) and Milla (Cameroon) 4 each.

The Final in Rome produced record match receipts of £4,300,000 and was watched by 73,609.

The fastest goal was scored by Safet Susic of Yugoslavia, after 3 minutes 58 seconds against the United Arab Emirates.

Total attendance for 52 matches of 2,514,074 was for 'tickets sold' but even this figure broke the record of the Mexico actual spectator count of 1986. The average gate per match was 48,346.

After the play-off match, Peter Shilton announced his retirement from international football at the age of 40. He played for England a record 125 times.

Parting shot from Desmond Lynam as he announced BBC TV's 'Goal of the World Cup' competition: 'This is what you do: pick a player, call 0898 991199... and if a girl called Mandy answers, you've got the wrong number.'

15th World Cup USA 1994

15th World Cup USA 1994 Facts

The problems thrown up by the Italian production of the World Cup in 1990 were tackled by FIFA with some success for the exciting presentation of the 15th tournament in the United States.

In a playing sense, the improvement was immediately obvious with 141 goals scored from the scheduled 52 matches for an average of 2.71 per game.

This was 26 more than were scored in Italy and nine more than Mexico in 1986.

One reason was the decision to encourage attacking play by easing up on the offside law relating to players not interfering with the play.

The decision to award three points for a win in the first-round group matches was ineffective in that there were still eight draws as in 1990. It was, however, an improvement on 1986 (11 draws) and 1982 (12 draws) for the same number of games played.

On the disciplinary front, the purge on violent play and the clampdown on the tackle from behind were welcomed.

This accounted for a huge increase in yellow cards compared with previous tournaments, although the sendings-off total of 15 was one fewer than 1990's record 16.

The original entry list totalled 144, by far the highest in World Cup history, although there were 12 withdrawals from the African nations before a ball was kicked.

The choice of USA as the first finals host outside Europe and South America heralded an increase in razzmatazz, starting as early as December 8, 1991, at Madison Square Garden for the qualifying round draw.

The first fixture was in the CONCACAF section between the Dominican Republic and Puerto Rico on March 21, 1992 - some 27 months before the opening match of the finals!

The great disappointment for British fans was the failure of all four nations, England, Northern Ireland, Scotland and Wales, to survive the qualifying round.

Fortunately, the home flag was kept flying by the Republic of Ireland and their rumbustious manager Jack Charlton for the second successive finals.

Charlton's squad of 22 was assembled purely from English and Scottish clubs and had a strong Aston Villa flavour led by the captain, Andy Townsend, whose accent did not betray his Irish ancestry.

Facts

15th World Cup
USA 1994

Ireland's numbered squad was: 1 Bonner (Celtic), 2 Irwin (Manchester United), 3 Phelan (Manchester City), 4 Moran (Blackburn), 5 McGrath (Aston Villa), 6 Keane (Manchester United), 7 Townsend (Aston Villa), 8 Houghton (Aston Villa), 9 Aldridge (Tranmere), 10 Sheridan (Sheffield Wednesday), 11 Staunton (Aston Villa), 12 G Kelly (Leeds), 13 Kernaghan (Manchester City), 14 Babb (Coventry), 15 Coyne (Motherwell), 16 Cascarino (Chelsea), 17 McGoldrick (Arsenal), 18 Whelan (Liverpool), 19 McLoughlin (Portsmouth), 20 D Kelly (Wolves), 21 McAteer (Bolton), 22 A Kelly (Sheffield United).

The luck of the Irish, it might be said, favoured the Republic in a desperate finish to the Group 4 qualifiers in the European sector.

Each team played 12 matches, a marathon of 42 in seven countries, starting in Spain on April 22, 1992, and also ending there on a championship-winning note on November 17, 1993.

Northern Ireland were in the same group but were never serious contenders, winning only five of their matches against four defeats.

Lithuania, Latvia and Albania virtually made up the numbers, with Spain, Eire and Denmark supplying the thrills in the last four fixtures - Ireland v Spain, Denmark v Northern Ireland (both October 13), Northern Ireland v Ireland and Spain v Denmark (both November 17).

Spain beat Ireland, and Denmark beat Northern Ireland, so that the last two matches started with the top three reading thus:

Country	P	W	D	L	F	A	Pts
Denmark	11	7	4	0	15	1	18
Spain	11	7	3	1	26	4	17
Republic of Ireland	11	7	3	1	18	5	17

Spain had been looking for goals from the outset and scored five in each of three of their matches. They won 5-0 at home to Latvia and Lithuania and 5-1 in Albania.

In the event, they beat Denmark 1-0, while the Republic of Ireland were being held to a 1-1 draw by their Northern neighbours in Belfast.

15th World Cup USA 1994 Facts

The Republic of Ireland thus crept through on the slimmest of goals totals, everything else being identical alongside the Danes. The final order:

Country	P	W	D	L	F	A	Pts
Spain	12	8	3	1	27	4	19
Republic of Ireland	12	7	4	1	19	6	18
Denmark	12	7	4	1	15	2	18

England's failure to qualify after a run of three finals was predictable soon after Graham Taylor had taken over the manager's job from Bobby Robson after the 1990 tournament.

Taylor had had great success with Watford, winning promotion to the First Division, and fared well with England in his early matches.

The wheels came off in the close season of 1992, with three uninspiring performances in the European Championship ending in a sad episode involving Taylor and his captain Gary Lineker which was to be repeated endlessly on the TV play-backs.

Having drawn 0-0 with Denmark and France, a win was called for in the last group match with the hosts, Sweden. Instead, they lost 2-1 and Lineker was called off by Taylor in the closing minutes, to be replaced by Alan Smith.

It was Lineker's 80th and final appearance for England and he was left one short of Bobby Charlton's international scoring record with 48 goals.

Denmark were to become European champions, a remarkable feat as they had only been called up to replace Yugoslavia, who were taken out on security grounds, just two weeks before the tournament started.

Five weeks before their first World Cup fixture, Taylor took his team to Santander to face Spain, with Stuart Pearce as skipper and Paul Ince a debutant. Result: a 1-0 defeat, the third time in four games England had failed to score.

The Group 2 draw presented formidable opponents in Norway, Poland and Holland, but Taylor's hopes of finishing in the top two were fairly high after surviving the first six of ten scheduled matches without defeat.

One of the major problems in England's case was weary limbs. Matches 5, 6 and 7, against their three toughest rivals, were played on April 28, May 29 and June 2. Draws with Holland and Poland and defeat in Norway alerted Fleet Street's prophets of doom.

Facts

15th World Cup
USA 1994

A 2-0 beating by Holland in Rotterdam in October, with Ronald Koeman and Dennis Bergkamp the second-half scorers, left England praying for a miracle - a cricket score against San Marino, Poland to beat Holland and America here we come!

Neither happened. San Marino hadn't read the script and scored in the first minute to double their goals tally of the previous nine matches and the Dutch won 3-1 in Poland.

Norway and Holland went through, England tossed their seven useless goals against San Marino at Bologna in the bin on the way out (four for Ian Wright) ... and Graham Taylor packed in his job. The top four:

Country	P	W	D	L	F	A	Pts
Norway	10	7	2	1	25	5	16
Holland	10	6	3	1	29	9	15
England	10	5	3	2	26	9	13
Poland	10	3	2	5	10	15	8

Scotland's run of five consecutive World Cup finals, albeit never getting beyond the first round, was seldom likely to continue in a powerful Group 1.

Even so, surprisingly, none of the five other contestants had emulated Scotland's feat of reaching the European finals in 1992.

Two points only from the three opening games, against Switzerland (1-3), Portugal (0-0) and Italy (0-0), meant that the return meeting in Portugal in April 1993 was the Scots' last hope.

15th World Cup USA 1994 Facts

The result was a humiliating 5-0 beating, Scotland's worst result since England hit them for the same scoreline in Glasgow 20 years earlier.

Portugal still failed to qualify, Italy beating them 1-0 at the group's vital stage to make sure of the trip to the States along with Switzerland.

Group 5 was reduced to five countries with Yugoslavia's exclusion, and Greece and Russia (back to basic after the USSR carve-up) were the lucky qualifiers with a minimum of leg weariness.

The Greeks enjoyed the easy fodder of Iceland, Hungary and Luxembourg, emerging unbeaten to win a place in the finals for the first time.

France were the great disappointment in Group 6, looking only a shadow of the team of the Eighties that twice reached the semi-finals only to be beaten each time by West Germany.

They looked to be coasting home before unaccountably losing their last two matches, both at home, 3-2 to Israel (that country's only win) and Bulgaria 2-1.

That defeat of France gave Bulgaria the second-place qualification below Sweden, with Austria among the also-rans.

Belgium and Romania headed Group 4 with similar results from ten games, with Czechoslovakia and Wales left to lick their wounds.

It might have been different but for the last four games of the group involving the four countries, with Wales needing to beat Romania and the Czechs requiring a positive result against the Belgians.

The Belgian defence stayed solid for the 0-0 draw required to guarantee an American adventure. They let in only five goals in 10 games.

Wales' hopes for a big win at Cardiff in order to squeeze a ticket to the States were soon quashed. Romania, 5-1 winners in Bucharest, completed the double with a hard-fought 2-1 margin.

Newcomers in this group were Faroe Islands, who had joined FIFA in 1988 and were still talking of a famous victory over Austria in a European Championship match.

Now the Faroe Islanders were back in the real world. Romania hit them for seven, Wales for six and their World Cup debut ended with figures of P10 W0 D0 L10 F1 A38 Pts0. The one goal came in Cyprus.

Belgium joined Germany (now unified) and Italy as Europe's three seeds, alongside USA, Brazil and Argentina, for the finals draw at Caesar's Palace, Las Vegas on December 19, 1993.

Facts

15th World Cup
USA 1994

The European 13 for the finals were: Germany (holders), Belgium, Bulgaria, Greece, Holland, Ireland, Italy, Norway, Romania, Russia, Spain, Sweden, Switzerland.

The South Americans' quartet for the finals were Argentina, Brazil, Bolivia and Colombia, but the qualifiers were not without drama.

Brazil came close to the unthinkable of failing to reach the World Cup finals for the first time in 15 tournaments.

The three-times Cup winners, having drawn 0-0 in their opening qualifier in Ecuador, were amazingly beaten 2-0 in Bolivia in the second match - the first time Brazil had ever lost a World Cup qualifying match.

Brazil finally got their act together, Romario made his peace with manager Carlos Alberto Parreira after feuding from a distance at his Eindhoven base, and Uruguay were beaten 2-0 in a concluding group match crucial for both nations.

Uruguay, twice World champions, were eliminated as Bolivia drew 1-1 in Ecuador on the same day.

Bolivia were in the finals for only the third time. Their previous disastrous record was: 1930, beaten 4-0 by Yugoslavia and Brazil; 1950, beaten 8-0 by Uruguay. 'Can do better' was the message for 1994.

Group B final placings:

Country	P	W	D	L	F	A	Pts
Brazil	8	5	2	1	20	4	12
Bolivia	8	5	1	2	22	11	11
Uruguay	8	4	2	2	10	7	10
Ecuador	8	1	3	4	7	7	5
Venezuela	8	1	0	7	4	34	2

15th World Cup USA 1994 Facts

Group A had shocks in store for Argentina, twice World Cup champions. Twice they were beaten by Colombia, the second time, unbelievably, 5-0 at home. Here's how the group finished:

Country	P	W	D	L	F	A	Pts
Colombia	6	4	2	0	13	2	10
Argentina	6	3	1	2	7	9	7
Paraguay	6	1	4	1	6	7	6
Peru	6	0	1	5	4	12	1

Colombia were in their second successive finals and recalling their 1-1 draw with West Germany in Italy. Now they had a bright young star called Faustino Asprilla in their ranks.

Argentina had to face a play-off with Australia, winners of the Oceania Group, to qualify. With the return of Maradona after drug exploits in Italy, they drew 1-1 in Australia and won the home leg 1-0.

This was Australia's third play-off! First they beat New Zealand twice, then survived for the Argentina match after a hairy second play-off with CONCACAF Group runners-up Canada.

Canada won 2-1 at home, as did the Australians in the return match, which necessitated a penalty shoot-out. The Aussies won it 4-1 and Canada were out after playing 14 times.

Mexico, banned from the 1990 finals, had already won the final round of the CONCACAF zone against Canada, El Salvador and Honduras to become the first nation to qualify for USA in May 1993.

Mexico were qualifying for the World Cup finals for the 10th time, with only six victories from 29 matches to their credit - three of those in their most recent appearances on home territory in 1986.

On the way to the States, Mexico recorded the highest score of the series, 11-0 against St Vincent in Mexico City, and beating Norway's 10-0 win over San Marino three months earlier.

The rapidly-improving standards of football across Africa were recognised in their being allocated three representatives in the finals for the first time.

Facts

15th World Cup
USA 1994

Late withdrawals contributed to the imbalance of some groups but three worthy challengers emerged in Cameroon, Morocco and Nigeria, the last-named in the finals for the first time.

Asia contributed the two remaining runners for the 1994 finals in Saudi Arabia and South Korea from a total of 29 competitors.

Saudi Arabia were deservedly Asian champions, having come through 11 games without defeat, and were to join Nigeria and Greece as first-time qualifiers among the 24 finals contestants.

The six seeds for the finals draw were USA, Brazil, Germany, Argentina, Italy and Belgium. The groups were drawn as follows:

Group A: Colombia, Romania, Switzerland, USA.

Group B: Brazil, Cameroon, Russia, Sweden.

Group C: Bolivia, Germany, South Korea, Spain.

Group D: Argentina, Bulgaria, Greece, Nigeria.

Group E: Ireland, Italy, Mexico, Norway.

Group F: Belgium, Holland, Morocco, Saudi Arabia.

Despite the fact that they had not reached a World Cup Final since 1970, Brazil were 3-1 favourites, followed by Germany at 7-2, Italy 5-1 and Holland 6-1. Saudi Arabia were a tempting 500-1 for wealthy sheiks.

Nine venues were selected for the finals: Boston, Chicago, Dallas, Detroit, Los Angeles, New York, Orlando, San Francisco, Washington.

The familiar system of six groups, followed by single matches, again applied, with penalty shoot-outs after extra time to decide all matches after the group stage.

On this occasion, history was written when the Final finished 0-0 after extra time and the tournament was decided by a shoot-out.

Eight teams were eliminated after the group matches but these did not include the host nation, to the delight of the American marketing team and the public in general.

The six bottom nations were Bolivia, Cameroon, Colombia, Greece, Morocco and Norway, the last-named being unlucky victims in a group which was by far the strongest.

The two others out in the group games were Russia, surprisingly, and South Korea with the fewest points of the third-placed teams.Group E was sad news for Norway, who had headed their qualifying section and largely sealed England's fate with scores of 2-0 and 1-1.

15th World Cup
USA 1994

Facts

The Norwegians missed the vital chance in their second match, with Italy, after beating Mexico 1-0 in their opening group game.

The Italian goalkeeper Gianluca Pagliuca was sent off for handling outside his area and manager Arrigo Sacchi astonishingly pulled off Roberto Baggio to allow the reserve 'keeper to go into goal.

The supporters of Italy at odds of 5-1 were resigned to losing - Jack Charlton's Irish had already beaten the Italians 1-0 - when Dino Baggio (no relation to Roberto) headed a second-half goal to give the ten men victory by a single goal.

The entire Irish and Italian population of New York, it seemed, made up the 75,000 at the Giants Stadium to see Ray Houghton score the vital goal for Ireland against the Azzurri.

They then lost at Orlando 2-1 to Mexico, where Charlton was fined $14,900 and banned from the bench for the next match after angry touchline scenes involving match officials.

John Aldridge, waiting impatiently to be signalled on as substitute, also became involved and was fined $1,850. He scored Ireland's late goal.

Ireland's third match was a goalless draw to end Norway's hopes in what became known as the Group of Death. The amazing final table read:

Country	P	W	D	L	F	A	Pts
Mexico	3	1	1	1	3	3	4
Eire	3	1	1	1	2	2	4
Italy	3	1	1	1	2	2	4
Norway	3	1	1	1	1	1	4

Facts

15th World Cup
USA 1994

The competitive nature of the 1994 series was illustrated by the fact that no country emerged 100 per cent from the group games and only four were unbeaten.

These were all from two groups, two in each: Brazil, Germany, Spain and Sweden. Only Brazil were to remain unbeaten on their way to the Final and their record fourth World Cup triumph.

Italy, having escaped an ignominious exit, were to continue on the tightrope with 2-1 wins in all of the next three rounds to the Final.

Greece, lucky to qualify, were outclassed in Group D and failed to register either a point or a goal in their three matches as finals debutants.Greece had daunting first opponents in Argentina, were a goal down in the first minute to Gabriel Batistuta - the fastest goal of the series - and were mesmerised by Maradona.

Batistuta went on to complete his hat-trick and Maradona made it 4-0, in what was to prove his penultimate World Cup appearance.

After another sparkling display in Argentina's 2-1 defeat of Nigeria, Maradona ended his 21st finals match by failing a dope test and being ordered home. He stayed on as a commentator.

Greece were next whipping boys for Bulgaria, whose 4-0 win was, remarkably, their first in a finals match - at the 18th attempt and in their sixth series, dating back to Chile 1962.

Bulgaria then beat Argentina 2-0 and were to continue their inspired run all the way to the semi-finals.

Nigeria headed the group to uphold Africa's reputation and earned further praise from 55,000 spectators in Boston by taking Italy to extra time before losing 2-1 in the second round.

Saudi Arabia also brought honour to Africa by beating Morocco and Belgium in Group F to move into the next stage.

Although they were beaten 2-1 by Holland after leading at half-time, Saudi Arabia finished with identical figures to the Dutch of P3 W2 D0 L1 F4 A3 Pts6.

Morocco failed to win a point but they wrote a line of history in meeting the Saudis in an all-Arab World Cup finals clash. It finished 2-1 to Saudi Arabia.

USA's one win in Group A, by 2-1 over Colombia in the crucial match for both countries, was shrouded in mystery and had a tragic sequel.

15th World Cup USA 1994 Facts

One of the Americans' goals was 'scored' by the Colombian midfielder, Andres Escobar, who paid for his unfortunate miskick with his life.

On his return to Colombia, he was shot dead as he left a restaurant in Medellin. There were dark rumours of a thwarted gambling coup as the motive for the murder.

Nearly 350,000 spectators watched the USA team's four finals matches, the last of which ended in an honourable second-round defeat by a single goal scored by Brazil's Bebeto in San Francisco.

Group C was won by Germany, although their form was far from convincing. They scored only five goals in collecting seven points to qualify for round two along with Spain.

It was fortunate for the Germans that Jurgen Klinsmann found his form, scoring four of the five goals. The other came from Karl-Heinz Riedle.

In their third group match, Germany were three up at half-time against South Korea, but wilted in the Dallas heat as goals from Hwang Sun-Hong and Hong Myung-Bo embarrassed defenders and commentators alike.

The crowd jeered Germany as the Koreans hit back and Stefan Effenberg responded with an easily recognised finger gesture. He was promptly sent home to Germany.

When Germany as champions played the first game at the opening ceremony, Bolivia's Marco Etcheverry was on the field as a substitute for only three minutes before being ordered off.

Bolivia also had Luis Cristaldo sent off against South Korea, and finished bottom of the group with one point.

Germany as usual showed their paces against sterner opposition in round two. They won a thrilling match 3-2 against Belgium in Chicago, with two goals from Voeller and another from Klinsmann.

Philippe Albert, beloved in Newcastle, got Belgium's second approaching injury time, but the after-match talking point was the decision to suspend the referee.

The 'crime' of Mr Roethlisberger of Switzerland was to ignore what was generally agreed to be a blatant foul by Germany's Helmer in his own penalty area. FIFA harshly decided to send the referee home.

In Group B, Cameroon were faced with formidable opponents in Brazil, Sweden and Russia. They went out, conceding 11 goals in all, after earning their only point in the opener with Sweden.

Rigobert Song, all of 17, had the unlikely distinction against Brazil of becoming the youngest player to be sent off in a World Cup finals match.

Facts

15th World Cup
USA 1994

Romario distinguished himself by scoring in all three of Brazil's group matches, but the goalscoring feat of this group - and of the series - was that of Oleg Salenko of Russia.

Salenko scored three in the first half against Cameroon and made it five after the break to record the only 'nap hand' in World Cup finals history.

Cameroon were beaten 6-1, but that man Roger Milla still had his moment of glory. Coming on as a substitute as always, he became the oldest player ever to score in a finals match.

Yet another record was written in Group B with the two ultimate qualifiers for the second round, Brazil and Sweden, meeting for the sixth time in the final stages of a World Cup. Latest 'score'... Brazil 4, Draws 2.

The eight matches for the next knock-out stage were: Brazil v USA, Germany v Belgium, Holland v Ireland, Mexico v Bulgaria, Nigeria v Italy, Romania v Argentina, Saudi Arabia v Sweden, Spain v Switzerland.

The outcome of the second phase was that seven European countries were to contest the quarter-finals, with Brazil alone representing the rest of the world. They still remained the bookies' favourites.

The footballing minnows all fought bravely - the Irish, Americans, Nigerians and Arabs alike - but were devoured by the big fish.

Nigeria came close to providing the shock of the tournament against Italy. They led after 27 minutes through Emmanuel Amunike and held out until two minutes from normal time when Roberto Baggio equalised.

Mexican referee Brizio flashed his yellow card some nine or ten times, then Gianfranco Zola saw red after being on as a substitute for barely 15 minutes.

Italy's class told in extra time, with Roberto Baggio earning a quarter-final place for his team from the penalty spot.

Bebeto's goal saw off the USA on July 4 - American Independence Day - to set up a Brazil v Holland quarter-final, a mouth-watering prospect made possible as the Dutch disposed of the Irish the same day in Orlando.

Dennis Bergkamp and Wim Jonk made it 2-0 to Holland in the first half and there it stayed as Jack Charlton's valiants melted in the Florida heat.

The Brazilians had played more than half the game with ten men, Leonardo having been dismissed after violin practice with an elbow, and their victory brought harsh American criticism of beaten manager Bora Milutinovic.

Milutinovic was setting up some kind of record by managing three different nations in three consecutive finals - Mexico (1986), Costa Rica (1990) and USA (1994).

15th World Cup USA 1994 Facts

Sixty thousand spectators in Dallas hoped for a surprise result as Saudi Arabia held Sweden to 1-1 at half-time, but the Swedes' prolific Kennet Andersson scored twice to end the dreams.

Bulgaria continued their newly-found winning streak at the Giants Stadium, New Jersey, where 71,000 saw a shambles of a match due to crazy refereeing by Syria's Al Sharif.

Bulgaria's Hristo Stoichkov scored first but Mexico equalised from a penalty through Garcia Aspe. Then Mr Sharif took over.

Emil Kremenliev, who escaped a sending-off for conceding the penalty although on a yellow card at the time, was then dismissed for no obvious reason, whereupon it became ten-a-side with Luis Garcia's red card for an equally obscure crime.

There was more farce when play was held up for 15 minutes while a broken crossbar was replaced.

The match then went into extra time before becoming the first penalty shoot-out of the series. Bulgaria won that easily 3-1.

Argentina's hopes of a third Final in succession died in front of 90,000 witnesses in Los Angeles, where a side stripped of Maradona and the injured Caniggia were removed by Romania.

Gheorghe Hagi was Romania's inspiration in a victory more complete than the 3-2 scoreline would suggest. Ilie Dumitrescu (2) and Hagi scored for the final farewell, with few regrets, to Argentina.

Switzerland, seldom a World Cup force since the memorable 12-goal epic with Austria in a 1958 quarter-final, were well beaten 3-0 in Washington by Spain to set up an interesting last-eight clash with Italy.

Facts

15th World Cup
USA 1994

The quarter-finals were thus Germany v Bulgaria (in New York), Italy v Spain (Boston), Brazil v Holland (Dallas), Sweden v Romania (San Francisco).

Brazil were meeting Holland for the first time in 20 years when, in West Germany, goals by Neeskens and Cruyff had deprived the South Americans of a place in the 1974 Final.

Holland were without Van Basten and Gullit but traded blow for blow for a goalless first half, but the Dutch looked well beaten after goals by Romario (52 minutes) and Bebeto (62 minutes).

Bergkamp (64 min) and Winter (77 min) then set up a thrilling finale. With nine minutes remaining, Brazil's experienced full-back Branco beat goalkeeper De Goey (later with Gullit at Chelsea) with a sizzling free kick from 30 yards.

Branco of Fluminense, playing because of Leonardo's suspension, was now back for keeps and was to figure in Brazil's triumphant drive to the Final.

The three other quarter-finals were closely-fought, with Sweden and Romania battling for 120 minutes followed by a penalty shoot-out.

The scoring chart tells the story: Brolin for Sweden (78 min), Raducioiu for Romania (88), Raducioiu again (100), Sweden's Schwarz sent off (101), K Andersson for Sweden (114).

Then the penalty shoot-out (Sweden first kick): Mild (over bar), Raducioiu (0-1), K Andersson (1-1), Hagi (1-2), Brolin (2-2), Lupescu (2-3), Ingesson (3-3), Petrescu (saved), Nilsson (4-3), Dumitrescu (4-4), Larsson (5-4), Beldedici (saved).

There was sympathy for Romania in this their second dismissal from the World Cup in successive finals on a 5-4 penalty shoot-out. The Irish had inflicted the first in Italy.

Germany had for them a disappointing tournament in that they were knocked out as early as the quarter-final stage for the first time since 1962.

Their conquerors at Giants Stadium were the 'new' Bulgaria, who were 50-1 outsiders before the start of the finals, compared with Germany's highly-backed 7-2.

All the action came in the second half, when Matthaus' penalty after 48 minutes looked sufficient until goals by Stoichkov (76 minutes) and Lechkov (78 minutes) floored the Germans.

Colombian referee J Torres Cadena made a name for himself and eight for his notebook by raising five yellow cards for Germany and three for Bolivia.

15th World Cup
USA 1994

Facts

Italy indulged in another cliffhanger finish with Spain. Dino Baggio scored in the first half, Caminero equalised in the 59th minute, then Roberto Baggio struck with the winner two minutes from time.

A blow for Italy was the suspension for eight matches and a hefty fine for defender Mauro Tassotti for elbowing Luis Enrique, whose nose was broken. The incident went unobserved by referee Sandor Puhl of Hungary, who was to control the Final, but FIFA went to work on the evidence of television.

A crowd of 84,500 in Pasadena bade farewell to Sweden, still leg-weary after their quarter-final marathon, though Brazil left it late for the kill.

There was no score when Jonas Thern, deputising for the suspended Stefan Schwarz, was also sent off after an hour and Brazil put them out with ten minutes to go, courtesy of Romario, to qualify for their fifth World Cup Final.

Italy won the other semi-final, thanks to two goals by the mercurial Roberto Baggio in the first 26 minutes. Stoichkov scored from the spot one minute before the interval to make it 2-1 and there it stayed, with Italy also through to their fifth Final.

Sweden summoned enough strength for a 4-0 defeat of Bulgaria in the third-place play-off, all the goals coming in the first half.

The Final in Pasadena was a direct contrast to the previous Final meeting of Italy and Brazil in Mexico in 1970.

On that occasion, Brazil won 4-1; in 1994, it was a goalless match for the first time, even after 120 minutes, and a first-ever penalty shoot-out decided it.

Brazil: Taffarel, Jorginho (sub Cafu 20 min), Aldair, Marcio Santos, Branco, Mazinho (sub Viola 106 min), Dunga (capt), Mauro Silva, Zinho, Romario, Bebeto.

Italy: Pagliuca, Mussi (sub Apolloni 34 min), Maldini, Baresi (capt), Benarrivo, Berti, Albertini, D Baggio (sub Evani 94 min), Donadoni, R Baggio, Massaro.

A remarkable event in an unremarkable Final was the reappearance of Franco Baresi, Italy's sweeper, who had undergone a cartilage operation after their second match against Norway 24 days earlier!

Baresi was the outstanding player for Italy for 120 minutes, but it was all in vain as he decided to lead from the front in the shoot-out . . and shot over the crossbar.

Penalty shoot-out (Italy first): Baresi (over bar), Marcio Santos (saved), Albertini (1-0), Romario (1-1), Evani (2-1), Branco (2-2), Massaro (saved), Dunga (2-3), R Baggio (over bar).

Facts

15th World Cup
USA 1994

Brazil were the winners 3-2 on penalties and received the trophy for the fourth time, once more than Italy and West Germany, making the score South America 8 Europe 7.

Attendances in the States broke all records, with 52 matches being watched by 3,567,415 spectators - more than a million higher than the previous best in 1990.

The average of 68,604 per match was also a record, being nearly 8,000 more than the previous best in Brazil in 1950.

Only one match of the USA series had below 50,000 spectators, the opening-round match between Nigeria and Bulgaria, which was watched by 44,132.

Fifteen penalties in all were awarded in open play and all were converted, yet the first penalty was missed in all three shoot-outs.

FIFA's award for the best player in the tournament went to Romario of Brazil, who also won the team awards for fair play and most entertaining.

The Lev Yashin Goalkeeper Award went to Michel Preud'homme of Belgium. He was beaten only once in three group matches, but fished three out of his net in the second-round game against Germany.

Lothar Matthaus (Germany) and Diego Maradona (Argentina) recorded their 21st World Cup finals appearances, each playing in his fourth series.

Only two others have played 21 times - Uwe Seeler (West Germany 1958-70) and Wladyslaw Zmuda (Poland 1974-86).

Leading goalscorers for the series were: Oleg Salenko (Russia), Hristo Stoichkov (Bulgaria) 6 each, Kennet Andersson (Sweden), Roberto Baggio (Italy), Jurgen Klinsmann (Germany), Romario (Brazil) 5 each.

USA 1994 ended without a further penalty shoot-out for the singer Diana Ross, who decided to end her short footballing career after aiming at an empty goal from ten feet during the opening ceremony. She missed.

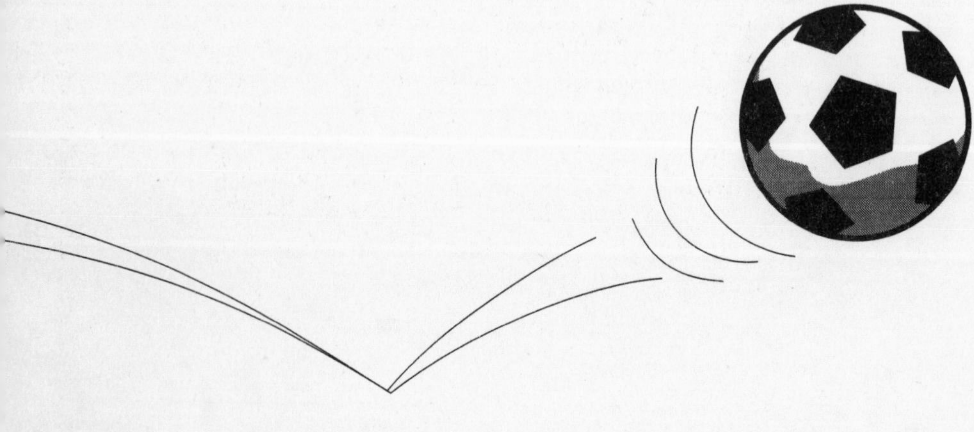

The Never-Ending Contest

Latest Score: South America 8, Europe 7

The Never-Ending Contest Facts

The battle for supremacy between football's great continents of Europe and South America continued relentlessly over the World Cup finals of 1986, 1990 and 1994.

Never had the lead been bigger than one series on either side since the first World Cup of 1930. The score after the Los Angeles triumph of Brazil stood at South America 8, Europe 7.

Here's how the contest raged over 15 series (South America first): 1-0, 1-1, 1-2, 2-2, 2-3, 3-3, 4-3, 4-4, 5-4, 5-5, 6-5, 6-6, 7-6, 7-7, 8-7.

No European country has yet won a World Cup outside Europe. Only once has South America successfully invaded Europe - Brazil in Stockholm in 1958. The conclusion? That Europe would draw level 8-8 in France and in to the Millennium ... with Germany or Italy catching up with Brazil on four wins each!

Forty-three countries took part in 156 matches over the three finals in the survey, Soviet Union/Russia and West Germany/Unified Germany counting as single units.

Britain's share of the action, apart from England's 1990 challenge, totalled a disappointing 21 matches, but the nine matches of Eire's 'League of Nations' in two finals was a shared interest for TV watchers.

The Germans again headed the three summarised series with 19 matches, followed by Argentina and Italy (18 each) and Brazil (16).

Notable improvements were shown by Belgium (15 matches) and Spain (14) to justify the support shown them in the betting shops for the 1998 finals in France.

Here is the A to Y summary of all countries who took part in the three tournaments:-

Algeria (3 matches): 1986, drew with Northern Ireland, lost to Brazil, Spain.

Argentina (18 matches): 1986, beat South Korea, Bulgaria, Uruguay, England, Belgium, West Germany, drew with Italy; 1990, beat Soviet Union, Brazil, Yugoslavia (on penalties), Italy (on penalties), drew with Romania, lost to Cameroon, West Germany; 1994, beat Greece, Nigeria, lost to Bulgaria, Romania.

Austria (3 matches): 1990, beat USA, lost to Italy, Czechoslovakia.

Belgium (15 matches): 1986, beat Iraq, Soviet Union, Spain (on penalties), drew with Paraguay, lost to Mexico, Argentina, France; 1990, beat South Korea, Uruguay, lost to Spain, England; 1994, beat Morocco, Holland, lost to Saudi Arabia, Germany.

Facts

The Never-Ending Contest

Bolivia (3 matches): 1994, drew with South Korea, lost to Germany, Spain.

Brazil (16 matches): 1986, beat Spain, Algeria, Northern Ireland, Poland, lost to France (on penalties); 1990, beat Sweden, Costa Rica, Scotland, lost to Argentina; 1994, beat Russia, Cameroon, USA, Holland, Sweden, Italy (on penalties), drew with Sweden.

Bulgaria (11 matches): 1986, drew with Italy, South Korea, lost to Argentina, Mexico; 1994, beat Greece, Argentina, Mexico (on penalties), Germany, lost to Nigeria, Italy, Sweden.

Cameroon (8 matches): 1990, beat Argentina, Romania, Colombia, lost to Soviet Union, England; 1994, drew with Sweden, lost to Brazil, Russia.

Canada (3 matches): 1986, lost to France, Hungary, Soviet Union.

Colombia (7 matches): 1990, beat United Arab Emirates, drew with West Germany, lost to Yugoslavia, Cameroon; 1994, beat Switzerland, lost to Romania, USA.

Costa Rica (4 matches): 1990, beat Scotland, Sweden, lost to Brazil, Czechoslovakia.

Czechoslovakia (5 matches): 1990, beat USA, Austria, Costa Rica, lost to Italy, West Germany.

Denmark (4 matches): 1986, beat Scotland, Uruguay, West Germany, lost to Spain.

Egypt (3 matches): 1990, drew with Holland, Ireland, lost to England.

Republic of Ireland (9 matches): 1990, beat Romania (on penalties), drew with England, Egypt, Holland, lost to Italy; 1994, beat Italy, drew with Norway, lost to Mexico, Holland.

England (12 matches): 1986, beat Poland, Paraguay, drew with Morocco, lost to Portugal, Argentina; 1990, beat Egypt, Belgium, Cameroon, drew with Ireland, Holland, lost to West Germany (on penalties), Italy.

France (7 matches): 1986, beat Canada, Hungary, Italy, Brazil (on penalties), Belgium, drew with Soviet Union, lost to West Germany.

Germany, Unified (5 matches): 1994, beat Bolivia, South Korea, Belgium, drew with Spain, lost to Bulgaria. (See also West Germany for earlier matches).

Greece (3 matches): 1994, lost to Argentina, Bulgaria, Nigeria.

Holland (9 matches): 1990, drew with Egypt, England, Ireland, lost to West Germany; 1994, beat Saudi Arabia, Morocco, Ireland, lost to Belgium, Brazil.

The Never-Ending Contest Facts

Hungary (3 matches): 1986, beat Canada, lost to Soviet Union, France.

Iraq (3 matches): 1986, lost to Paraguay, Belgium, Mexico.

Italy (18 matches): 1986, beat South Korea, drew with Bulgaria, Argentina, lost to France; 1990, beat Austria, USA, Czechoslovakia, Uruguay, Ireland, England, lost to Argentina (on penalties); 1994, beat Norway, Nigeria, Spain, Bulgaria, drew with Mexico, lost to Ireland, Brazil (on penalties).

Mexico (9 matches): 1986, beat Belgium, Iraq, Bulgaria, drew with Paraguay, lost to West Germany (on penalties); 1994, beat Ireland, drew with Italy, lost to Norway, Bulgaria (on penalties).

Morocco (7 matches): 1986, beat Portugal, drew with Poland, England, lost to West Germany; 1994, lost to Belgium, Saudi Arabia, Holland.

Nigeria (4 matches): 1994, beat Bulgaria, Greece, lost to Argentina, Italy.

Northern Ireland (3 matches): 1986, drew with Algeria, lost to Spain, Brazil.

Norway (3 matches): 1994, beat Mexico, drew with Ireland, lost to Italy.

Paraguay (4 matches): 1986, beat Iraq, drew with Mexico, Belgium, lost to England.

Poland (4 matches): 1986, beat Portugal, drew with Morocco, lost to England, Brazil.

Portugal (3 matches): 1986, beat England, lost to Poland, Morocco.

Romania (9 matches): 1990, beat Soviet Union, drew with Argentina, lost to Cameroon, Ireland (on penalties); 1994, beat Colombia, USA, Argentina, lost to Switzerland, Sweden (on penalties).

Russia (3 matches): 1994, beat Cameroon, lost to Brazil, Sweden. (See also Soviet Union for earlier matches).

Saudi Arabia (4 matches): 1994, beat Morocco, Belgium, lost to Holland, Sweden.

Scotland (6 matches): 1986, drew with Uruguay, lost to Denmark, West Germany; 1990, beat Sweden, lost to Costa Rica, Brazil.

South Korea (9 matches): 1986, drew with Bulgaria, lost to Argentina, Italy; 1990, lost to Belgium, Spain, Uruguay; 1994, drew with Spain, Bolivia, lost to Germany.

Soviet Union (7 matches): 1986, beat Hungary, Canada, drew with France, lost to to Belgium; 1990, beat Cameroon, lost to to Romania, Argentina.

Facts

The Never-Ending Contest

Spain (14 matches): 1986, beat Northern Ireland, Algeria, Denmark, lost to to Brazil, Belgium (on penalties); 1990, beat South Korea, Belgium, drew with Uruguay, lost to Yugoslavia; 1994, beat Bolivia, Switzerland, drew with South Korea, Germany, lost to Italy.

Sweden (10 matches): 1990, lost to Brazil, Scotland, Costa Rica; 1994, beat Russia, Saudi Arabia, Romania (on penalties), Bulgaria, drew with Cameroon, Brazil, lost to Brazil.

Switzerland (4 matches): 1994, beat Romania, drew with USA, lost to Colombia, Spain.

United Arab Emirates (3 matches): 1990, lost to Colombia, West Germany, Yugoslavia.

Uruguay (8 matches): 1986, drew with West Germany, Scotland, lost to Denmark, Argentina; 1990, beat South Korea, drew with Spain, lost to Belgium, Italy.

USA (7 matches): 1990, lost to Czechoslovakia, Italy, Austria; 1994, beat Colombia, drew with Switzerland, lost to Romania, Brazil.

West Germany (14 matches): 1986, beat Scotland, Morocco, Mexico (on penalties), France, drew with Uruguay, lost to Denmark, Argentina; 1990, beat Yugoslavia, United Arab Emirates, Holland, Czechoslovakia, England (on penalties), Argentina, drew with Colombia.

Yugoslavia (5 matches): 1990, beat Colombia, United Arab Emirates, Spain, lost to West Germany, Argentina (on penalties).

Referees for the three Finals were from; 1986 Brazil (Filho), 1990 Mexico (Codesal), 1994 Hungary (Puhl).

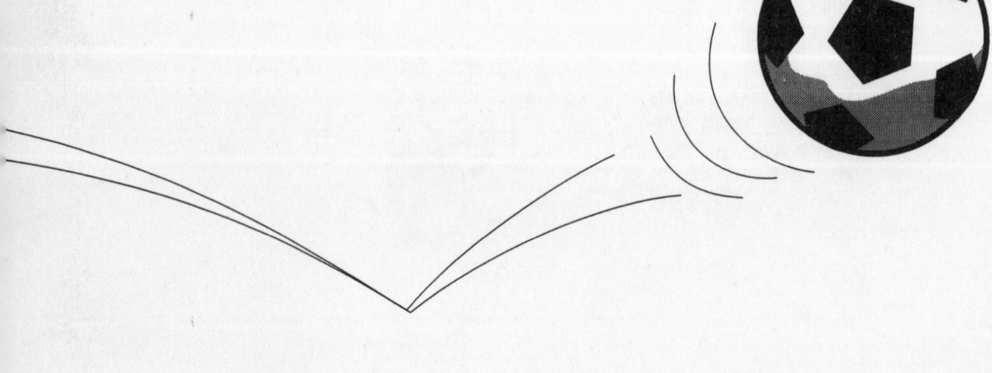

16th World Cup France 1998

The Qualifying Rounds

16th World Cup – France 1998 The Qualifying Rounds Facts

On March 10, 1996, Dominica met Antigua in the first of 639 scheduled qualifying-round matches in the 16th World Cup. It was a 3-3 draw.

The first match of the finals was due to kick off in Paris on June 10, 1998... twenty-seven months later.

There is no record of any losing bets from Dominican or Antiguan fans, but even then, Brazil the holders were quoted at a measly 4-1 to win their fifth World Cup Final of the 20th Century.

Records were broken all along the way to the finals in France, starting with an astonishing entry of 171 countries, not counting hosts France and holders Brazil, from 197 FIFA members.

Although Bermuda and the Bahamas withdrew before the start for financial reasons, the line-up was vastly more than the original record entry of 144 in the previous tournament - and some dozen or so of those pulled out before a ball was kicked.

The first World Cup was contested by 13 countries (with no qualifying rounds), and only four of these from Europe. In 1998, there was to be a biggest-ever total of 32 countries in the finals, with 15 from Europe alone. This meant 64 matches, as against 52 in 1994.

Yet Sepp Blatter, FIFA secretary-general, once said: 'In some countries you have a big match on television every day. It is too much and a threat to the game.'

The Brazilian president of FIFA, Joao Havelange, announced that he planned to retire after the 1998 Final in his 81st year, having been head of world football for 24 years.

France were chosen to stage the finals for the second time, the first occasion having been 1938 when only 15 countries played on a straight knock-out basis.

Sixty years on, the man in charge of headaches was Michel Platini, former captain and coach of France, in his capacity as president of FIFA's World Cup Organising Committee.

Ten of the 13 contestants of 1930 were to appear in the 1998 finals, the missing countries being Uruguay, twice champions, Bolivia and Peru - all South American.

The ten at the Class of '30 old boys' reunion were Argentina, Belgium, Brazil, Chile, France, Mexico, Paraguay, Romania, USA and Yugoslavia.

The decision to award three points for a win in all the qualifiers for the first time added spice to the early rounds - and especially in the South American zone where, in addition to Brazil, four tickets to France were on offer.

Facts

16th World Cup – France 1998
The Qualifying Rounds

Argentina, Paraguay and Colombia were comfortable winners of the first three places in their 16 round-robin matches.

Argentina, twice champions, qualified for the 12th time, Paraguay for their fourth, as also did Colombia.

Paraguay are coached by an old Brazilian World Cup player, Paulo Cesar Carpeggiani, and a versatile goalkeeper in Jose Luis Chilavert.

Chilavert always likes to be where the action is. He is a free-kick specialist and shook a 58,000 Buenos Aires crowd by forcing a 1-1 draw after Batistita had given Argentina the lead.

Chilavert, however, was not around for the closing stages of the qualifiers, having been banned for four matches after a punch-up with Faustino Asprilla during their 2-1 win over Argentina.

Uruguay, with a record of nine finals, started their campaign badly with defeats by Paraguay, Colombia and Chile, and had four different coaches in 18 months.

They fell out of the running for fourth spot, thus failing to qualify for the second finals in succession, when a much-needed win against Argentina never materialised, and the game ended 0-0.

The previous month Uruguay had lost 2-1 in Peru, who were involved in a desperate fight with Chile and Ecuador for the last qualification place in their 16th and final games.

Chile clinched it to qualify for their first World Cup finals for 16 years, thanks largely to the 23 goals scored in the 16 matches by Marcello Salas and Ivan Zamorano.

The last deciding match, in which Chile beat Bolivia 3-0 in Santiago, was watched by Alex Ferguson, the Manchester United manager, who had ideas of signing Salas. The Chilean rose to the occasion by scoring.

The Asian competition produced a fascinating quartet of qualifiers in Iran, Japan, Saudi Arabia and South Korea.

South Korea were runaway winners of Group B, having clinched their place with two of their eight games still to play.

South Korea were in their fourth consecutive finals and fifth in all, having played 11 finals matches – yet they are still looking for their first win.

Apart from their earliest appearance in 1954, when they were swamped by a 16-goal tidal wave from Hungary and Turkey, South Korea have drawn with Bulgaria, Spain and Bolivia, and were beaten only 3-2 by Italy (1986) and Germany (1994).

16th World Cup – France 1998 The Qualifying Rounds Facts

One South Korean player to watch is Choi Yong-Soo, who scored all three goals in the opening win over Kazakhstan. Their coach Cha Bum Kun played as a striker with Eintracht Frankfurt in the late Seventies.

Saudi Arabia finished top of Group A to qualify for the finals for the second consecutive time, thanks to a vital one-goal win over Iran. The Saudis' scoring hero was Khaled Mussad.

Who would be a coach for Saudi? By the end of 1997, they had fired seven of them since their 1994 finals spell in the USA.

The Iranians then had to win their place in the finals the hard way. They were beaten by Japan in the play-off between the two group runners-up and were faced with a two-match play-off with Australia, winners of the Oceania qualifying section.

The hero for Japan was a substitute, Masayuki Okano, who came on to score the golden goal with one minute left in extra time.

Japan, on their way to the second-round group games, were merciless in their two preliminary matches against Macao, winning 10-0 each time.

Japan were qualifying for a World Cup finals for the first time, along with Croatia, Jamaica and South Africa.

The Australia-Iran clashes were in themselves a mini-World Cup, accompanied as they were by widespread publicity and the last of the 32 qualifiers hanging on their results.

Australia had beaten New Zealand 3-0 and 2-0 to finish Oceania champions, having earlier plastered the Solomon Islands 13-0 in Sydney.

On the form-book, that wasn't sufficient! Nine days earlier at Damascus, the Iranians had beaten the Maldives Republic 17-0 to set an all-time World Cup scoring record. (Six days later the Maldives conceded 12 to Syria).

The last painful intelligence from the Maldives was that Romulo Cortez is no longer the national coach.

At the higher level it was dead level, so to speak. Australia made the 1974 finals (lost two, drew with Chile) and Iran were there in 1978 (lost two, drew with Scotland).

The first match in Teheran was given the build-up of World War Three, with the 'Iran Daily' newspaper declaring that 'one shouldn't accept too much from a nation that started out as a prison camp of the British'.

Australia's coach, Terry Venables, once England's manager, first had a pop at FIFA for granting an amnesty to four Iranian players' bookings 'because Iran has played 14 games in the tournament already, compared with Australia's six'.

Facts

16th World Cup – France 1998
The Qualifying Rounds

Australia's players coped well with the high-octane atmosphere created by 128,000 fanatics in the Azadi Stadium. The match was also watched by a domestic TV audience of 40 million, two-thirds of Iran's population.

The result was 1-1, Leeds teenager Harry Kewell scoring for Venables' foreign legion and Khodadad Azizi equalising just before half-time.

Iran's Brazilian coach Valdir Vieira, only two weeks into the job, said: 'Venables should not count on going to France yet. We were dancing around Australia.'

Venables said: 'We got a result and we got a goal. We've got to be satisfied with that.'

Australia's 12-match unbeaten record and promise of World Cup fame attracted 85,022 spectators to Melbourne Cricket Ground for the second leg on November 29, 1997, the last match before the finals draw in Marseille five days hence.

Australia's 'Socceroos' dominated the game for 75 minutes, scoring twice, then Iran stole in twice to equalise for a 3-3 aggregate and a priceless victory on the away-goals rule.

Harry Kewell again stood out, scoring the Aussies' first goal and providing the headed pass for Aurelio Vidmar to net the second.

In the 75th minute, Karim Bagheri made it 2-1, and three minutes later came the Iran equaliser and the winner by Khodadad Azizi.

Coach Vieira said: 'God has helped us and he has helped our goalkeeper.' Coach Venables said: 'We terrorised them for a lot of the time.'

The referee of this final qualifier was, oddly, the referee of the 1994 Final, Sandor Puhl of Hungary, who was voted FIFA's No 1 ref for the three subsequent years in an international poll.

16th World Cup – France 1998
The Qualifying Rounds

Facts

Sadly, Mr Puhl's was a shooting star. He later failed to punish Paul Bosvelt of Feyenoord for a sickening tackle on Denis Irwin of Manchester United in a Champions League match and was suspended by FIFA for the rest of the season.

One established record was that the crowd at the MCG far exceeded the previous highest for a soccer match of 36,200 for the Olympic Games Final of 1956.

The rapid development of African football was recognised by the award of five qualifying places, a record number for the continent.

Africa's five finalists were Cameroon, Morocco, Nigeria, South Africa and Tunisia, with Cameroon becoming the first African nation to appear in three consecutive World Cup finals series.

Cameroon and Morocco were in their fourth World Cup finals. Nigeria were following on 1994 with a second appearance and Tunisia also were doubling their score, having previously qualified in 1978.

Most encouraging and exciting was the emergence of South Africa, fast rejoining the world of sport after three decades of isolation because of apartheid.

They finished convincing winners of their group of four, with home victories over Congo and Zambia and the double against Zaire, who were the only one of the quartet to have previously qualified (1974).

England saw South Africa's capabilities first-hand at Old Trafford on May 24, 1997, when they were beaten only 2-1 in their first-ever meeting, and later in the year they kept defeat by France down to the same margin.

Their team is composed of players largely experienced in European football, among them Phil Masinga, ex-Leeds United, who scored four of their seven qualifying goals.

South Africa were then managed by Clive Barker and were known in Zulu-speak as 'Bafana Bafana' - The Boys. Their players also include Lucas Radebe of Leeds United and Mark Fish of Bolton Wanderers.

Nigeria had their group wrapped up before losing their final game against Guinea. Their excellent form in USA in 1994, when they took Italy to extra time after beating Bulgaria and Greece, had been maintained.

Cameroon were already well known on the World Cup stage before qualifying unbeaten in six games, but their group table conveyed the warning message of another emerging African nation.

Facts

16th World Cup – France 1998
The Qualifying Rounds

Angola drew twice with Nigeria, 0-0 and 1-1, to finish unbeaten:

Country	P	W	D	L	F	A	Pts
Cameroon	6	4	2	0	10	4	14
Angola	6	2	4	0	7	4	10

Cameroon, the Lions of Africa, had a World Cup record leading up to the 1998 finals of P11 W3 D4 L4 F11 A21, their finest hour coming on July 1, 1990, when they lost to England 3-2 after extra time in a quarter-final match in Italy.

Their star performer is goalkeeper and captain Jacques Song'o. He plays for Deportivo La Coruna in Spain and kept goal for the Rest of the World against Europe at the World Cup draw in Marseille.

Cameroon could suffer a few tabloid headlines in the event of any scoring lapses by one of their strikers in France. He is a Frenchman with Cameroon roots . . . Jean-Jacques Misse Misse.

England's coaching team took a closer look at Tunisia's impressive qualifying record after the World Cup draw, where they won five out of six and drew 0-0 in Cairo with Egypt, who were strongly fancied to qualify.

This was the Group 2 qualifying table:

Country	P	W	D	L	F	A	Pts
Tunisia	6	5	1	0	10	1	16
Egypt	6	3	1	2	15	5	10
Liberia	6	1	1	4	2	10	4
Namibia	6	1	1	4	6	17	4

Tunisia's 1997 record also included reaching the finals of the African Champions Cup and Cup-Winners' Cup.

Morocco were overwhelming winners of Group 5, their only blemish being a 2-2 draw in Ghana. Their record: P6 W5 D1 L0 F14 A2 Pts16.

16th World Cup – France 1998 The Qualifying Rounds Facts

Morocco's achievement in their three previous finals, in Mexico twice and the United States, adds up to one win in 10 matches, but they have only once been hit for three goals - by Peru.

Against that, they have held England and Poland to goalless draws, lost 2-1 and 1-0 to West Germany and beaten Portugal 3-1. Their record: P10 W1 D3 L6 F7 A13.

Morocco's star player is Salaheddine Bassir, now with Deportivo La Coruna and with a goals return of 10 from his first 16 international appearances.

The three qualifiers from the CONCACAF section were Mexico for the 11th time, USA for the sixth time with the last three in succession, and first-timers The Reggae Boys - as the Jamaican team will be known for ever more.

Mexico won the group comfortably but nothing seems to please either their ruling body or their volatile supporters.

Nearly 115,000 fans booed Mexico off the park after an excruciating goalless draw against USA at the Azteca Stadium.

The head that rolled was that of their time-traveller coach, Bora Milutinovic, whose 'crime' was to take his fourth different country to the World Cup finals in consecutive tournaments.

Jamaica achieved the impossible with the help of a jumble of players from England's Premiership, local lads from the various leagues of Jamaica, and the experience and skills of their Brazilian coach, Rene Simoes.

After clinching a World Cup place by drawing 0-0 with USA in Kingston, the Jamaican players were promised free plots of land and a fund was launched with the aim of giving them £20,000 each.

Derby County player Deon Burton found himself on the heroes' pedestal hitherto reserved for Jamaica's cricketers after scoring in each of his first three World Cup matches.

Facts

16th World Cup – France 1998
The Qualifying Rounds

They were all vital goals. He was the scorer in each of the 1-0 wins against Costa Rica and Canada, and the other goal was in the 1-1 draw away to USA.

Burton is one of the quartet qualified through their parentage to play for Jamaica. Robbie Earle (Wimbledon), Fitzroy Simpson and Paul Hall (both Portsmouth) are the others.

Casting their net wider before France 1998, the Jamaican FA were checking on such names as Frank Sinclair (Chelsea), Dean Sturridge and Chris Powell (Derby), Ian Taylor (Aston Villa), Marcus Gayle (Wimbledon) and Noel Blake (Exeter).

Nobody could have predicted all this after Jamaica's stuttering start to the final qualifying round. They were bottom of the table with only one win from five games, having suffered a nightmare 6-0 defeat in Mexico.

USA were grateful to goalkeeper Kasey Keller of Leicester and key man John Harkes of the 1994 squad for their unexpected qualification.

There were 49 entries for the European section, with 14 places in the finals to be won alongside France as hosts.

They were drawn in groups of five or six, with the nine winners and the best runner-up to go through automatically. The eight other runners-up were paired home and away to produce the four remaining qualifiers.

The Home Countries' hopes rested mainly with Scotland and England, although neither was among the first seeds, while the Republic of Ireland were hopeful of completing a hat-trick of consecutive appearances in the finals, this time under a new manager, Mick McCarthy.

England were also under a new chief, Chelsea's player-manager Glenn Hoddle taking over as head coach at 39 from Terry Venables.

Venables had a successful run from 1993 to 1996, culminating in a semi-final appearance in the European Championship. He resigned to become chief executive of Portsmouth and manager of Australia's national side.

Hoddle played 53 times for England while with Tottenham and Monaco, before becoming manager of Swindon Town in 1991 and moving to Stamford Bridge in 1993. He scored eight international goals.

Hoddle's first match in charge was against Moldova away, for which he appointed as skipper Alan Shearer. He was in fact England's 100th captain in the nation's history.

The first seeds were, in group order one to nine: Denmark, Italy, Norway, Sweden, Russia, Spain, Holland, Romania, Germany.

16th World Cup – France 1998
The Qualifying Rounds

Facts

Group 2 was virtually a two-horse race from the outset, although England and Italy especially were to find tough opposition in Poland and Georgia. Moldova were also there as fodder in the chase for good goal-difference statistics which could prove absolutely vital.

England started with a 3-0 win in Moldova, their first goal under Hoddle coming from Nick Barmby in the Everton man's only game in the World Cup.

Poland gave England a fright by scoring first in seven minutes at Wembley but Shearer kept up his scoring run with two goals to make his tally eight in seven games.

Some seven months later, Georgia were beaten 2-0 for nine points from three games. Then came the shocker - beaten by Gianfranco Zola's only goal of the match for Hoddle's first reverse.

Luckily, the Italians dropped four precious points in drawing 0-0 in Poland and Georgia, while England regained their winning vein with three victories for eight goals and none conceded.

The third win, 4-0 against Moldova at Wembley, was memorable for its one-minute silence for Diana, Princess of Wales. After the match, England players donated their fees of £30,000 to the Fund.

The scene was set for a last-minute heart-stopper against Italy on October 11, 1997, at Rome's 82,000-capacity Stadio Olimpico.

The situation was crystal clear. Italy had to win to qualify; England knew a draw would suffice. This was the scenario:

Country	P	W	D	L	F	A	Pts
England	7	6	0	1	15	2	18
Italy	7	5	2	0	11	1	17

Who said a 0-0 must be boring? The tension on the pitch was almost unbearable, the scenes off it sickening. Police brutality, chaotic administration and hooliganism at its most frightening were all to blame as FIFA and security forces on both sides sat in judgment.

Gianfranco Zola said before the match: 'At Wembley we managed a miracle and we will have to repeat that feat in Rome. We can do it.'

There was no repeat for Italy, less still for Zola as he trudged off to be substituted, pursued by the mocking echo of his prediction.

Facts

16th World Cup – France 1998
The Qualifying Rounds

England had qualified and Italy, three times World Cup holders, faced the daunting task of two play-off matches with Russia.

David Beckham played in all eight England ties, the only man in the squad with such a 100 per cent record.

Paul Ince captained the England side in the continuing absence of Alan Shearer and was a wounded hero, with bandaged head and blood-spattered shirt.

The England team (3-5-2 formation): Seaman; Campbell, Adams, Southgate; Beckham, Batty, Ince (capt), Gascoigne (sub Butt, 88min), Le Saux; Sheringham, Wright.

Hoddle waxed lyrical over the total backing of the fans for the four Wembley group matches, which averaged 73,700 per game.

Scotland also stayed cool and positive to finish second to Austria in Group 4 and qualified for the finals as the best European runners-up.

Unpredictable as ever in World Cup action, the Scots drew and won their ties with Austria, then lost to Sweden, who finished third.

This was Scotland's only defeat in ten matches, with clean sheets in eight and only three goals given away - two to Sweden and one to Belarus.

Craig Brown's management of Scotland was widely praised, while Gary McAllister was an inspiring captain in all his nine appearances.

Denmark headed Group 1 with a last-match 0-0 draw in Greece, Peter Schmeichel of Manchester United performing heroically in the Danish goal. Their only previous finals appearance was in 1986.

Group 3 was an easy ride for Norway, full of English-based players. They finished unbeaten, eight points clear of Hungary and, like England, gave away only two goals in eight games.

Group 5 was a two-horse race from the start between Bulgaria and Russia, with Israel, Cyprus and poor little Luxembourg (lost all eight games, goals for 2, against 22) making up the numbers. Bulgaria won the group by one point.

Spain were impressive winners of Group 6, with Yugoslavia runners-up, followed by the Czech Republic and Slovakia.Out of their class in this group were Malta, pointless from ten games (goals for 2, against 37), and the Faroe Islands, who lost all their games apart from a double over the Maltese.

Holland were back to their best in winning Group 7 ahead of Belgium. Wales were never in the race and ended up P8 W2 D1 L5 F20 A21 Pts7.

16th World Cup – France 1998
The Qualifying Rounds

Facts

San Marino ran away with the booby prize in this section by failing to score or earn a point in their eight games. Even Wales took them for 11 in two meetings and San Marino's final tally was 42 goals against.

Liechtenstein fared even worse in Group 8 with figures of 10-0-0-10 and 52 goals conceded, including an 11-1 whipping by Macedonia.

Romania romped home in this group, losing their 100 per cent record in their last match, a 1-1 draw so vital to opponents from the Republic of Ireland who thus qualified for the runners-up play-offs, one point ahead of Lithuania.

Germany won Group 9 without a defeat in ten games, but they looked shaky at times with four draws. The runners-up place went to Ukraine, who pipped Portugal by a single point.

Northern Ireland were never in the hunt, with Albania their only victims (Albania won the return match to record their only win), though the Irish did surprise even themselves by holding the European Champions to a goalless draw in Germany.

The four remaining European names for the finals draw were to result from those two-leg matches: Russia v Italy, Hungary v Yugoslavia, Croatia v Ukraine, Belgium v Republic of Ireland.

Yugoslavia emerged from their civil war turmoil to slaughter the Hungarians 12-1 over two legs, seven goals coming from the Real Madrid player Predrag Mijatovic.

Belgium put the pressure on Ireland with an away goal (result 1-1), although it was not decisive in the end as the Belgians won the second match 2-1 for a 3-2 aggregate.

Italy, like Belgium, drew 1-1 away in the first leg with Russia. They won the return match by a single goal for a 2-1 aggregate.

Croatia cushioned themselves with a 2-0 home win against Ukraine, drew 1-1 in the second leg and qualified for their first World Cup finals with a 3-1 aggregate.

FIFA finally named the top seeds: Brazil (holders), France (hosts), Italy, Germany, Argentina, Holland, Spain, Romania.

The opening match, scheduled for Paris on June 10, 1998, was Brazil v Scotland.

Craig Brown, the Scots' manager, said: 'We have to be optimistic.' And so say all of us!

Wingless Wonders

England's 1966 World Cup winners

Wingless Wonders **Facts**

GORDON BANKS (Leicester City)

Sheffield-born youngest of four sons of a steel foundry worker, Gordon Banks was a goalkeeper from his early schooldays.

Bert Trautmann, of Manchester City, was the 'keeper on whom he modelled himself and inspired him to a professional career.

His lucky break came while he was working as a coalman's mate. He went to watch a local match and was asked to stand in for a missing goalkeeper.

Gordon was in his mid-twenties when he took over from Ron Springett in the England goal for the first of 73 caps.

His first cap was against Scotland at Wembley in April 1963 (lost 1-2). His last cap was also against Scotland, away (won 1-0).

He kept a clean sheet in an incredible 35 England games, and conceded only 57 international goals.

He played in nine World Cup matches, conceding only four goals - and two of those were on his most memorable day... Wembley, July 30, 1966.

Gordon's opposite number that day in the West German team, Tilkowski, was nicknamed 'Dracula' by the England lads - because he disliked crosses!

The England 'keeper rated the semi-final against Portugal as the classiest match he ever played in, despite the fact that he was finally beaten for the first time after a wonderful run of seven clean sheets.

That goal haunted him long after it was scored, from the penalty spot, by Eusebio, who had already converted two in Portugal's quarter-final with North Korea.

Gordon knew he usually shot to the 'keeper's right and some of his England teammates were also pointing in that direction. Portugal's skipper Coluna spotted them and whispered to Eusebio.

The 'keeper assumed he was telling Eusebio to change his direction, so dived to the left as the ball was struck. Eusebio went, as usual, to the right.

Facts

Wingless Wonders

Gordon re-lived the moment a thousand times. 'I could have cried,' he said.

Of the Final, he recalls saying to himself after Peters made it 2-1: 'Come on, Gordon - composure, control, concentration.'

Another satisfying recollection of the 1966 World Cup is the unheard-of instance of a player winning an argument with Alf Ramsey.

Before the match with France, the manager proposed that a defender should stand on the goal-line alongside Gordon for free-kicks, having seen Garrincha the Brazilian's 'banana shots'.

The 'keeper said it was 'a stupid idea' and when other members of the side agreed with him, Alf abandoned the ploy.

In 1972, Banks was named Footballer of the Year by the Football Writers' Association. The only previous goalkeeper to receive the award was his schoolboy idol Bert Trautmann in 1956.

Five months later, at the age of 34, Gordon lost an eye in a road accident, ending a first-class career comprising spells at Chesterfield (one season), Leicester City (eight) and Stoke City (five).

Banks later played in the United States for two years with Fort Lauderdale Strikers.

GEORGE COHEN (Fulham)

George Cohen played for Fulham in the days when Craven Cottage was in big black capitals on the football maps.

From the time he started his career in 1957 as a 17-year-old, he was strictly a 'one-club' man.

His starting wage was £7 a week, not a fortune for a club on the fringe of promotion to the First Division, but George was a happy Londoner playing the game he loved - and for a London club.

He made his debut for Fulham against Liverpool as a full-back in 1957, the first of 408 appearances for the club.

Wingless Wonders **Facts**

Seven years after joining the club, he was capped for the first time on May 6, 1964 against Uruguay at Wembley. England won 2-1, Johnny Byrne scoring both goals.

George took over the right-back position from Jimmy Armfield in that match, at the same time Bobby Moore was assuming Armfield's role as England captain on a regular basis.

It was the start of a long partnership with Ray Wilson, considered by many critics to be the most successful in England's history.

Cohen and Wilson played together as England's full-backs on 28 occasions, including all six matches in the 1966 World Cup finals.

George won 37 caps in all and was the last Fulham player to be picked for England.

His League career ended prematurely when he underwent major knee surgery in 1970, after 13 happy years with Fulham.

His last game for England was on November 22, 1967, against Northern Ireland in a European Championship qualifier at Wembley. England won 2-0... and Ray Wilson was his full-back partner.

George vainly attempted a comeback with a few games in the Southern League before moving into the building trade.

Between 1976 and 1990, he took on another battle - this time with stomach cancer.

He won the struggle and came out of hospital in 1990 a fit man again.

RAY WILSON (Everton)

Ray Wilson's career took off the day he had a quiet chat with Roy Goodall at Huddersfield Town's ground after doing his National Service.

Goodall, Town's trainer and pre-war player with England and Huddersfield, suggested that instead of playing as an inside-forward, Ray Wilson should try switching to full-back.

It was an inspired thought. Ray took to his new position like a duck to water and went on to play left-back 63 times for England.

Goodall knew his onions and his Huddersfield, having played right-back for the club in three successive League Championship sides and two FA Cup Finals in the Twenties.

Facts

Wingless Wonders

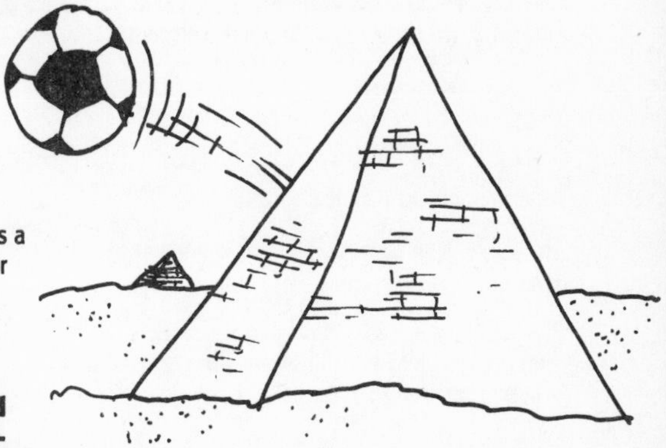

Derbyshire-born Ray joined Huddersfield's ground staff at the age of 16 'cleaning boots during the daytime and training at night.'

He played in the junior team as a pro before going away at 18 for his two-year Army stint, some of it in Egypt.

On being demobbed, he had a trial with Huddersfield and was signed on for a season. That's when Roy Goodall talked to him.

Ray was soon a regular in Town's side at left-back and in 1960 won his first cap for England, before a massive Hampden Park crowd, on April 19, 1960. The final score was 1-1.

His 63 international appearances were for many years the highest number for a full-back for England.

Only Kenny Sansom (86) and Stuart Pearce (76 by the end of 1997) have played in more England matches at full-back.

As the World Cup 1966 finals approached, Ray struck up a regular and highly successful partnership with George Cohen, but fate almost took a hand in its infancy.

In June 1966, Ray collapsed with a back injury during England training at Lilleshall and was ordered to lie on fracture boards for 24 hours. Alf Ramsey gave trainer Harold Shepherdson one week only in which to get him fit for action.

The target was achieved thanks largely to therapy at RAF Cosford's swimming pool.

Wilson, smaller in stature and quick of foot, and Cohen, a heavier, formidable figure, gelled so well that they played alongside each other 28 times for England.

Ray played his heart out in the World Cup finals. In the quarter-final, his initial move resulted in Geoff Hurst's winning goal. In the semi-final against Portugal, he set up a move that brought a Bobby Charlton goal.

Wingless Wonders Facts

During his time with Huddersfield, Ray was constantly asking for a transfer until finally, he moved across the Pennines to Everton for £40,000.

The next four years were the most rewarding of his career, with 1966 a golden year.

In May he walked up the Wembley steps for an FA Cup winners' medal. Everton had beaten Sheffield Wednesday 3-2.

In July he was mounting those 39 steps again to receive his World Cup winners' medal.

Two years later, and still playing regularly for Everton and England, he was 'up them thar stairs' a third time - but this time for an FA Cup losers' medal. West Bromwich Albion 1 Everton 0.

On reflection, Ray said he was glad to have had the experience of winning and losing a Cup Final so that he knew the elation of one and the downside of the other.

Losing, he said, was 'just waiting for the ground to open up and swallow you!'

The Cohen-Wilson combination was together for the last time in November 1967, England beating Northern Ireland 2-0 in a European Championship qualifying match at Wembley.

Ray played six more games after the break-up with three different partners - Cyril Knowles, Keith Newton and Tommy Wright.

His last two England appearances were in Italy in 1968 in the European Championship finals. England lost 1-0 to Yugoslavia in their semi-final, but won 2-0 against the Soviet Union in the third-place play-off.

Following a knee injury, Ray spent a year in Everton reserves before going to Oldham Athletic to play what he considered 'a necessity.'

At 35 he was made Oldham skipper before making his final move to Bradford City as coach.

He turned down an offer to manage the club because he always said that soccer management was not in his future plans. Instead, he joined the family firm of funeral directors.

So ended the illustrious football career of the man Denis Law once described as 'the defender I find most difficult to pass.'

Facts

Wingless Wonders

NOBBY STILES (Manchester United)

Born in 1942. Won 28 England caps. Height 5ft 5in, on a clear day.

Son of a football-mad undertaker in the Collyhurst district of Manchester.

First introduction to football was retrieving the ball from a river for his dad's team.

Decided to join Manchester United at the age of six, after his first view of the team in action from Dad's shoulders.

Known worldwide as the Toothless Tiger - but simply 'Happy' to his teammates. The name given to him by victims of his crunching tackles is unfit for family reading.

Played for United juniors at 16 before making his first-team debut.

Nobby's crisis match was the Group 1 meeting with France in the 1966 World Cup finals. A mistimed tackle earned him a referee's caution and there was consequent pressure on Ramsey from FA officials to drop him.

'No,' growled Alf, 'I pick the teams' – and this was followed by Nobby's vital contribution to the 1-0 quarter-final win against Argentina.

He had played all six World Cup matches in 1966, but for him the unforgettable moment came as he entered the arena for the quarter-final game with Argentina. Ninety thousand fans chanted 'Stiles-Stiles-Stiles.'

Nobby was then deputed to deal with the renowned skills of Portugal's Eusebio, who had just scored four in the 5-3 win over North Korea.

Nobby closed the door on the Portuguese genius, and two goals from his United pal Bobby Charlton paved the Wembley Way to the Final with West Germany.

Wingless Wonders Facts

In the final, 'Happy' lifted his exhausted teammates after 90 minutes, facing extra time, by saying over and over again: 'We can win it'.

The game restarted with Ramsey's epic cry: 'You've won it once. Now go out and win it again,' and Nobby obeyed his master's voice.

At the nailbiting stage, he set up the move that led to Hurst's second goal, and the vital 3-2 lead. Nobby knew then they'd 'won it again'.

Nobby, socks below his ankles, did his famous jig with the trophy but knotted legs refused to run any more and he completed the lap of honour at a slow walk.

Clutching his winners' medal after holding the trophy, he said: 'They can't take this away from us.'

Nobby's international career had an odd top-and-tail feature, in that his first and final caps were won against Scotland at Wembley and Hampden Park.

JACK CHARLTON (Leeds United)

Big Jack Charlton, 6ft 2in without his boots on, wanted to be a bobby when he left school.

He settled for a footballer's life and did the bobby's job for England in 1966.

He never wore a helmet but he did earn 35 international caps to keep his thinning thatch dry.

Jack Charlton was born on May 8, 1935 - two years earlier than brother Bobby.

Dad was a coal miner, mother Cissie a member of the talented and football-mad Milburn family.

Jack wrote for a career with the police and was accepted. Luckily for Don Revie and Alf Ramsey, and eventually for the whole of southern Ireland, the letter came a day too late.

Facts

Wingless Wonders

Twenty-four hours earlier, he had agreed to the offer of a football future with Leeds United.

Leeds took young Jack as an amateur at 15 and started paying him at the age of 17.

He played 629 League matches for Leeds in his 21-year stay with them.

He was awarded his first cap for England on April 10, 1965, against Scotland at Wembley - one month before his 30th birthday.

The score was 2-2, the England goals scored by Jimmy Greaves and, naturally... Jack's brother Bobby Charlton.

England's first six that day was: Banks, Cohen, Wilson, Stiles, J Charlton, Moore. It read the same 22 internationals and 15 months later in the World Cup Final.

It was a different story up front, where the line-up read P Thompson, Greaves, Bridges, Byrne, R Charlton. Only Bobby - 'our kid' - was still there for The Big Match.

Jack and Bobby were together through all six World Cup finals matches in 1966, and were given a thank-you evening by the locals of their hometown Ashington.

Thousands lined the streets as they travelled to the council office reception in an open-topped Rolls-Royce.

They each received a gold watch and an inscribed tankard, both highly-treasured mementos.

The crowning glory for Jack was being voted Footballer of the Year 1966-67, the year after Bobby had had the same recognition.

Jack was called 'The Giraffe' by his fellow players because of his height, solid bearing on the pitch - and his telescopic neck.

During the World Cup, two players from each team were selected for random dope tests. Jack was chosen so many times that the rest of the team presented him with a baby's potty and named him 'England's Jimmy Riddle Champion'!

On April 15, 1967, playing against Scotland in a European Championship qualifier at Wembley, he scored even though suffering a broken toe early on. Scotland won 3-2.

England's other goal in that match was scored, naturally, by ... Bobby Charlton.

In the previous match, against Wales at Wembley on November 16, 1966, again in a European Championship qualifier, Jack scored one of five England goals.

Wingless Wonders **Facts**

Also among the scorers for England that day was, that's right ... Bobby Charlton.

One of Jack's happiest memories is of a game against Romania at Wembley in January 1969. Brother Bobby captained the side and Jack scored the goal in a 1-1 draw.

Altogether, he scored six times for England - a remarkably high return for 35 games from the centre-half spot.

It is said that he suffered the one big put-down from Alf Ramsey. After picking him, Alf confided that he was not the best centre-half around but that he just happened to fit in with his game plan.

Jack's career with Leeds brought him two League Championships, two European Fairs Cups and three FA Cup Final medals (twice losers, once winners).

He then went into club management at Middlesbrough, Sheffield Wednesday and Newcastle United.

In 1986 he took charge of the lowly Republic of Ireland team, moulding them into a formidable force with the help of new 'Irishmen' with the strangest and most tenuous Irish family connections.

His Republic teams qualified for the 1990 and 1994 World Cup finals and Jack became the national hero.

It was said in corridors of power that had he so wished, he could have been President of the Republic!

He has also graduated to the TV commentators' ranks, but his idea of a good day out is hunting, shooting or fishing. Preferably all three!

Always complimentary about brother Bobby, he did not hesitate when asked to name his team of all-time greats. 'Our kid' was there ...

BOBBY MOORE (West Ham United)

Robert Frederick Chelsea Moore was England's most successful World Cup captain.

He played 108 times for England, all but eight matches under Alf Ramsey.

He captained England 90 times, equalling the record of Billy Wright, who played 105 times for his country.

Facts

Wingless Wonders

He made his international debut against Peru in Lima on May 20, 1962, taking over from Bobby Robson at right-half. England won 4-0.

Eleven days later he made his World Cup debut at Rancagua, Chile, against Hungary. England lost 2-1.

In his twelfth game for England, he stood in as captain for Jimmy Armfield against Czechoslovakia in Bratislava. England won 4-2.

He was only 22 at the time - England's youngest-ever skipper.

One year later, he started his long run in charge against Uruguay at Wembley. England won 2-1.

He was captain in his last game for England against Italy at Wembley on November 14, 1973. Italy won 1-0.

He scored twice for England in 1966 in the run-up to the World Cup - at home to Poland (1-1) and away to Norway (won 6-1).

He played in three World Cup series, 1962, 1966 and 1970, for a total of 14 appearances. He never played in a qualifying round.

Gordon Banks said of his captain: 'He was a clinically cold professional who never put a foot wrong from the first whistle in the World Cup to the last.'

Bobby Moore was an East Londoner, born at Barking on April 12, 1941.

His leadership qualities emerged at an early age with the England Youth team, for whom he played a record 18 times.

He made his debut for West Ham at the age of 17 and won eight Under-23 caps before his promotion to the senior England side.

Bobby's peak success period came in the mid-sixties, when he climbed Wembley's famous 39 steps three times in successive years.

In 1964, he shared in a shock 3-1 victory in an FA Cup semi-final against Manchester United, the holders, at Hillsborough.

He went on to earn a winners' medal in West Ham's Final triumph by 3-2 over Preston North End.

In 1965, he helped the Hammers to win the European Cup-Winners' Cup at Wembley, beating Munich 1860 by 2-0.

Also in that West Ham team were Geoff Hurst and Martin Peters, who were at Bobby's side the following golden year.

Wingless Wonders Facts

He was voted Footballer of the Year by the critics in 1964, the only West Ham player ever to be so honoured.

Two years later, at the end of the World Cup series, his prowess earned him the Player of Players award.

Ron Greenwood, Moore's club manager at the time, said: 'We all take Bobby too much for granted. His play is so good that we only notice him when he makes a mistake.'

He was Mr Perfect when he went up to collect the World Cup from the Queen, who was wearing white gloves, so he quicky wiped his muddy hands down his England jersey before they shook hands.

His dark moment came in 1970, after England had played matches against Colombia and Ecuador for climatic experience before the series in Mexico.

On a shopping trip during a stop-over in Bogota, he was wrongfully accused of stealing a bracelet in a jeweller's shop.

Although it was later proved to be a trumped-up charge, he was delayed for four days from joining his team-mates in Mexico.

Moore's 16 years and 545 League matches for West Ham ended when he was transferred in 1974 to Second Division Fulham, managed by Alec Stock, for £25,000.

The Fulham minnows, inspired by Bobby and old international pal Alan Mullery, caused a sensation by reaching the FA Cup Final of 1975.

There the dream ended when they were beaten 2-0... by his old club West Ham.

A glittering playing career ended in the North American Soccer League in 1976, where he played 24 times for San Antonio Thunder.

He also played in America with Seattle Sounders and ended his career at Fulham in the 1976-77 season.

Bobby played 40 times, missing only two matches, in his last League season with Fulham.

Altogether in senior games, he played exactly 1,000 times.

Facts

Wingless Wonders

After spells as manager at Oxford City and Southend United, he continued his football connection with newspapers and broadcasting.

Bobby Moore died from cancer on February 24, 1993, at the age of 51.

ALAN BALL (Blackpool)

The Shropshire lad, son of a professional footballer, was steeped in the game from the time he could walk.

Alan James Ball, born on May 12, 1945, had only one target before he even started school - to play for England.

He played in the back garden before school; he played for the school team; he played in the park after school.

If anybody wanted to buy him a present, be it Christmas or his birthday or Pancake Tuesday, his father, Alan Ball Senior, always said: `Buy the lad a football.'

By the time he was ten, he vowed to Dad that he would play for England before he was 20.

He was true to his word, making his debut against Yugoslavia in Belgrade three days before his 20th birthday in a 1-1 draw.

He played again three days later on his birthday at Nuremberg, where West Germany were beaten 1-0, and he completed three England games in eight days in Gothenburg with a 2-1 win over Sweden.

He freely admitted that his fiery temper matched his red hair, and he was first sent off at school by one of the supervising masters at the age of 12... for being cheeky.

By the time he was 20, he had been booked nine times and had a suspension.

During a schoolboy trial, he was substituted after 20 minutes because an official said he was `too small'.

While still at school, young Alan played for Ashton United in the Lancashire Combination, managed by Dad.

He was called before an FA inquiry team to explain how an amateur could be paid £3 a week.

Wingless Wonders Facts

Alan junior said that it was to cover match travel expenses. The men from the FA believed little Cherub Face.

At 16 and having just left school, after failing all seven GCE exams, he signed as an amateur for Bolton Wanderers.

In Ball's second colts match, feeling pleased with himself having scored six, he was urged by a club official to 'stop hogging the ball'. Words were exchanged and the fiery redhead was moved from the middle to the wing.

Disillusioned Alan then signed pro forms for Blackpool at 17, helped them beat Liverpool 2-1 in his League debut and was soon picked for England Under-23.

With World Cup '66 looming, he was sent off in an Under-23 game and thought he had blown his chances of senior honours.

Alf Ramsey let him sweat for 24 hours before quietly telling him: 'You must learn to accept the referee's decision - good or bad.' Then Alf named him in the World Cup squad.

Alan wore the No 7 shirt in four of the six England Cup games, missing out to Paine (v Mexico) and Callaghan (v France).

He never forgot his Dad's words when he was having problems with his game at Blackpool: 'Chase, chase, chase in every game.'

In the Final with West Germany, in the words of one critic, he 'covered twice as much ground as any of the players on either side.'

He went on to play for England 72 times, including all four World Cup games in Mexico (one as substitute) and in three of the four Qualifying Round matches of the 1974 World Cup. He scored eight goals.

Facts

Wingless Wonders

In the twilight of his England career, he captained them in six consecutive matches and ended on a high note.

They won four and drew two, the sixth one his last appearance for his country resulting in a glorious 5-1 home win over Scotland on May 24, 1975.

England's trainer in 1966 said of Ball: 'He is a true professional in every sense of the word. He gives his all every time he puts on a football shirt.'

At club level, Alan joined Everton in August 1966 for a fee of £112,000, and moved to Arsenal for a then record fee of £220,000 in December 1971.

He was on the losing side in two FA Cup Finals, with Everton in 1968 and Arsenal in 1972.

He won a First Division championship medal with Everton in season 1969-70.

He stayed in the game on retirement as a player and has managed a number of clubs.

GEOFF HURST (West Ham United)

Geoffrey Charles Hurst got his call to No 10 on February 23, 1966, for his first summit with West Germany.

He made his final appearance at No 10 on April 9, 1972, against West Germany.

In between, he had three more meetings with the West Germans, one of which was a World Summit on July 30, 1966.

It was the day the World was conquered, this time as a No 8, an historic occasion that will live long after the hero has departed.

As every red-blooded English person knows, Geoff Hurst established a unique record by scoring a hat-trick in the World Cup Final. England 4 West Germany 2 after extra time.

That's when the Lancastrian's love affair with London - at West Ham and Wembley - hit its peak on football's passion register.

Geoff Hurst played 49 times for England and scored 24 goals to occupy eighth position in the all-time list of England marksmen.

He was worth every goal of that great eight scorers' roll, which includes two of his squad mates in that World Cup campaign of 1966, Bobby Charlton and Jimmy Greaves.

Wingless Wonders Facts

The top seven England goalscorers are: Charlton 49, Lineker 48, Greaves 44, Finney and Lofthouse 30 each, Platt 27, Bryan Robson 26.

Geoff was a war baby, born at Ashton-under-Lyne on December 8, 1941.

He moved to Essex as a boy and played for Chelmsford Schools, but he had no ambition to make a career in football and showed a greater keenness for cricket.

Then he went to watch West Ham and was hooked. He joined the Hammers' ground staff at the age of 17.

He turned pro with the club a year later, won six youth caps and was an FA Youth Cup finalist in 1959.

His captain at West Ham, Bobby Moore, was his team-mate during the three golden years of the mid-Sixties.

Three times he climbed the 39 steps of Wembley behind Moore after winning an FA Cup Final (1964), European Cup-Winners' Cup (1965) and the World Cup (1966).

Hurst scored his first goal for England in his second international, at Hampden Park in a 4-3 win over Scotland.

Geoff thought his World Cup chances had gone when Jimmy Greaves retrieved his place in the England side and scored four goals against Norway only 12 days before the first World Cup group match with Uruguay.

Geoff missed selection for the first three World Cup matches, but was back for the quarter-final against Argentina when Greaves was injured.

The ball ran for Geoff now as he scored the only goal of the Argentina match, a header from his Hammers team-mate Martin Peters' cross.

There was speculation that the fit-again Greaves would take over for the Final with West Germany, but Alf Ramsey decided to stick with his winning team from the semi-final with Portugal.

His three goals in the Final changed Geoff's life. Radio, TV and newspapers all wanted him and there were advertising offers galore. 'I felt ten feet tall,' he recalled.

Another hat-trick for England followed eight months after the Final, again at his beloved Wembley, in a 5-0 victory over France.

The season after the World Cup, he scored 29 goals for West Ham, and in October 1968 helped himself to six against Sunderland.

Facts

Wingless Wonders

He scored a total of 180 League goals for West Ham before joining Stoke City in 1972.

His League playing career ended in a brief period with West Bromwich Albion, for whom he scored twice in 10 games.

There followed a season of football in the States with Seattle, then a spell as player-manager with Telford United.

In 1977, Geoff accepted an offer from Ron Greenwood, the England manager and his former boss at West Ham, to work with the England training team.

His managerial experience took him to Stamford Bridge and Chelsea, where he stayed until the end of the 1980-81 season.

He continued to play cricket at every opportunity, often as wicket-keeper, and played once in 1962 for Essex.

Wiingless Wonders **Facts**

BOBBY CHARLTON (Manchester United)

He was born to be a footballer... and knighted as England's finest football ambassador.

Between those milestones, Bobby Charlton played 106 times for England and scored 49 goals. The goals record still stands.

He played in all six World Cup games of 1966 along with brother Jack, a unique entry for the *Guinness Book of Records*.

He scored England's first goal of the finals, against Mexico.

He scored the two memorable goals that swept away Portugal in the semi-final.

That same year, he was voted Footballer of the Year in England and European Footballer of the Year.

He played for Manchester United for 20 years, retiring in 1973.

He won every major honour in the game - World Cup, European Cup, FA Cup, League Championship.

When he retired, after 754 first-class matches, he had scored 247 goals.

Long before the knighthood in 1994, he was awarded the OBE, largely in recognition of his impeccable behaviour throughout his playing career.

Sir Matt Busby once paid him the ultimate compliment: 'He was as near perfection as man and player as it is possible to be.'

Born on October 11, 1937, at Ashington, Co Durham, Bobby was influenced as a toddler by his grandfather 'Tanner' Milburn, once a fair old player himself with Ashington.

The Milburn name was a by-word in the North-East. George, Jim and Stan all played for Leeds, and Jackie Milburn - 'Wor Jackie' of Newcastle - was capped 13 times for England a decade before Bobby.

Facts

Wingless Wonders

Old Tanner watched the lad's inevitable progress, from junior school sides at 10 to his first England cap at 15, playing for England Boys against Wales.

Bobby was on target straight away, scoring two goals in a 3-3 draw.

As many as 15 clubs wanted to sign him at the time, but he settled for Manchester United at the age of 17.

His brother Jack, who is two years older, had signed for Leeds United two years earlier.

One of his uncles bought young Bob his first pair of football boots, made of pigskin with thick, square toecaps. He broke them in by standing in a bowl of water for an hour, leaving them to dry on his feet.

Bobby scored his first goal for England on his debut against Scotland at Hampden Park on April 19, 1958. England won 4-0.

That match came, incredibly, only 10 weeks after he had been rescued from the wreckage of the Munich air crash.

In the previous England match against France, which they also won 4-0, his United pals Roger Byrne, Duncan Edwards and Tommy Taylor were in the line-up. They were all victims of the crash.

Bobby's rehabilitation continued a couple of weeks later when he played at centre-forward for United in the FA Cup Final against Bolton. They lost 2-0.

Twelve months earlier he had been at inside-left for them in the Final with Aston Villa. United lost 2-1, and six of that team died at Munich.

Bobby kept his England place for the next three matches, but was not chosen for any of the matches in the 1958 World Cup finals in Sweden.

His FA Cup winners' medal finally came in 1963 at the third try, United beating Leicester 3-1.

He played in all four England matches in the Chile 1962 finals and was a 'regular' all the way to Wembley Way 1966.

Another milestone year was 1968. Bobby scored twice in United's 4-1 defeat of Benfica after extra time in the European Cup.

Another 'first' here... it was the first time an English club had won the European Cup of Champions.

Great delight the same year came with the knighting of Matt Busby, Bobby's mentor. They came together later as members of the Manchester United board.

Wingless Wonders Facts

On April 21, 1970, Bobby played his 100th match for England against Northern Ireland at Wembley - and he scored in the 3-1 win.

Bobby played in the World Cup for the third time in 1970 in Mexico, which was his international swansong.

He appeared in all four England games, the last of which was the final match of his international career, against the old enemy of 1966, West Germany, in the quarter-finals.

The Germans won this time, 3-2 in extra time, and Bobby was substituted at No 9 by Colin Bell.

He captained England twice at Wembley in Bobby Moore's absence, against Romania in 1969 and Holland in 1970. Both games were drawn.

His 106 caps took him one ahead of Billy Wright, and the figure has been surpassed by only two other England players, Bobby Moore (108) and Peter Shilton (125).

Nobby Stiles said of Bobby: 'He is the greatest footballer in the world. A wonderful all-round player with the grace of a gazelle.'

Bobby Moore: 'Bobby Charlton is world-class, with lovely skill and two tremendous feet. He could run all day and scored magical goals.'

Describing the 1966 semi-final with Portugal, Gordon Banks said that Bobby 'gave the greatest performance of his life, moving with the grace of a ballet dancer and the power of a panther.'

Jimmy Greaves: 'Bobby was the perfect foil, with the strength and tenacity of two men. I fed off him for years.'

ROGER HUNT (Liverpool)

Roger Hunt was a long time waiting for his dream of being a professional footballer to become a reality.

Twenty-one years slipped by from the cradle to Anfield, with a few hiccups and disappointments en route.

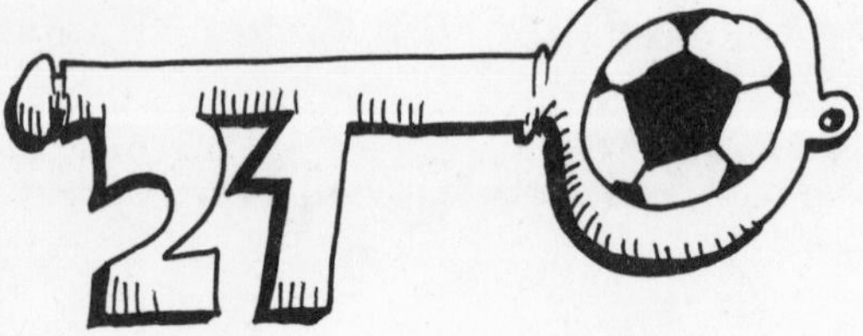

Facts

Wingless Wonders

Roger, born at Golborne, Lancashire, on July 20, 1938, developed his game playing for Glazebury, a village team near Warrington, and later for Stockton Heath.

His hopes were high when Bury signed him on amateur forms. They nosedived when he was told his application for pro status had been rejected.

Roger joined the Army and his luck changed while he was playing with a team near Swindon. Both Swindon Town and Liverpool came to him with professional contracts.

Swindon's offer was the better deal, but Anfield was nearer home and he signed for Liverpool in 1959.

His first League appearance was in a Second Division match against Scunthorpe, standing in for the injured Billy Liddell. Liverpool won 2-0.

Liverpool finished third in his first two seasons with the club, but in 1962 won promotion to the First Division by eight clear points, due in no small measure to Roger.

He scored 41 times in the promotion season, including a hat-trick against Tottenham at White Hart Lane.

His intelligent and unselfish football caught the selectors' eyes and his first England cap came against Austria at Wembley on April 4, 1962. He scored one in the 3-1 win.

Jimmy Greaves was back for the following international, claiming an inside-forward spot for the next 14 matches before Roger got his second chance.

Again he scored, helping England to a 2-1 away win over East Germany, and again he was in and out of the team frustratingly before Alf Ramsey made him a 'regular' in the run-up to the World Cup.

During the in-out spell, Roger enjoyed 90 minutes against the USA in New York in May 1964, and helped himself to four goals in England's 10-0 avalanche.

He played in all six World Cup matches at Wembley, scoring once against Mexico and claiming both goals against France.

He had a close-up view of Geoff Hurst's controversial extra-time goal off the underside of the crossbar in the Final with West Germany.

He saw that the ball was over the goal-line and triumphantly raised his arms. It was argued that he could surely have applied the *coup de grace* had he not believed his own eyes.

Roger now had a World Cup winner's award to add to two First Division Championship medals and an FA Cup winners' medal.

Wingless Wonders Facts

He was on the mark at Wembley in Liverpool's 2-1 FA Cup Final win over Leeds United in 1965.

The following year, he figured in the Merseysiders' Cup-Winners' Cup Final match with Borussia Dortmund at Hampden Park. The German team won 2-1 in extra time, Roger scoring Liverpool's goal.

With Liverpool, he scored a record 245 goals in 401 games. His 18 FA Cup goals, 17 European goals and the haul of 41 in the 1961-62 season were all club record feats.

Bill Shankly said of Hunt: `He's a great player with a big heart ... always hungry for goals.'

Bob Paisley said of him: `Unselfish, fearless, a man in the true Liverpool mould and a glutton for work.'

After playing his 34th match for England, a 1-1 draw with Romania at Wembley, Roger asked Sir Alf not to consider him again for selection.

Despite his trojan work for England, the press were calling for the return of Greaves to replace him.

Roger scored 18 goals for England to take 13th equal place with Johnny Haynes in the all-time list of the country's scorers.

At the end of 1969, he was reluctantly transferred to Bolton Wanderers for a fee of £32,000. He retired from the game in 1971.

In a memorable career, he was booked only twice and was affectionately nicknamed `Sir Roger' by the Anfield fans.

They showed their love for him at his 1972 Anfield testimonial match, when 56,000 spectators were there in pouring rain to salute him.

Roger Hunt had come a long way since winning his first award - a Warrington Guardian Cup competition medal.

MARTIN PETERS (West Ham United)

Wartime baby, born at Plaistow within the sound of Bow Bells.

Son of a Thames lighterman to complete the authentic Cockney stamp.

Famously dubbed by Alf Ramsey as `ten years ahead of his time'. Martin Peters, 25 at the time, wasn't quite sure how to take it.

Facts

Wingless Wonders

Martin thought he could be in his mid-thirties dotage before he caught up with himself.

Opposition fans were heard to shout that they would come and see him 10 years later to see if he'd improved at all!

Football career started as a goalkeeper for Fenshawe School, Dagenham, at the age of nine.

The following season, he scored 40 goals as the school's centre-forward.

A year later he was centre-half for Dagenham Boys under-11s.

Progressing towards the big-time, Martin found himself at centre-half for Dagenham Boys under-14s (with a promising lad called Venables alongside at wing-half) and left-back for the under-15s in the same season.

Next stop London Boys, then left-back for his first Boys international against Scotland at Derby in April 1959. England lost 3-2.

Before the 1966 World Cup Final, Martin had played in two England v West Germany games.

His first encounter in 1959 was in the winning England Boys team as a wing-half at Wembley. He would be about seven years ahead of his time then.

In 1962 he captained England Youth against the German Youth side at Derby. Again England won, Martin scoring the only goal.

That little affair at Wembley on July 30, 1966, completed a neat hat-trick of victories over the old enemy. And he scored.

One player also involved in those three encounters was the German forward Wolfgang Overath. They have never discussed their three meetings.

Jimmy Greaves had been Martin's hero since he was 10 when he went to see his school team play Kingswood School, Dagenham. Jimmy's school won 13-0. Greaves, aged 15, scored eleven.

At the World Cup Final, Martin was said to be devastated when Greaves was not chosen for the Big Match. That said, Greaves' replacement from West Ham didn't do too badly.

Martin played 67 times for England between 1966 and 1974 while with West Ham and Tottenham.

He made his debut for England against Yugoslavia (won 2-0) and scored his first international goal in the next match away to Finland (won 3-0).

Wingless Wonders **Facts**

He played in five of the six 1966 World Cup games, taking the place of John Connelly after the first match against Uruguay.

He also played in all four games in the World Cup finals of 1970 and in the two qualifying matches against Poland in 1973.

He captained England four times, including the World Cup qualifying home match with Poland.

He scored 20 goals for England, two of them in World Cup matches - both against West Germany.

Martin's nickname was 'The Ghost' because of the uncanny way he could suddenly 'appear' unseen at the far post to head in goals.

A final tribute from World Cup colleague Nobby Stiles: 'He must be football's most solid ghost. You can't pin him down or keep him out.'

ALF RAMSEY (England Manager)

Alf Ramsey, as a manager and player, was a man of few words and great achievements - at Tottenham, Ipswich and Wembley.

As a player he won a League Championship medal with Spurs and 32 England caps.

Facts

Wingless Wonders

As a club manager he won Divisions Three, Two and One Championships.

As the national manager he won the World Cup.

As for the few words, his two one-liners are written in football history.

On appointment as manager of England in October 1963, he said: 'We shall win the World Cup.' They did.

On July 30, 1966, just before extra time in the World Cup Final, he told his tired team: 'You've won it once. Now go and win it again.' They did.

Alf was born in 1920 at Dagenham, Essex, youngest of four sons of a smallholder.

He started his football career as a full-back with Southampton, moving to Tottenham Hotspur in 1949.

He won his first international cap at Highbury in December 1948, England beating Switzerland 6-0.

He made his World Cup debut against Scotland at Hampden Park on April 15, 1950. England won 1-0 to qualify for the finals in Brazil.

He was a member of the side that was sensationally beaten 1-0 by the USA on England's blackest day - June 29, 1950.

Alf was once asked if he had played in that game. He replied that he was 'the only one who had'.

He captained England three times in Billy Wright's absence.

Ramsey scored three goals for England, one of them in 1953 in a 4-4 draw with a FIFA XI.

He also scored in his final international match, the memorable 6-3 defeat by Hungary at Wembley on November 25, 1953.

At the age of 35, he was appointed manager of Ipswich Town, where he had remarkable success.

In his first season they finished third in Division 3 South, and then won promotion as champions the following year.

Ipswich won the Second Division title in 1961 and the League Championship in their first season in Division 1.

Alf was always the perfectionist as a player and manager and was always a players' man. He expected complete respect and loyalty from his team and offered the same in return.

Wingless Wonders — Facts

He had a bad start as England manager - a 5-2 defeat by France in Paris in a European Championship match, and beaten 2-1 by Scotland at Wembley.

A string of successes followed during the next three years, including a 10-0 win over the United States.

The England v Hungary match in May 1965 at Wembley was of special significance for Alf. He produced a film of the 1953 game and insisted on the squad watching the mistakes he and his team-mates had made.

England then went on to win by a single goal scored by Jimmy Greaves, bringing a rare smile to the manager's face!

An interesting note about Alf's team that day. The first six of Banks, Cohen, Wilson, Stiles, Jack Charlton and Moore was also the future World Cup Final line-up.

Numbers 7 to 11, comprising Paine, Greaves, Bridges, Eastham and Connelly, all failed to survive for the 1966 Final.

The disciplinarian in Alf never faltered. Before leaving for Lisbon to play Portugal in 1964, seven of the team went out for a drink. It was after 1 am when they returned to find their passports on their pillows.

Nothing was said until after the final training stint in Portugal, when Alf remarked that he thought there were seven players who would want to stay behind.

He told them in no uncertain terms that he was not impressed by their behaviour and that had he had sufficient players he would have dropped all seven as a punishment. England won 4-3.

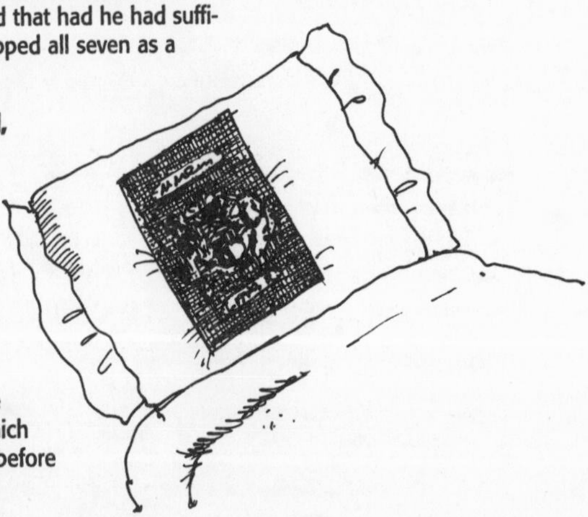

As the 1966 finals approached, he decided on the 4-3-3 formation which was instantly dubbed the 'Wingless Wonders'. The idea worked, as everyone knows, and it was as Sir Alf Ramsey that he led the team to the Mexico finals of 1970.

West Germany had their revenge in the quarter-finals, a match which England appeared to have won before the last dramatic 20 minutes.

Facts

Wingless Wonders

Sir Alf took off Bobby Charlton and Martin Peters, hoping to save them for the semi-final that never was, and brought on Norman Hunter and Colin Bell.

The Germans equalised, then Muller won it with a goal in extra time: West Germany 3 England 2.

When England failed to qualify for the World Cup finals in West Germany, Sir Alf was shown the door on Mayday 1974, ultimately to be replaced by Don Revie.

Lady Ramsey would never forget that quarter-final match in Leon. She went to claim her reserved seat only to find it occupied by a Mexican who refused to move.

Without further ado, she returned to her hotel and watched the match on TV in the silence of her room.

In Alf's 11 years as manager, England's record was: P113 W69 D27 L17.

Sir Alf managed Birmingham City for a short time during the 1977-78 season before ill health forced him into early retirement.

HAROLD SHEPHERDSON (England trainer)

England's first professional trainer was appointed by Walter Winterbottom in 1957, after the team manager had tried out several during his first 10 years in charge.

He chose Harold Shepherdson, trainer at Middlesbrough and a qualified physiotherapist.

Harold was to remain throughout the rest of Winterbottom's reign and also that of his successor, Alf Ramsey, for an incredible 171 international matches.

Middlesbrough-born Harold was football-mad from early childhood, with the burning ambition to play for Boro.

He played as a youngster with Hugh Bell School, Middlesbrough, and for Yorkshire Boys before signing professional forms for Boro in 1936.

Two years later, at the age of 18, he made his League debut at Highbury against Arsenal, and was given the formidable task of facing Ted Drake. He survived and Middlesbrough won 2-1.

After five war years with the Army Physical Training Corps, during which he played guest matches for Darlington, Luton, Brentford and Northampton, he returned to play a few games for Middlesbrough before his transfer to Southend on May 29, 1947.

Wingless Wonders **Facts**

Harold never played for Southend. During the close season he developed a knee problem, was advised by a specialist to retire and went back to Middlesbrough on the training staff.

He became the club's trainer in 1950 and eventually shared his time on England duties. He was Winterbottom's trainer for 50 matches.

Harold once assessed the merits of the two England managers. Walter was `a great gentleman and a fine theorist'. Alf, too, a great fellow to work with but also `a very fine professional in charge of a magnificent squad of players'.

Harold described the World Cup Final win as the greatest single match memory of his footballing life: `It was like the weather . . . mingled sunshine, showers, thunder and lightning.'

Usually a quiet spectator with Alf at matches, he was so overcome with joy when England won that he jumped from his seat, arms raised in triumph. The manager told him, quietly but firmly, to `sit down'.

Harold was awarded the MBE in 1969 and continued with Alf until the partnership ended in 1974, when Harold also stepped down.

Harold Shepherdson died at the age of 76.

England's World Cup Teams

England's World Cup Teams — Facts

(Q = Qualifying, F = Finals, Scorers in brackets)

BRAZIL 1950:

Q. Wales (a) won 4-1: Williams, Mozley, Aston, W Wright (capt), Franklin, Dickinson, Finney, Mortensen (1), Milburn (3), Shackleton, Hancocks.

Q. Northern Ireland (h) won 9-2: Streten, Mozley, Aston, W Watson, Franklin, W Wright (capt), Finney, Mortensen (2), J Rowley (4), Pearson (2), J Froggatt (1).

Q. Scotland (a) won 1-0: Williams, Ramsey, Aston, W Wright (capt), Franklin, Dickinson, Finney, Mannion, Mortensen, Bentley (1), Langton.

F. Chile won 2-0: Williams, Ramsey, Aston, W Wright (capt), L Hughes, Dickinson, Finney, Mannion (1), Bentley, Mortensen (1), Mullen.

F. USA lost 0-1: Williams, Ramsey, Aston, W Wright (capt), L Hughes, Dickinson, Finney, Mannion, Bentley, Mortensen, Mullen.

F. Spain lost 0-1: Williams, Ramsey, Eckersley, W Wright (capt), L Hughes, Dickinson, S Matthews, Mortensen, Milburn, E Baily, Finney.

SWITZERLAND 1954:

Q. Wales (a) won 4-1: Merrick, Garrett, Eckersley, W Wright (capt), Johnston, Dickinson, Finney, Quixall, Lofthouse (2), Wilshaw (2), Mullen.

Q. Northern Ireland (h) won 3-1: Merrick, Rickaby, Eckersley, W Wright (capt), Johnston, Dickinson, S Matthews, Quixall, Lofthouse (1), Hassall (2), Mullen.

Q. Scotland (a) won 4-2: Merrick, Staniforth, R Byrne, W Wright (capt), H Clarke, Dickinson, Finney, Broadis (1), R Allen (1), Nicholls (1), Mullen (1).

F. Belgium draw 4-4: Merrick, Staniforth, R Byrne, W Wright (capt), Owen, Dickinson, S Matthews, Broadis (2), Lofthouse (2), T Taylor, Finney.

F. Switzerland won 2-0: Merrick, Staniforth, R Byrne, McGarry, W Wright (capt), Dickinson, Finney, Broadis, T Taylor, Wilshaw (1), Mullen (1).

F. Uruguay lost 2-4: Merrick, Staniforth, R Byrne, McGarry, W Wright (capt), Dickinson, S Matthews, Broadis, Lofthouse (1), Wilshaw, Finney (1).

Facts

England's World Cup Teams

SWEDEN 1958:

Q. Denmark (h) won 5-2: Ditchburn, Hall, R Byrne, Clayton, W Wright (capt), Dickinson, S Matthews, Brooks, T Taylor (3), Edwards (2), Finney.

Q. Eire (h) won 5-1: Hodgkinson, Hall, R Byrne, Clayton, W Wright (capt), Edwards, S Matthews, Atyeo (2), T Taylor (3), Haynes, Finney.

Q. Denmark (a) won 4-1: Hodgkinson, Hall, R Byrne, Clayton, W Wright (capt), Edwards, S Matthews, Atyeo (1), T Taylor (2), Haynes (1), Finney.

Q. Eire (a) draw 1-1: Hodgkinson, Hall, R Byrne, Clayton, W Wright (capt), Edwards, Finney, Atyeo (1), T Taylor, Haynes, Pegg.

F. Soviet Union draw 2-2: McDonald, D Howe, T Banks, Clamp, W Wright (capt), Slater, Douglas, R Robson, Kevan (1), Haynes, Finney (1).

F. Brazil draw 0-0: McDonald, D Howe, T Banks, Clamp, W Wright (capt), Slater, Douglas, R Robson, Kevan, Haynes, A'Court.

F. Austria draw 2-2: McDonald, D Howe, T Banks, Clamp, W Wright (capt), Slater, Douglas, R Robson, Kevan (1), Haynes (1), A'Court.

F. Soviet Union lost 0-1: McDonald, D Howe, T Banks, Clayton, W Wright (capt), Slater, Brabrook, Broadbent, Kevan, Haynes, A'Court.

CHILE 1962:

Q. Luxembourg (a) won 9-0: R Springett, Armfield, McNeil, R Robson, Swan, R Flowers, Douglas, Greaves (3), R Smith (2), Haynes (capt) (1), R Charlton (3).

Q. Portugal (a) draw 1-1: R Springett, Armfield, McNeil, R Robson, Swan, R Flowers (1), Douglas, Greaves, R Smith, Haynes (capt), R Charlton.

Q. Luxembourg (h) won 4-1: R Springett, Armfield (capt), McNeil, R Robson, Swan, R Flowers, Douglas, Fantham, Pointer (1), Viollet (1), R Charlton (2).

Q. Portugal (h) won 2-0: R Springett, Armfield, Wilson, R Robson, Swan, R Flowers, Connelly (1), Douglas, Pointer (1), Haynes (capt), R Charlton.

F. Hungary lost 1-2; R Springett, Armfield, Wilson, Moore, Norman, R Flowers (1), Douglas, Greaves, Hitchens, Haynes (capt), R Charlton.

F. Argentina won 3-1: R Springett, Armfield, Wilson, Moore, Norman, R Flowers (1), Douglas, Greaves (1), Peacock, Haynes (capt), R Charlton (1).

England's World Cup Teams **Facts**

F. Bulgaria draw 0-0: R Springett, Armfield, Wilson, Moore, Norman, R Flowers, Douglas, Greaves, Peacock, Haynes (capt), R Charlton.

F. Brazil lost 1-3: R Springett, Armfield, Wilson, Moore, Norman, R Flowers, Douglas, Greaves, Hitchens (1), Haynes (capt), R Charlton.

ENGLAND 1966:

F. Uruguay draw 0-0: G Banks, Cohen, Wilson, Stiles, J Charlton, Moore (capt), Ball, Greaves, R Charlton, Hunt, Connelly.

F. Mexico won 2-0: G Banks, Cohen, Wilson, Stiles, J Charlton, Moore (capt), Paine, Greaves, R Charlton (1), Hunt (1), Peters.

F. France won 2-0: G Banks, Cohen, Wilson, Stiles, J Charlton, Moore (capt), Callaghan, Greaves, R Charlton, Hunt (2), Peters.

F. Argentina won 1-0: G Banks, Cohen, Wilson, Stiles, J Charlton, Moore (capt), Ball, Hurst (1), R Charlton, Hunt, Peters.

F. Portugal won 2-1: G Banks, Cohen, Wilson, Stiles, J Charlton, Moore (capt), Ball, Hurst, R Charlton (2), Hunt, Peters.

F. West Germany won 4-2: G Banks, Cohen, Wilson, Stiles, J Charlton, Moore (capt), Ball, Hurst (3), R Charlton, Hunt, Peters (1).

Facts

England's World Cup Teams

MEXICO 1970:

F. Romania won 1-0: G Banks, Newton, Cooper, Mullery, Labone, Moore (capt), F Lee, Ball, R Charlton, Hurst (1), Peters. Subs: T Wright, Osgood.

F. Brazil lost 0-1: G Banks, T Wright, Cooper, Mullery, Labone, Moore (capt), F Lee, Ball, R Charlton, Hurst, Peters. Subs: Astle, Bell.

F. Czechoslovakia won 1-0: G Banks, Newton, Cooper, Mullery, J Charlton, Moore (capt), Bell, R Charlton, Astle, A Clarke (1), Peters. Subs: Ball, Osgood.

F. West Germany lost 2-3: Bonetti, Newton, Cooper, Mullery (1), Labone, Moore (capt), F Lee, Ball, R Charlton, Hurst, Peters (1). Subs: Bell, Hunter.

WEST GERMANY 1974:

Q. Wales (a) won 1-0: Clemence, Storey, E Hughes, Hunter, McFarland, Moore (capt), Keegan, Chivers, Marsh, Bell (1), Ball.

Q. Wales (h) draw 1-1: Clemence, Storey, E Hughes, Hunter (1), McFarland, Moore (capt), Keegan, Bell, Chivers. Marsh, Ball.

Q. Poland (a) lost 0-2: Shilton, Madeley, E Hughes, Storey, McFarland, Moore (capt), Ball, Bell, Chivers, A Clarke, Peters.

Q. Poland (h) draw 1-1: Shilton, Madeley, E Hughes, Bell, McFarland, Hunter, Currie, Channon, Chivers, A Clarke (1), Peters (capt). Sub: Hector.

ARGENTINA 1978:

Q. Finland (a) won 4-1: Clemence, Todd, Mills, Phil Thompson, Madeley, Cherry, Keegan (2), Channon (1), Pearson (1), Brooking, G Francis (capt).

Q. Finland (h) won 2-1: Clemence, Todd, Beattie, P Thompson, Greenhoff, Wilkins, Keegan (capt), Channon, Royle (1), Brooking, Tueart (1). Subs: Mills, G Hill.

Q. Italy (a) lost 0-2: Clemence, Clement, Mills, Greenhoff, McFarland, E Hughes, Keegan (capt), Channon, Bowles, Cherry, Brooking. Sub: Beattie.

Q. Luxembourg (h) won 5-0: Clemence, Gidman, Cherry, R Kennedy (1), Dave Watson (1974-82), E Hughes, Keegan (capt) (1), Channon (2), Royle, T Francis (1), Hill. Sub: Mariner.

England's World Cup Teams **Facts**

Q. Luxembourg (a) won 2-0: Clemence, Cherry, Watson, E Hughes (capt), Kennedy (1), Callaghan, McDermott, Wilkins, T Francis, Mariner (1), Hill. Subs: Whymark, Beattie.

Q. Italy (h) won 2-0: Clemence, Neal, Cherry, Wilkins, Watson, E Hughes (capt), Keegan (1), Coppell, Latchford, Brooking (1), P Barnes. Subs: Pearson, T Francis.

SPAIN 1982:

Q. Norway (h) won 4-0: Shilton, Anderson, Sansom, P Thompson (capt), Watson, B Robson, Gates, McDermott (2), Mariner (1), Woodcock (1), Rix.

Q. Romania (a) lost 1-2: Clemence, Neal, Sansom, P Thompson (capt), Watson, Robson, Rix, McDermott, Birtles, Woodcock (1), Gates. Subs: Cunningham, Coppell.

Q. Romania (h) draw 0-0: Shilton, Anderson, Samson, Robson, Watson (capt), Osman, Wilkins, Brooking, Coppell, T Francis, Woodcock. Sub: McDermott.

Q. Switzerland (a) lost 1-2: Clemence, Mills, Samson, Wilkins, Watson, Osman, Keegan (capt), Robson, Coppell, Mariner, T Francis. Subs: McDermott (1), Barnes.

Q. Hungary (a) won 3-1: Clemence, Neal, Mills, Thompson, Watson, Robson, Keegan (capt) (1), McDermott, Mariner, Brooking (2), Coppell. Sub: Wilkins.

Q. Norway (a) lost 1-2: Clemence, Neal, Mills, Thompson, Osman, Robson (1), Keegan (capt), T Francis, Mariner, Hoddle, McDermott. Subs: Withe, Barnes.

Q. Hungary (h) won 1-0: Shilton, Neal, Mills, Thompson, Martin, Robson, Keegan (capt), Coppell, Mariner (1), Brooking, McDermott. Sub: Morley.

F. France won 3-1: Shilton, Mills (capt), Sansom, Thompson, Butcher, Robson (2), Coppell, T Francis, Mariner (1), Rix, Wilkins. Sub: Neal.

F. Czechoslovakia won 2-0: Shilton, Mills (capt), Sansom, Thompson, Butcher, Robson, Coppell, T Francis (1), Mariner, Rix, Wilkins. (One own goal). Sub: Hoddle.

F. Kuwait won 1-0: Shilton, Neal, Mills (capt), Thompson, Foster, Hoddle, Coppell, T Francis (1), Mariner, Rix, Wilkins.

F. West Germany draw 0-0: Shilton, Mills (capt), Sansom, Thompson, Butcher, Robson, Coppell, T Francis, Mariner, Rix, Wilkins. Sub: Woodcock.

F. Spain draw 0-0: Shilton, Mills (capt), Sansom, Thompson, Butcher, Robson, Rix, T Francis, Mariner, Woodcock, Wilkins. Subs: Brooking, Keegan.

Facts

England's World Cup Teams

MEXICO 1986:

Q. Finland (h) won 5-0: Shilton, Duxbury, Sansom (1), Williams, M Wright, Butcher, Robson (capt) (1), Wilkins, Hateley (2), Woodcock (1), J Barnes. Subs: G A Stevens (Tottenham), Chamberlain.

Q. Turkey (a) won 8-0: Shilton, Anderson (1), Sansom, Williams, Wright, Butcher, Robson (capt) (3), Wilkins, Withe, Woodcock (2), Barnes (2). Subs: G A Stevens, Francis.

Q. Northern Ireland (a) won 1-0: Shilton, Anderson, Sansom, Steven, Martin, Butcher, Stevens (Everton & Rangers), Wilkins (capt), Hateley (1), Woodcock, Barnes. Sub: Francis.

Q. Romania (a) draw 0-0: Shilton, Anderson, Sansom, Steven, Wright, Butcher, Robson (capt), Wilkins, Mariner,Francis, Barnes. Subs: Lineker, Waddle.

Q. Finland (a) draw 1-1: Shilton, Anderson, Sansom, Steven, Fenwick, Butcher, Robson (capt), Wilkins, Hateley (1), Francis, Barnes. Sub: Waddle.

Q. Romania (h) draw 1-1: Shilton, Stevens, Sansom, Reid, Wright, Fenwick, Robson (capt), Hoddle (1), Hateley, Lineker, Waddle. Subs: Woodcock, Barnes.

Q. Turkey (h) won 5-0: Shilton, Stevens, Sansom, Hoddle, Wright, Fenwick, Robson (capt) (1), Wilkins, Hateley, Lineker (3), Waddle (1). Subs: Steven, Woodcock.

Q. Northern Ireland (h) draw 0-0: Shilton, G A Stevens, Sansom, Hoddle, Wright, Fenwick, Bracewell, Wilkins (capt), K Dixon, Lineker, Waddle.

F. Portugal lost 0-1: Shilton, Stevens, Sansom, Hoddle, Fenwick, Butcher, Robson (capt), Wilkins, Hateley, Lineker, Waddle. Subs: Hodge, Beardsley.

F. Morocco draw 0-0: Shilton, Stevens, Sansom, Hoddle, Fenwick, Butcher, Robson (capt), Wilkins, Hateley, Lineker, Waddle. Subs: Hodge, G A Stevens.

F. Poland won 3-0: Shilton (capt), Stevens, Sansom, Hoddle, Fenwick, Butcher, Hodge, Reid, Beardsley, Lineker (3), Steven. Subs: Waddle, Dixon.

F. Paraguay won 3-0: Shilton (capt), Stevens, Sansom, Hoddle, Martin, Butcher, Hodge, Reid, Beardsley (1), Lineker (2), Steven. Subs: G A Stevens, Hateley.

F. Argentina lost 1-2: Shilton (capt), Stevens, Sansom, Hoddle, Fenwick, Butcher, Hodge, Reid, Beardsley, Lineker (1), Steven. Subs: Waddle, Barnes.

England's World Cup Teams Facts

ITALY 1990:

Q. Sweden (h) draw 0-0: Shilton, Stevens, Pearce, Webb, Adams, Butcher, Robson (capt), Beardsley, Waddle, Lineker, Barnes. Subs: Walker, Cottee.

Q. Albania (a) won 2-0: Shilton, Stevens, Pearce, Webb, Walker, Butcher, Robson (capt) (1), Rocastle, Waddle, Lineker, Barnes (1). Subs: Beardsley, A Smith.

Q. Albania (h) won 5-0: Shilton, Stevens, Pearce, Webb, Walker, Butcher, Robson (capt), Rocastle, Beardsley (2), Lineker (1), Waddle (1). Subs: Parker, Gascoigne (1).

Q. Poland (h) won 3-0: Shilton, Stevens, Pearce, Webb (1), Walker, Butcher, Robson (capt), Waddle, Beardsley, Lineker (1), Barnes (1). Subs: Rocastle, A Smith.

Q. Sweden (a) draw 0-0: Shilton, Stevens, Pearce, Webb, Walker, Butcher (capt), Beardsley, McMahon, Waddle, Lineker, Barnes. Subs: Gascoigne, Rocastle.

Q. Poland (a) draw 0-0: Shilton, Stevens, Pearce, McMahon, Walker, Butcher, Robson (capt), Rocastle, Beardsley, Lineker, Waddle.

F. Eire draw 1-1: Shilton, Stevens, Pearce, Gascoigne, Walker, Butcher, Waddle, Robson (capt), Beardsley, Lineker (1), Barnes. Subs: McMahon, Bull.

F. Holland draw 0-0: Shilton, Parker, Pearce, Wright, Walker, Butcher, Robson (capt), Waddle, Gascoigne, Lineker, Barnes. Subs: Platt, Bull.

F. Egypt won 1-0: Shilton (capt), Parker, Pearce, Gascoigne, Walker, Wright (1), McMahon, Waddle, Bull, Lineker, Barnes. Subs: Platt, Beardsley.

F. Belgium won 1-0: Shilton, Parker, Pearce, Wright, Walker, Butcher (capt), McMahon, Waddle, Gascoigne, Lineker, Barnes. Subs: Platt (1), Bull.

F. West Germany draw 1-1: Shilton, Parker, Pearce, Wright, Walker, Butcher (capt), Platt, Waddle, Gascoigne, Lineker (1), Beardsley. Sub: Steven.

F. Italy lost 1-2: Shilton (capt), Stevens, Dorigo, Parker, Walker, Wright, Platt (1), Steven, McMahon, Lineker, Beardsley. Subs: Waddle, Webb.

USA 1994:

Q. Norway (h) draw 1-1: Woods, L Dixon, Pearce (capt), Batty, Walker, Adams, Platt (1), Gascoigne, Shearer, I Wright, Ince. Subs: Palmer, Merson.

Facts

England's World Cup Teams

Q. Turkey (h) won 4-0: Woods, Dixon, Pearce (capt) (1), Palmer, Walker, Adams, Platt, Gascoigne (2), Shearer (1), I Wright, Ince.

Q. San Marino (h) won 6-0: Woods, Dixon, Dorigo, Palmer (1), Walker, Adams, Platt (capt) (4), Gascoigne, Ferdinand (1), Barnes, Batty.

Q. Turkey (a) won 2-0: Woods, Dixon, Sinton, Palmer, Walker, Adams, Platt (capt) (1), Gascoigne (1), Barnes, I Wright, Ince. Subs: Clough, Sharpe.

Q. Holland (h) draw 2-2: Woods, Dixon, Keown, Palmer, Walker, Adams, Platt capt (1), Gascoigne, Ferdinand, Barnes (1), Ince. Sub: Merson.

Q. Poland (a) draw 1-1: Woods, Bardsley, Dorigo, Palmer, Walker, Adams, Platt (capt), Gascoigne, Sheringham, Barnes, Ince. Subs: I Wright (1), Clough.

Q. Norway (a) lost 0-2: Woods, Dixon, Pallister, Palmer, Walker, Adams, Platt (capt), Gascoigne, Ferdinand, Sheringham, Sharpe. Subs: Clough, I Wright.

Q. Poland (h) won 3-0: Seaman, Jones, Pearce (capt) (1), Ince, Pallister, Adams, Platt, Gascoigne (1), Ferdinand (1), I Wright, Sharpe.

Q. Holland (a) lost 0-2: Seaman, Parker, Dorigo, Ince, Pallister, Adams, Platt (capt), Palmer, Shearer, Merson, Sharpe. Subs: Sinton, I Wright.

Q. San Marino (a) won 7-1: Seaman, Dixon, Pearce (capt), Ince (2), Pallister, Walker, Platt, Ripley, Ferdinand (1), I Wright (4), Sinton.

FRANCE 1998:

Q. Moldova (a) won 3-0: Seaman, G Neville, Pearce, Ince, Pallister, Southgate, Beckham, Gascoigne (1), Shearer (capt) (1), Barmby (1), Hinchcliffe. Subs: Batty, Le Tissier.

Q. Poland (h) won 2-1: Seaman, G Neville, Pearce, Ince, Southgate, Hinchcliffe, Beckham, Gascoigne, Shearer (capt) (2), Ferdinand, McManaman. Sub: Pallister.

Q. Georgia (a) won 2-0: Seaman, Campbell, Hinchcliffe, Ince, Adams (capt), Southgate, Beckham, Gascoigne, Ferdinand (1), Sheringham, Batty. Sub: I Wright.

Q. Italy (h) lost 0-1: Walker, G Neville, Pearce, Ince, Campbell, Le Saux, Beckham, Batty, Shearer (capt), Le Tissier, McManaman. Subs: I Wright, Ferdinand, Merson.

Q. Georgia (h) won 2-0: Seaman, G Neville, Campbell, Batty, Adams, Le Saux, Beckham, Ince, Shearer (capt) (1), Sheringham (1), Lee. Subs: Southgate, Redknapp.

England's World Cup Teams Facts

Q. Poland (a) won 2-0: Seaman, G Neville, Campbell, Ince, Southgate, Le Saux, Beckham, Gascoigne, Shearer (capt) (1), Sheringham (1), Lee. Subs: P Neville, Batty.

Q. Moldova (h) won 4-0: Seaman (capt), G Neville, Campbell, Southgate, P Neville, Beckham, Batty, Gascoigne (1), Scholes (1), Ferdinand, I Wright (2). Subs: Ripley, Butt, Collymore.

Q. Italy (a) draw 0-0: Seaman, Campbell, Southgate, Adams, Le Saux, Beckham, Ince (capt), Batty, Gascoigne, I Wright, Sheringham. Sub: Butt.

Scotland's World Cup Teams

Scotland's World Cup Teams — Facts

Q = Qualifying, F = Finals, Scorers in brackets

BRAZIL 1950:

Q. Northern Ireland (a) won 8-2: Cowan, Young capt, Cox, Evans, Woodburn, Aitken, Waddell (2), Mason (1), Morris (3), Steel (1), Reilly (1).

Q. Wales (h) won 2-0: Cowan, Young capt, Cox, Evans, Woodburn, Aitken, Liddell, McPhail (1), Linwood (1), Steel, Reilly.

Q. England (h) lost 0-1: Cowan, Young capt, Cox, McColl, Woodburn, Forbes, Waddell, Moir, Bauld, Steel, Liddell.

SWITZERLAND 1954:

Q. Northern Ireland (a) won 3-1: Farm, Young capt, Cox, Evans, Brennan, Cowie, Waddell, Fleming (2), McPhail, Watson, Henderson (1).

Q. Wales (h) draw 3-3: Farm, Young capt, Cox, Evans, Telfer, Cowie, McKenzie, Johnstone (1), Reilly (1), Brown (1), Liddell.

Q. England (h) lost 2-4: Farm, Haughney, Cox capt, Evans, Brennan, Aitken, McKenzie, Johnstone, Henderson, Brown (1), Ormond (1).

F. Austria lost 0-1: Martin, Cunningham capt, Aird, Docherty, Davidson, Cowie, McKenzie, Fernie, Mochan, Brown, Ormond.

F. Uruguay lost 0-7: Martin, Cunningham capt, Aird, Docherty, Davidson, Cowie, McKenzie, Fernie, Mochan, Brown, Ormond.

SWEDEN 1958:

Q. Spain (h) won 4-2: Younger, Caldow, Hewie (1), McColl, Young capt, Docherty, Smith, Collins, Mudie (3), Baird, Ring.

Q. Switzerland (a) won 2-1: Younger, Caldow, Hewie, McColl, Young capt, Docherty, Smith, Collins (1), Mudie (1), Baird, Ring.

Facts

Scotland's World Cup Teams

Q. Spain (a) lost 1-4: Younger, Caldow, Hewie, Mackay, Evans, Docherty capt, Smith (1), Collins, Mudie, Baird, Ring.

Q. Switzerland (h) won 3-2: Younger, Parker, Caldow, Fernie, Evans, Docherty capt, Scott (1), Collins, Mudie (1), Robertson (1), Ring.

F. Yugoslavia draw 1-1: Younger capt, Caldow, Hewie, Turnbull, Evans, Cowie, Leggat, Murray (1), Mudie, Collins, Imlach.

F. Paraguay lost 2-3: Younger capt, Parker, Caldow, Turnbull, Evans, Cowie, Leggat, Collins (1), Mudie (1), Robertson, Fernie.

F. France lost 1-2: Brown, Caldow, Hewie, Turnbull, Evans capt, Mackay, Collins, Murray, Mudie, Baird (1), Imlach.

CHILE 1962:

Q. Eire (h) won 4-1: Leslie, Shearer, Caldow capt, Crerand, McNeill, Baxter, McLeod, Quinn, Herd (2), Brand (2), Wilson.

Q. Eire (a) won 3-0: Leslie, Shearer, Caldow capt, Crerand, McNeill, Baxter, McLeod, Quinn, A Young (2), Brand (1), Wilson.

Q. Czechoslovakia (a) lost 0-4: Leslie, Shearer, Caldow capt, Crerand, McNeill, Baxter, McLeod, McMillan, Herd, Brand, Wilson.

Q. Czechoslovakia (h) won 3-2: Brown, McKay, Caldow capt, Crerand, McNeill, Baxter, Scott, White, St John (1), Law (2), Wilson.

Q. Czechoslovakia (a) lost 2-4: Connachan, A Hamilton, Caldow capt, Crerand, Ure, Baxter, Brand, White, St John (2), Law, Robertson.

ENGLAND 1966:

Q. Finland (h) won 3-1: Forsyth, A Hamilton, Kennedy, Greig, McGrory, Baxter, Johnstone, Gibson (1), Chalmers (1), Law capt (1), Scott.

Q. Poland (a) draw 1-1: Brown, A Hamilton, McCreadie, Greig, McNeill capt, Crerand, Henderson, Collins, Martin, Law (1), Hughes.

Scotland's World Cup Teams **Facts**

Q. Finland (a) won 2-1: Brown, A Hamilton, McCreadie, Crerand, McNeill capt, Greig (1), Henderson, Law, Martin, W Hamilton, Wilson (1).

Q. Poland (h) lost 1-2: Brown, A Hamilton, McCreadie, Crerand, McNeill capt (1), Greig, Henderson, Bremner, Gilzean, Law, Johnston.

Q. Italy (h) won 1-0: Brown, Greig (1), Provan, Murdoch, McKinnon, Baxter capt, Henderson, Bremner, Gilzean, Martin, Hughes.

Q. Italy (a) lost 0-3: Blacklaw, Provan, McCreadie, Murdoch, McKinnon, Greig capt, Forrest, Bremner, Yeats, Cooke, Hughes.

MEXICO 1970:

Q. Austria (h) won 2-1: Simpson, Gemmell, McCreadie, Bremner capt (1), McKinnon, Greig, Johnstone, Cooke, Hughes, Law (1), Lennox. Sub: Gilzean.

Q. Cyprus (a) won 5-0: Herriot, Fraser, McCreadie, Bremner capt, McKinnon, Greig, McLean, Murdoch (1), Stein (2), Gilzean (2), Cooke. Subs: McNeill, Lennox.

Q. West Germany (h) draw 1-1: Lawrence, Gemmell, McCreadie, Murdoch (1), McKinnon, Greig, Johnstone, Bremner capt, Law, Gilzean, Lennox. Sub: Cooke.

Q. Cyprus (h) won 8-0: Herriot, McCreadie, Gemmell (1), Bremner capt, McNeill (1), Greig, Henderson (1), Cooke, Stein (4), Gilzean, E Gray (1).

Q. West Germany (a) lost 2-3: Herriot, Greig, Gemmell, Bremner capt, McKinnon, McNeill, Johnstone (1), Cormack, Gilzean (1), E Gray, Stein.

Q. Austria (a) lost 0-2: McGarr, Greig, Burns, Murdoch, McKinnon, Stanton, Cooke, Bremner capt, Gilzean, Curran, E Gray. Subs: Lorimer, Stein.

WEST GERMANY 1974:

Q. Denmark (a) won 4-1: Clark, Brownlie, A Forsyth, Bremner capt, Colquhoun, Buchan, Lorimer, Macari (1), Bone (1), Graham, Morgan (1). Subs: Dalglish, Harper (1).

Q. Denmark (h) won 2-0: Harvey, Brownlie, Donachie, Bremner capt, Colquhoun, Buchan, Lorimer (1), Dalglish (1), Harper, Graham, Morgan. Sub: Carr.

Facts

Scotland's World Cup Teams

Q. Czechoslovakia (h) won 2-1: Hunter, Jardine, McGrain, Bremner capt, Holton (1), Connelly, Hay, Law, Morgan, Dalglish, Hutchison. Sub: Jordan (1).

Q. Czechoslovakia (a) lost 0-1: Harvey, Jardine, McGrain, T Forsyth, Blackley, Hay capt, Morgan, Jordan, Law, Dalglish, Hutchison. Sub: Ford.

F. Zaire won 2-0: Harvey, Jardine, McGrain, Bremner capt, Holton, Blackley, Dalglish, Hay, Lorimer (1), Jordan (1), Law. Sub: Hutchison.

F. Brazil draw 0-0: Harvey, Jardine, McGrain, Holton, Buchan, Bremner capt, Hay, Dalglish, Morgan, Jordan, Lorimer.

F. Yugoslavia draw 1-1: Harvey, Jardine, McGrain, Holton, Buchan, Bremner capt, Dalglish, Hay, Morgan, Jordan (1), Lorimer. Sub: Hutchison.

ARGENTINA 1978:

Q. Czechoslovakia (a) lost 0-2: Rough, McGrain, Donachie, Buchan, McQueen, Rioch, Dalglish, Masson, Jordan, A Gray, Gemmill capt. Subs: Burns, Hartford.

Q. Wales (h) won 1-0: Rough, McGrain, Donachie, Blackley, McQueen, Rioch, Burns, Dalglish, Jordan, Gemmill capt, E Gray. (One own goal). Subs: Hartford, Pettigrew.

Q. Czechoslovakia (h) won 3-1: Rough, Jardine, McGrain, T Forsyth, McQueen, Rioch capt, Dalglish (1), Masson, Jordan (1), Hartford (1), Johnston.

Q. Wales (a) won 2-0: Rough, Jardine, Donachie, Masson capt (1), McQueen, T Forsyth, Dalglish (1), Hartford, Jordan, Macari, Johnston. Sub: Buchan.

Scotland's World Cup Teams **Facts**

F. Peru lost 1-3: Rough, Kennedy, Burns, Buchan, T Forsyth, Rioch capt, Masson, Hartford, Dalglish, Jordan (1), Johnston. Subs: Gemmill, Macari.

F. Iran draw 1-1: Rough, Jardine, Burns, Donachie, Buchan, Gemmill capt, Macari, Hartford, Dalglish, Jordan, Robertson. (One own goal). Subs: T Forsyth, Harper.

F. Holland won 3-2: Rough, Kennedy, Buchan, Donachie, T Forsyth, Rioch capt, Gemmill (2), Hartford, Souness, Dalglish (1), Jordan.

SPAIN 1982:

Q. Sweden (a) won 1-0: Rough, McGrain, F Gray, Miller, McLeish, Hansen, Dalglish, Strachan (1), A Gray, Gemmill capt, Robertson. Sub: Archibald.

Q. Portugal (h) draw 0-0: Rough, McGrain, F Gray, Souness, Hansen, Miller, Strachan, Dalglish, A Gray, Gemmill capt, Robertson.

Q. Israel (a) won 1-0: Rough, McGrain, F Gray, Souness, McLeish, Burns, Wark, Dalglish (1), Archibald, Gemmill capt, Robertson. Subs: Miller, A Gray.

Q. Northern Ireland (h) draw 1-1: Rough, McGrain, F Gray, Burns, McLeish, Miller, Wark (1), Archibald, A Gray, Gemmill capt, Robertson. Subs: Thomson, Hartford.

Q. Israel (h) won 3-1: Rough, McGrain capt, F Gray, Souness, McLeish, Hansen, Provan (1), Archibald, Jordan, Hartford, Robertson (2).

Q. Sweden (h) won 2-0: Rough, McGrain capt, F Gray, Wark, McLeish, Hansen, Provan, Dalglish, Jordan (1), Hartford, Robertson (1). Sub: A Gray.

Q. Northern Ireland (a) draw 0-0: Rough, Stewart, Hansen, Miller, F Gray, Strachan, Souness, Hartford capt, Robertson, Dalglish, Archibald. Sub: A Gray.

Q. Portugal (a) lost 1-2: Thomson, Stewart, F Gray, Souness, Hansen, Miller, Provan, Strachan, Archibald, Hartford capt, Sturrock (1). Subs: Kennedy, Dalglish.

Facts

Scotland's World Cup Teams

F. New Zealand won 5-2: Rough, McGrain capt, Hansen, Evans, F Gray, Souness, Strachan, Dalglish (1), Wark (2), Brazil, Robertson (1). Subs: Narey, Archibald (1).

F. Brazil lost 1-4: Rough, Narey (1), Miller, Hansen, F Gray, Wark, Souness capt, Strachan, Hartford, Archibald, Robertson. Subs: Dalglish, McLeish.

F. Soviet Union draw 2-2: Rough, F Gray, Hansen, Miller, Strachan, Narey, Souness capt (1), Jordan (1), Wark, Robertson, Archibald. Subs: McGrain, Brazil.

MEXICO 1986:

Q. Iceland (h) won 3-0: Leighton, Nicol, Albiston, Souness capt, McLeish, Miller, Dalglish, McStay (2), Johnston, Bett, Cooper. Sub: Nicholas (1).

Q. Spain (h) won 3-1: Leighton, Nicol, Albiston, Souness capt, McLeish, Miller, Dalglish (1), McStay, Johnston (2), Bett, Cooper.

Q. Spain (a) lost 0-1: Leighton, Gough, Albiston, Souness capt, McLeish, Miller, Archibald, McStay, Johnston, Bett, Cooper. Subs: Nicholas, Strachan.

Q. Wales (h) lost 0-1: Leighton, Nicol, Albiston, Souness capt, McLeish, Miller, Dalglish, McStay, Johnston, Bett, Cooper. Subs: Hansen, Nicholas.

Q. Iceland (a) won 1-0: Leighton, Gough, Malpas, Aitken, McLeish, Miller, Strachan, Souness capt, A Gray, Bett (1), Sharp. Sub: Archibald.

Q. Wales (a) draw 1-1: Leighton, Gough, Malpas, Aitken, McLeish, Miller capt, Nicol, Strachan, Sharp, Bett, Speedie. Subs: Rough, Cooper (1).

Q. Australia (h) won 2-0: Leighton, Nicol, Malpas, Souness capt, McLeish, Miller, Dalglish, Strachan, McAvennie (1), Aitken, Cooper (1). Subs: Sharp, Bett.

Q. Australia (a) draw 0-0: Leighton, Gough, Malpas, Souness capt, McLeish, Miller, Speedie, McStay, McAvennie, Aitken, Cooper. Sub: Sharp.

F. Denmark lost 0-1: Leighton, Gough, Malpas, McLeish, Miller, Souness capt, Aitken, Nicol, Nicholas, Strachan, Sturrock. Subs: Bannon, McAvennie.

Scotland's World Cup Teams Facts

F. West Germany lost 1-2: Leighton, Gough, Narey, Miller, Malpas, Nicol, Bannon, Souness capt, Strachan (1), Aitken, Archibald. Subs: McAvennie, Cooper.

F. Uruguay draw 0-0: Leighton, Gough, Miller capt, Narey, Albiston, Strachan, Aitken, McStay, Nicol, Sharp, Sturrock. Subs: Cooper, Nicholas.

ITALY 1990:

Q. Norway (a) won 2-1: Leighton, Nicol, Malpas, Gillespie, McLeish, Miller, Aitken capt, McStay (1), Johnston (1), McClair, Gallacher. Sub: Durrant.

Q. Yugoslavia (h) draw 1-1: Goram, Gough, Malpas, Nicol, McLeish, Miller, Aitken capt, McStay, Johnston (1), McClair, Bett. Subs: Speedie, McCoist

Q. Cyprus (a) won 3-2: Leighton, Gough (2), Malpas, Aitken capt, McLeish, Narey, Nicol, McStay, McClair, Speedie, Johnston (1). Subs: Ferguson, McInally.

Q. France (h) won 2-0: Leighton, Gough, Malpas, Aitken, McLeish capt, Gillespie, Nicol, McStay, McCoist, Ferguson, Johnston (2). Subs: McClair, Strachan.

Q. Cyprus (h) won 2-1: Leighton, Gough, Malpas, Aitken capt, McLeish, McPherson, Nevin, McStay, Johnston (1), McCoist (1), Durie. Subs: Nicholas, Speedie.

Q. Yugoslavia (a) lost 1-3: Leighton, Gillespie, Malpas, Aitken capt, McLeish, Miller, Nicol, McStay, McCoist, MacLeod, Durie (1). Sub: McInally.

Q. France (a) lost 0-3: Leighton, Gough, Malpas, Nicol, McLeish, Aitken capt, Strachan, McStay, McCoist, MacLeod, Johnston. Subs: McInally, Bett.

Q. Norway (h) draw 1-1: Leighton, McPherson, Malpas, Aitken capt, McLeish, Miller, Johnston, McStay, McCoist (1), Bett, Cooper. Subs: MacLeod, McClair.

F. Costa Rica lost 0-1: Leighton, Gough, McLeish, McPherson, Malpas, Aitken capt, McStay, Bett, McCall, Johnston, McInally. Subs: McKimmie, McCoist.

Facts

Scotland's World Cup Teams

F. Sweden won 2-1: Leighton, McLeish, Malpas, McPherson, Levein, Aitken capt, MacLeod, Durie, McCall (1), Johnston (1), Fleck. Subs: McStay, McCoist.F.

F. Brazil lost 0-1: Leighton, McKimmie, McLeish, McPherson, Aitken capt, Malpas, McStay, McCall, MacLeod, Johnston, McCoist. Subs: Gillespie, Fleck.

USA 1994:

Q. Switzerland (a) lost 1-3: Goram, Gough capt, Malpas, McCall, Boyd, McPherson, Durie, McAllister, McCoist (1), McStay, McClair. Subs: Gallacher, Durrant.

Q. Portugal (h) draw 0-0: Goram, Malpas, Boyd, McCall, Whyte, Levein, Gallacher, McStay capt, McCoist, McAllister, Collins. Subs: McClair, Durrant.

Q. Italy (h) draw 0-0: Goram, McPherson, Malpas, McStay capt, McLaren, Whyte, Durie, McAllister, McCoist, Durrant, Boyd. Subs: Jess, J Robertson.

Q. Malta (h) won 3-0: Goram, McPherson, Boyd, McStay capt, McLeish, McLaren, Nevin (1), McAllister, McCoist (2), Collins, Jess. Subs: J Robertson, Ferguson.

Q. Portugal (a) lost 0-5: Goram, Gough, McInally, McPherson, McKimmie, Levein, McStay capt, McCall, McCoist, Collins, Gallacher. Subs: Nevin, Durrant.

Q. Estonia (a) won 3-0: Gunn, Wright, Boyd, McStay capt, Hendry, Irvine, Gallacher (1), Bowman, J Robertson, McClair, Collins (1). Subs: McLaren, Booth (1).

Q. Estonia (h) won 3-1: Gunn, McLaren, Boyd, McStay capt, Hendry, Irvine, Gallacher, Ferguson, McClair (1), Collins, Nevin (2). Subs: J Robertson, Booth.

Q. Switzerland (h) draw 1-1: Gunn, McKimmie, D Robertson, Levein, Irvine, Nevin, Bowman, McAllister capt, Collins (1), Booth, Durie. Subs: O'Donnell, Jess.

Q. Italy (a) lost 1-3: Gunn, McKimmie, Irvine, McLaren, Boyd, Bowman, McAllister capt, McCall, Durie, Gallacher (1), Jess. Sub: Durrant.

Q. Malta (a) won 2-0: Leighton, McLaren, McKinnon, Durrant, Hendry (1), Irvine, Ferguson, W McKinlay (1), Nevin, McAllister capt, Gallacher. Subs: Boyd, Booth.

Scotland's World Cup Teams Facts

FRANCE 1998:

Q. Austria (a) draw 0-0: Goram, Burley, Boyd, Calderwood, Hendry, T McKinlay, D Ferguson, McCall, McCoist, McAllister capt, Collins. Sub: Durie.

Q. Latvia (a) won 2-0: Goram, Burley, Boyd, Calderwood, Whyte, T McKinlay, Spencer, McCall, Jackson (1), McAllister capt, Collins (1). Subs: McNamara, Dodds, Lambert.

Q. Sweden (h) won 1-0: Leighton, Calderwood, Hendry capt, Boyd, McNamara, Burley, W McKinlay, Collins, T McKinlay, McGinlay (1), Jackson. Subs: Lambert, McCoist, Gallacher.

Q. Estonia (a) draw 0-0: Goram, McNamara, Boyd, McStay, Hendry, Calderwood, Gallacher, McAllister capt, D Ferguson, McGinlay, Collins. Subs: I Ferguson, T McKinlay, McCoist.

***Note: This match was played at Monaco, a neutral ground, by order of FIFA. The match was originally arranged to be played at Tallinn, Estonia, but the home team failed to turn up when the kick-off was rescheduled from evening to afternoon because of inadequate floodlights.**

Q. Estonia (h) won 2-0: Leighton, Burley, Boyd (1), T McKinlay, Calderwood, Hendry, Gemmill, Jackson, Gallacher, McAllister capt, McStay. (One own goal). Subs: W McKinlay, McGinlay.

Q. Austria (h) won 2-0: Leighton, Calderwood, Hendry, Boyd, Lambert, Burley, McAllister capt, Collins, T McKinlay, Gallacher (2), Jackson. Subs: McStay, McCoist, McGinlay.

Q. Sweden (a) lost 1-2: Leighton, Calderwood, Hendry, Boyd, Burley, McAllister capt, Lambert, Collins, T McKinlay, Jackson, Gallacher (1). Subs: Gemmill, Durie.

Q. Belarus (a) won 1-0: Leighton, Burley, Boyd, Dailly, Hopkin, Lambert, McAllister capt (1), Jackson, T McKinlay, Gallacher, Durie. Subs: Dodds, B McAllister.

Q. Belarus (h) won 4-0: Leighton, Burley, Boyd, Calderwood, Dailly,T McKinlay, Gallacher (2), Lambert, Durie, McAllister capt, Collins. Subs: Hopkin (2), Dodds.

Q. Latvia (h) won 2-0: Leighton, Burley, Boyd, Calderwood, Hendry, Dailly, Gallacher (1), Lambert, Durie (1), McAllister capt, Collins. Subs: W McKinlay, T McKinlay, Donnelly.

World Cup 1998 Facts & Fixtures

World Cup 1998 Facts & Fixtures

Facts

Past World Cup Finals

Year	Venue	Winners	Runners-Up	Result	Third
1930	Montevideo	Uruguay	Argentina	4-2	-
1934	Rome	Italy	Czechoslovakia	2-1	Germany
1938	Paris	Italy	Hungary	4-2	Brazil
*1950	Rio de Janeiro	Uruguay	Brazil	2-1	-
1954	Berne	Germany	Hungary	3-2	Austria
1958	Stockholm	Brazil	Sweden	5-2	France
1962	Santiago	Brazil	Czechoslovakia	3-1	Chile
1966	Wembley	England	W Germany	4-2	Portugal
1970	Mexico City	Brazil	Italy	4-1	W Germany
1974	Munich	W Germany	Holland	2-1	Poland
1978	Buenos Aires	Argentina	Holland	3-1	Brazil
1982	Madrid	Italy	W Germany	3-1	Poland
1986	Mexico City	Argentina	W Germany	3-2	France
1990	Rome	W Germany	Argentina	1-0	Italy
**1994	Los Angeles	Brazil	Italy	0-0	Sweden

* Final pool decided the winner

** Brazil won 3-2 on pens

Facts

World Cup 1998
Facts & Fixtures

How They Qualified for France 98

ENGLAND (Winners Group 2)

Moldova	Away	W 3-0	(Barmby, Gascoigne, Shearer)
Poland	Home	W 2-1	(Shearer 2)
Georgia	Away	W 2-0	(Sheringham, Ferdinand)
Italy	Home	L 0-1	
Georgia	Home	W 2-0	(Sheringham, Shearer)
Poland	Away	W 2-0	(Shearer, Sheringham)
Moldova	Home	W 4-0	(Scholes, Wright 2, Gascoigne)
Italy	Away	D 0-0	

P8, W6, D1, L1, Goals 15-2, Pts 19

Scorers: Shearer 5, Sheringham 3, Gascoigne 2, Wright 2, Barmby 1, Ferdinand 1, Scholes 1.

SCOTLAND (Best runners-up)

Austria	Away	D 0-0	
Latvia	Away	W 2-0	(Collins, Jackson)
Sweden	Home	W 1-0	(McGinlay)
Estonia	Neutral	D 0-0	(Monaco)
Estonia	Home	W 2-0	(Boyd, Opp. og)
Austria	Home	W 2-0	(Gallacher 2)
Sweden	Away	L 1-2	(Gallacher)
Belarus	Away	W 1-0	(McAllister pen)
Belarus	Home	W 4-1	(Gallacher 2, Hopkin 2)
Latvia	Home	W 2-0	(Gallacher, Durie)

P10, W7, D2, L1, Goals 15-3, Pts 23

Scorers: Gallacher 6, Hopkin 2, Boyd 1, Collins 1, Durie 1, Jackson 1, McAllister 1 (pen), McGinlay 1, Opponent 1.

World Cup 1998
Facts & Fixtures

Facts

1998 Finals Match Schedule

GROUP A:	Venue	Date	K.O (BST)
Brazil v Scotland	Paris, St-Denis	June 10	4.30
Morocco v Norway	Montpellier	June 10	8.00
Brazil v Morocco	Nantes	June 16	8.00
Scotland v Norway	Bordeaux	June 16	4.30
Brazil v Norway	Marseille	June 23	8.00
Scotland v Morocco	St Etienne	June 23	8.00
GROUP B:			
Italy v Chile	Bordeaux	June 11	4.30
Cameroon v Austria	Toulouse	June 11	8.00
Italy v Cameroon	Montpellier	June 17	8.00
Chile v Austria	St Etienne	June 17	4.30
Italy v Austria	Paris, St-Denis	June 23	3.00
Chile v Cameroon	Nantes	June 23	3.00
GROUP C:			
France v South Africa	Marseille	June 12	8.00
Saudi Arabia v Denmark	Lens	June 12	4.30
France v Saudi Arabia	Paris, St-Denis	June 18	8.00
South Africa v Denmark	Toulouse	June 18	4.30
France v Denmark	Lyon	June 24	3.00
South Africa v Saudi Arabia	Bordeaux	June 24	3.00

Facts

World Cup 1998
Facts & Fixtures

GROUP D:	Venue	Date	K.O (BST)
Paraguay v Bulgaria	Montpellier	June 12	1.30
Spain v Nigeria	Nantes	June 13	1.30
Spain v Paraguay	St Etienne	June 19	8.00
Nigeria v Bulgaria	Paris, Parc-des-Princes	June 19	4.30
Spain v Bulgaria	Lens	June 24	8.00
Nigeria v Paraguay	Toulouse	June 24	8.00
GROUP E:			
Holland v Belgium	Paris, St-Denis	June 13	8.00
South Korea v Mexico	Lyon	June 13	4.30
Holland v South Korea	Marseille	June 20	8.00
Belgium v Mexico	Bordeaux	June 20	1.30
Holland v Mexico	St Etienne	June 25	3.00
Belgium v South Korea	Paris, Parc-des-Princes	June 25	3.00
GROUP F:			
Yugoslavia v Iran	St Etienne	June 14	1.30
Germany v USA	Paris, Parc-des-Princes	June 15	8.00
Germany v Yugoslavia	Lens	June 21	4.30
USA v Iran	Lyon	June 21	8.00
Germany v Iran	Montpellier	June 25	8.00
USA v Yugoslavia	Nantes	June 25	8.00

World Cup 1998 Facts & Fixtures — Facts

GROUP G:	Venue	Date	K.O (BST)
Romania v Colombia	Lyon	June 15	4.30
England v Tunisia	Marseille	June 15	1.30
Romania v England	Toulouse	June 22	8.00
Colombia v Tunisia	Montpellier	June 22	4.30
Romania v Tunisia	Paris, St-Denis	June 26	8.00
Colombia v England	Lens	June 26	8.00
GROUP H:			
Argentina v Japan	Toulouse	June 14	4.30
Jamaica v Croatia	Lens	June 14	8.00
Japan v Croatia	Nante	June 20	4.30
Argentina v Jamaica	Paris, Parc-des-Princes	June 21	1.30
Argentina v Croatia	Bordeaux	June 26	3.00
Japan v Jamaica	Lyon	June 26	3.00

SECOND ROUND:	Venue	Date	K.O (BST)
1. Winner Gr A v Rn-Up Gr B	Paris, Parc-des-Princes	June 27	8.00
2. Winner Gr B v Rn-Up Gr A	Marseille	June 27	3.30
3. Winner Gr C v Rn-Up Gr D	Lens	June 28	3.30
4. Winner Gr D v Rn-Up Gr C	Paris, St-Denis	June 28	8.00
5. Winner Gr E v Rn-Up Gr F	Toulouse	June 29	8.00
6. Winner Gr F v Rn-Up Gr E	Montpellier	June 29	3.30
7. Winner Gr G v Rn-Up Gr H	Bordeaux	June 30	3.30
8. Winner Gr H v Rn-Up Gr G	St Etienne	June 30	8.00

Facts

World Cup 1998
Facts & Fixtures

QUARTER-FINALS:			
A: Winner 2 v Winner 3	Paris, St-Denis	July 3	3.30
B: Winner 1 v Winner 4	Nantes	July 3	8.00
C: Winner 5 v Winner 8	Marseille	July 4	3.30
D: Winner 6 v Winner 7	Lyon	July 4	8.00
SEMI-FINALS:			
Winner A v Winner C	Marseille	July 7	8.00
Winner B v Winner D	Paris, St-Denis	July 8	8.00
THIRD PLACE:	Paris, Parc-des-Princes	July 11	8.00
THE FINAL:	Paris, St-Denis	July 12	8.00

Quiz Score Sheets

Quiz Score Sheets

Quiz Score Sheets

Quiz Score Sheets

Quiz Score Sheets

Quiz Score Sheets

Quiz Score Sheets